Q ANTHOLOGY

Q ANTHOLOGY

A selection from
the prose and verse of

SIR ARTHUR QUILLER-COUCH

Compiled and edited

by

F. BRITTAIN, LITT.D.

Fellow of Jesus College, Cambridge
Author of
Arthur Quiller-Couch, a Biographical Study of Q'

LONDON: J. M. DENT & SONS LTD.

Made in Great Britain
by
The Temple Press · Letchworth · Herts.
First published 1948

INTRODUCTION

ARTHUR THOMAS QUILLER-COUCH, known to so many of his readers and friends simply as 'Q,' was born in 1863 at Bodmin, the county town of Cornwall. His mother was a Devonian, but his father was born at the fishing village of Polperro, on the south coast of Cornwall, where both the Quillers and the Couches had long been settled. The Quillers, it is true, were reputed to have come from France some five or six generations back, but the Couches bore a Cornish name and had probably lived in Cornwall from time immemorial. None of them can ever have loved their native county more than Q, whose books overflow with his devotion to the people, the life, the legends, and the scenery of Cornwall.

Q had a proper affection for his father, who was a doctor, and for the memory of his paternal grandfather (also a doctor) whom he remembered meeting only once. He pays warm tributes to both of them, and to their professional work, in his books. His conversation in private life nevertheless showed that he shared Napoleon's mistrust of the medical profession as a whole. This mistrust was perhaps a piece of atavism, for most of Q's ancestors before his grandfather's time had been hardy seafarers—men who probably scorned the learned professions in general, who seldom needed the services of a doctor or, if they needed them, were seldom able to get them.

Q resembled these remoter ancestors also in the great interest that he took in the sea, in seamen, and in shipping of every kind. This interest went very deep and was life-long. It was in fact a passion and, as a consequence, there are very few of his numerous books from which the sea is completely absent, whatever their subject or wherever their scene is laid. He possessed the rugged, weather-beaten features of a seafaring man and shared in some of the superstitions of the old type of sailor.

He found, too, when the test came, that he could not live happily for long out of sight of the sea.

When Q was only ten years old he was sent away to school at Newton Abbot in Devon, where his mother's parents lived, but he spent his holidays at home, and during them he explored the country around Bodmin thoroughly. It was on one of these schoolboy expeditions that he first visited the charming little port of Fowey—the place that was to inspire so much of his writing and from which his name will always be inseparable. He was entranced by Fowey as soon as he saw it and resolved that, if he could, he would live in it. He was only fifteen at the time; but his boyish delight in the town, far from proving to be merely a passing fancy, developed into a devotion that became more and more intense as he grew older.

From Newton Abbot Q went on to Clifton College, Bristol, for further schooling, and here he gained his first literary success by winning the school prize for a poem about Athens. This was afterwards privately printed by his parents—his first published work. He left Clifton in 1882 for Trinity College, Oxford, where he had been awarded a scholarship.

The love of Greek and Latin letters that he had acquired in his schooldays was inevitably strengthened by his five years at Oxford, where he took his degree in classics and stayed for a further year as lecturer in classics at his college. After he left Oxford he had no further occasion to study the classics systematically, but he never lost his love for them and they exerted a steady influence on him for the rest of his life. One might say that his classical education was to a great extent responsible for the clarity, conciseness, and common sense for which his English style became famous.

At Clifton, Q had edited the school magazine; at Oxford, while still in his early twenties, he wrote his first novel, *Dead Man's Rock*, which was very manifestly in the style of R. L. Stevenson. He also wrote regularly for the newly founded *Oxford Magazine*, contributing to it parodies and other poems that still give him a high place among English writers of light verse. It was also to *The Oxford Magazine* that he contributed, several years after he had left the university, his beautiful poem, *Alma Mater*—probably the best known of all his poems. In it he expressed, in haunting language, his lifelong devotion to Oxford, 'mother and mistress and queen—and yet not three goddesses but one goddess,' as he called the city many years later.

In 1887 Q left Oxford for London, where he lived until 1892, working partly as a free-lance journalist, but most of the time for a firm of publishers. During these five years he wrote three more novels and several other books, and from 1890 he was assistant editor of a new Liberal weekly paper, *The Speaker,* to which he contributed a short story every week and literary articles and reviews frequently. He was working all day and half the night in an attempt to make his name as a writer, and also in a gallant and ultimately successful effort to wipe out some family debts for which he was not responsible and which he had no obligation to pay. All the time, too, he was supporting his widowed mother and his two brothers; and from 1889 he also had a wife to support, and from 1890 a son as well.

It is not surprising, therefore, that his health broke down and that he left London in 1892, under medical advice, to live by the sea. Fowey, the 'Troy Town' of his novels and short stories, which he had frequently revisited and from which his wife came, was his obvious choice. There, in a white-painted house called 'The Haven,' with its narrow steep garden washed by the water of the harbour, and with a view of the open sea from his study window, he lived in great happiness until his death more than fifty years later. He had to work hard, but with a wife who was devoted to him and to whom he was equally devoted he was unafraid of the future. In a poem addressed to her he wrote:

> dear my wife, be blithe
> To bid the New Year hail. . . .

For though the snows he 'll shake
  Of winter from his head,
To settle, flake by flake,
  On ours instead,

Yet we be wreathèd green
  Beyond his blight or chill
Who kissed at seventeen
  And worship still.

Except that he continued for a few years to write short stories and articles for *The Speaker*, Q earned his living during his first twenty years at Fowey entirely as a free-lance writer. His output consequently had to be considerable and was in fact amazing, amounting as it did to two books every year on the average. More than half of this was fiction, but he was also writing serious verse, light verse (such as the delightful *Ballad of the Jubilee Cup*), and literary studies, and was compiling anthologies. The best of these—the most successful anthology in our language—was *The Oxford Book of English Verse*, which made his name familiar wherever the English language was spoken or English literature studied.

All this time Q was taking an ever-increasing part in Cornish public affairs, particularly in education and politics. His experiences as a member of the county education committee are reflected in his novels (especially *Shining Ferry*) and other writings, and his political activities appear sporadically in his stories and sketches. An Anglican and yet a Liberal, he held very definite opinions both ecclesiastically and politically and made no attempt to conceal them. Yet, though this was a time when religious and political feeling ran very high, his integrity was such that he became a very popular figure—an institution in himself. The Dutch novelist, Maarten Maartens, who paid him a visit in 1904, described him to a friend as 'King of Fowey in a quiet way'; and when W. H. Hudson went to Fowey some years later and received a letter from his wife saying that she

had been told that Q lived there he wrote to a friend: 'I replied
to her that she had sent me wonderful news, that I had been
hearing that Quiller-Couch lived at Fowey all my life and that
in Cornwall you heard it every day.'   It was like a sea-shanty,
he said, or the chorus of *John Brown's Body*:

> Glory glory halleluja,
> Glory glory halleluja,
> Glory glory halleluja,
>   Quiller-Couch lives at Fowey.

Q's services to literature, coupled with his public and political
services and his outstanding character, brought him recognition
from the Liberal Government in 1910, when (to his great surprise) he was knighted.   He had never been a blind partisan of
the Liberal party, neither did his knighthood make him one.
On the contrary, only two years later he openly attacked the
Liberal Government's Mental Deficiency Bill in the columns of
The Eye-Witness, comparing the minister responsible for the
introduction of the Bill to a strumpet.   His attack was written
at white heat, and was all the more effective from being one of
the very few examples of satire to be found in the whole of
his works.

Nor was Q ever a blind partisan of the Church of England.
It is beyond all doubt that he strongly disliked Nonconformity
—his private letters would make that abundantly clear, even if
there were no other evidence—yet some of his closest friends
were ardent Nonconformists; and in his *Eye-Witness* articles he
makes an outspoken and sustained attack on a bishop of the
Church of England—his former Oxford tutor—for siding with
the Liberal Government's Bill.   He puts to the bishop the
direct question: 'Do you still press me to join your damned
Association?' and immediately signs himself 'Your lordship's
obedient servant (but not in this).'

A few weeks after these attacks appeared in print the Liberal
Government showed its magnanimity by appointing Q—again,

greatly to his surprise—to the King Edward VII Professorship of English Literature in the University of Cambridge. He was almost simultaneously elected a fellow of Jesus College, and from then onward he lived during term in his rooms at college, but always returned to his beloved Fowey at the earliest possible moment for each vacation.

From the first, Q was as popular and as prominent at Cambridge as he had long been in Cornwall. His inaugural lecture was packed to the doors and beyond. Like all his subsequent lectures, it was prepared and delivered with the greatest care. His lectures were such works of art, and were so stimulating and so entertaining, that attendance at them was for years a fashionable pursuit among people of all ages at Cambridge—somewhat to Q's embarrassment at times.

His publications, though inevitably less numerous than they had been, continued to appear at the rate of a volume or more each year. He had little time now for the writing of fiction, and after 1918 he published no more novels or volumes of short stories: his most important books during the Cambridge period were collections of lectures, published under such titles as *The Art of Writing*, *The Art of Reading*, and *Studies in Literature*. In all of them, as Mr. George Sampson has said, 'literature is consistently presented, with convincing enthusiasm and creative understanding, as something for hearty, rational, disciplined enjoyment by normal human beings.'

Perhaps the best known of all Q's lectures is the entertaining *Interlude on Jargon*, which appeared in the earliest volume. It should be studied by everybody who intends to write. One lecture that deserves to be better known than it is was delivered twenty years later, when Q was seventy years of age, and is entitled *Tradition and Orthodoxy*. It is the reply of a lifelong Liberal to an attack on Liberalism by a convert to Toryism —Mr. T. S. Eliot. In style it reminds one of Q's open letters to the Bishop of Exeter in *The Eye-Witness* more than twenty years earlier. A writer who is himself an admirer of Mr.

Eliot has described it as 'a superb example of the magisterial rebuke.'

After that Q wrote no new books, apart from his unfinished *Memories and Opinions*, but he wrote a number of charming introductions to books by younger writers, a few more short stories and poems, and compiled a new edition of *The Oxford Book of English Verse*. Honours came to him in his old age. In three consecutive years he was made a freeman of Bodmin, of Fowey, and of Truro, and—what probably gave him even more pleasure—in 1937 he was elected mayor of Fowey. Being a life-long optimist, full of confidence in the younger generation, he accepted the outbreak of the Second World War in 1939 philosophically, having no doubt about ultimate victory. Unperturbed by air raids, he continued to travel backwards and forwards between Cambridge and Fowey as he had done ever since 1912. He kept his eightieth birthday at Fowey in 1943, and (as he would have wished) it was at Fowey that he died on 12th May in the following year, and at Fowey that he was buried.

Q was one of the most versatile as well as one of the most prolific of modern writers. He produced more than twenty novels, a dozen volumes of short stories, another dozen of literary studies, half a dozen books for children, two volumes of original verse, a number of anthologies, and a large quantity of miscellaneous prose, including some dozens of introductions to books by other writers or to his own selections from English literature.

What is even more remarkable than the quantity or the range of his writing is the high standard that he maintained through all of it. This was partly due to his natural gifts, but even more to the severe discipline to which he subjected himself whenever he wrote—whether he was writing a novel, a university lecture, a parody, a translation from the classics, or a limerick. As in his dress and his daily routine, so in his writing he was thorough in every detail. His chief contribution to English letters was his style, in which there lives again the chivalrous, hospitable Q who loved bright colours, dressed with great care, was accurate but not pedantic, and refused ever to be hurried.

* * *

This anthology aims at providing as representative a selection from Q's writing as is possible in the compass.   Since each item is given unabbreviated, it is obvious that no novel could be included.

The items are arranged in the order in which they were first published, as nearly as it can be ascertained.   Some of them have previously appeared only in periodicals or in other publications equally difficult to obtain.

Q's CHIEF WORKS

AUTOBIOGRAPHY

Memories and Opinions, an Unfinished Autobiography, 1944.

LITERARY CRITICISM

Adventures in Criticism, 1896; *From a Cornish Window*, 1906; *Poetry*, 1914; *On the Art of Writing*, 1916; *Shakespeare's Workmanship*, 1918; *Studies in Literature* (First Series), 1918; *On the Art of Reading*, 1920; Introductions to Shakespeare's Comedies in the New Cambridge Edition, 14 vols., 1921–31; *Studies in Literature* (Second Series), 1922; *Charles Dickens and Other Victorians*, 1925; *The Age of Chaucer*, 1926; *A Lecture on Lectures*, 1927; *Studies in Literature* (Third Series), 1929; *The Poet as Citizen, and Other Papers*, 1934.

NOVELS

Dead Man's Rock, 1887; *Troy Town*, 1888; *The Splendid Spur*, 1889; *The Blue Pavilions*, 1891; *Ia*, 1896; *The Ship of Stars*, 1899; *The Westcotes*, 1902; *The Adventures of Harry*

Revel, 1903; *Hetty Wesley*, 1903; *Fort Amity*, 1904; *Shining Ferry*, 1905; *Sir John Constantine*, 1906; *The Mayor of Troy*, 1906; *Poison Island*, 1907; *Major Vigoureux*, 1907; *True Tilda*, 1909; *Lady Good-for-Nothing*, 1910; *Brother Copas*, 1911; *Hocken and Hunken*, 1912; *Nicky-Nan, Reservist*, 1915; *Foe-Farrell*, 1918.

COLLECTIONS OF SHORT STORIES

Noughts and Crosses, 1891; *I Saw Three Ships*, 1892; *The Delectable Duchy*, 1893; *Wandering Heath*, 1895; *Old Fires and Profitable Ghosts*, 1900; *The Laird's Luck*, 1901; *The White Wolf*, 1902; *Two Sides of the Face*, 1903; *Shakespeare's Christmas*, 1905; *Merry Garden*, 1907; *Corporal Sam*, 1910; *News from the Duchy*, 1913; *Mortallone and Aunt Trinidad*, 1917.

CHILDREN'S BOOKS

Fairy Tales Far and Near Retold, 1895; *The Sleeping Beauty and other Fairy Tales Retold*, 1910; *The Roll Call of Honour*, 1912; *In Powder and Crinoline : Old Fairy Tales Retold*, 1913.

MISCELLANEOUS PROSE

The Warwickshire Avon, 1892; *A Blot of Ink* (translated from the French of René Bazin by Q and P. M. Francke), 1892; *Historical Tales from Shakespeare*, 1899; *Memoir of Arthur John Butler*, 1917.

VERSE

Green Bays, 1893; *Poems and Ballads*, 1896; *The Vigil of Venus and Other Poems*, 1912; *Poems* (a new edition of *Poems and Ballads*, together with the whole of *The Vigil of Venus* and other items), 1929; *Green Bays* (new and enlarged edition), 1930.

ANTHOLOGIES

The Golden Pomp, 1895; *English Sonnets*, 1897; *The Oxford Book of English Verse (1250–1900)*, 1900; *The Pilgrim's Way*, 1906; *The Oxford Book of Ballads*, 1910; *The Oxford Book of Victorian Verse*, 1912; *The Oxford Book of English Prose*, 1925; *Pages of English Prose*, 1930; *Felicities of Thomas Traherne*, 1934; *English Sonnets* (new and enlarged edition), 1935; *The Oxford Book of English Verse* (new edition, 1250–1918), 1939.

ACKNOWLEDGMENTS

This selection from the works of Sir Arthur Quiller-Couch is reprinted by kind permission of his literary executors and of the following publishers and editors:

J. W. Arrowsmith (London) Ltd.; Blackie & Son Ltd.; *The Cambridge Review*; The Cambridge University Press; Cassell & Co. Ltd.; The Clarendon Press; Hutchinson & Co. (Publishers) Ltd.; *The Oxford Magazine*; The Oxford University Press; *The Spectator*; *Time and Tide*; *The Times*; *The Times Literary Supplement*; G. P. Putnam's Sons of New York; and Charles Scribner's Sons of New York.

CONTENTS

Contents

BEHOLD! I AM NOT ONE THAT GOES TO LECTURES

BY W. W.

BEHOLD! I am not one that goes to Lectures or the pow-
wow of Professors.

The elementary laws never apologize: neither do I apologize.

I find letters from the Dean dropt on my table—and every one
is signed by the Dean's name—

And I leave them where they are; for I know that as long
as I stay up

Others will punctually come for ever and ever.

I am one who goes to the river,

I sit in the boat and think of 'life' and of 'time.'

How life is much, but time is more; and the beginning is
everything,

But the end is something.

I loll in the Parks, I go to the wicket, I swipe.

I see twenty-two young men from Foster's watching me, and
the trousers of the twenty-two young men,

I see the Balliol men *en masse* watching me.—The Hottentot
that loves his mother, the untutored Bedowee, the
Cave-man that wears only his certificate of baptism,
and the shaggy Sioux that hangs his testamur with
his scalps.

I see the Don who ploughed me in Rudiments watching me:
and the wife of the Don who ploughed me in
Rudiments watching me.

I see the rapport of the wicket-keeper and umpire.

I cannot see that I am out.

Oh! you Umpires!

I am not one who greatly cares for experience, soap, bull-dogs,
    cautions, majorities, or a graduated Income Tax,
The certainty of space, punctuation, sexes, institutions, copious-
    ness, degrees, committees, delicatesse, or the fetters
    of rhyme—
    For none of these do I care: but least for the fetters of rhyme.
    Myself only I sing.   Me Imperturbe!   Me Prononcé!
    Me progressive and the depth of me progressive,
        And the βάθος, *Anglicé* bathos
        Of me hirsute, nakedly whooping,
Me over the tiles to the Cosmos endlessly whooping
        The song of Simple Enumeration.

FIRE!

BY SIR W. S.

*Written on the occasion of the visit of the United Fire
Brigades to Oxford, 1887*

I

ST. GILES'S street is fair and wide,
  St. Giles's street is long;
But long or wide, may naught abide
  Therein of guile or wrong;
For through St. Giles's, to and fro,
The mild ecclesiastics go
  From prime to evensong.
It were a fearsome task, perdie!
To sin in such good company.

II

Long had the slanting beam of day
Proclaimed the Thirtieth of May
Ere now, erect, its fiery heat
Illumined all that hallowed street,
And breathing benediction on
Thy serried battlements, St. John,
Suffused at once with equal glow
The cluster'd Archipelago,
The Art Professor's studio
  And Mr. Greenwood's shop,
Thy building, Pusey, where below
The stout Salvation soldiers blow
  The cornet till they drop;
Thine, Balliol, where we move, and oh!
  Thine, Randolph, where we stop.

3

III

But what is this that frights the air,
And wakes the curate from his lair
  In Pusey's cool retreat,
To leave the feast, to climb the stair,
  And scan the startled street?
As when perambulate the young
And call with unrelenting tongue
  On home, mamma, and sire;
Or voters shout with strength of lung
  For Hall & Co.'s Entire;
Or Sabbath-breakers scream and shout—
The band of Booth, with drum devout,
Eliza on her Sunday out,
  Or Farmer with his choir:—

IV

E'en so, with shriek of fife and drum
  And horrid clang of brass,
The Fire Brigades of England come
  And down St. Giles's pass.
Oh grand, methinks, in such array
To spend a Whitsun Holiday
  All soaking to the skin!
(Yet shoes and hose alike are stout;
The shoes to keep the water out,
  The hose to keep it in.)

V

They came from Henley on the Thames,
  From Berwick on the Tweed,
And at the mercy of the flames
They left their children and their dames,

To come and play their little games
    On Morrell's dewy mead.
Yet feared they not with fire to play—
The pyrotechnics (so they say)
    Were very fine indeed.

VI

(P.S. BY LORD MACAULAY)

Then let us bless Our Gracious Queen and eke the Fire Brigade,
And bless no less the horrid mess they've been and gone and
    made;
Remove the dirt they chose to squirt upon our best attire,
Bless all, but most the lucky chance that no one shouted 'Fire!'

TWILIGHT

BY W—LL—M C—WP—R

'TIS evening.   See with its resorting throng
Rude Carfax teems, and waistcoats, visited
With too-familiar elbow, swell the curse
Vortiginous.   The boating man returns,
His rawness growing with experience—
Strange union! and directs the optic glass
Not unresponsive to Jemima's charms,
Who wheels obdurate, in his mimic chaise
Perambulant, the child.   The gouty cit,
Asthmatical, with elevated cane
Pursues the unregarding tram, as one
Who, having heard a hurdy-gurdy, girds
His loins and hunts the hurdy-gurdy-man,
Blaspheming.   Now the clangorous bell proclaims
The *Times* or *Chronicle*, and Rauca screams
The latest horrid murder in the ear
Of nervous dons expectant of the urn
And mild domestic muffin.

                    To the Parks
Drags the slow Ladies' School, consuming time
In passing given points.   Here glow the lamps,
And tea-spoons clatter to the cosy hum
Of scientific circles.   Here resounds
The football-field with its discordant train,
The crowd that cheers yet not discriminates,
As ever into touch the ball returns
And shrieks the whistle, while the game proceeds
With fine irregularity well worth
The paltry shilling.—

                  Draw the curtains close
While I resume the night-cap dear to all
Familiar with my illustrated works.

THE SPLENDID SPUR

NOT on the neck of prince or hound,
   Nor on a woman's finger twined,
May gold from the deriding ground
   Keep sacred that we sacred bind:
         Only the heel
         Of splendid steel
   Shall stand secure on sliding fate,
   When golden navies weep their freight.

The scarlet hat, the laurelled stave,
   Are measures, not the springs, of worth;
In a wife's lap, as in a grave,
   Man's airy notions mix with earth.
         Seek other spur
         Bravely to stir
   The dust in this loud world, and tread
   Alp-high among the whisp'ring dead!

Trust in thyself,—then spur amain!
   So shall Charybdis wear a grace,
Grim Etna laugh, the Libyan plain
   Take roses to her shrivelled face.
         This orb—this round
         Of sight and sound—
   Count it the lists that God hath built
   For haughty hearts to ride a-tilt.

OLD AESON

JUDGE between me and my guest, the stranger within my gates, the man whom in his extremity I clothed and fed.

I remember well the time of his coming: for it happened at the end of five days and nights during which the year passed from strength to age; in the interval between the swallow's departure and the redwing's coming; when the tortoise in my garden crept into his winter quarters, and the equinox was on us, with an east wind that parched the blood in the trees, so that their leaves for once knew no gradations of red and yellow, but turned at a stroke to brown, and crackled like tin-foil.

At five o'clock in the morning of the sixth day I looked out. The wind whistled across the sky, but now without the obstruction of any cloud. Full in front of my window Sirius flashed with a whiteness that pierced the eye. A little to the right, the whole constellation of Orion was suspended, clear over a wedge-like gap in the coast, wherein the sea could be guessed rather than seen. And, travelling yet farther, the eye fell on two brilliant lights, the one set high above the other—the one steady and a fiery red, the other yellow and blazing intermittently— the one Aldebaran, the other revolving on the lighthouse top, fifteen miles away.

Half-way up the east, the moon, now in her last quarter and decrepit, climbed with the dawn close at her heels. And at this hour they brought in the Stranger, asking if my pleasure were to give him clothing and hospitality.

Nobody knew whence he came—except that it was from the wind and the night—seeing that he spoke in a strange tongue, moaning and making a sound like the twittering of birds in a chimney. But his journey must have been long and painful;

8

for his legs bent under him, and he could not stand when they lifted him. So, finding it useless to question him for the time, I learnt from the servants all they had to tell—namely that they had come upon him, but a few minutes before, lying on his face within my grounds, without staff or scrip, bareheaded, spent, and crying feebly for succour in his foreign tongue; and that in pity they had carried him in and brought him to me.

Now for the look of this man, he seemed a century old, being bald, extremely wrinkled, with wide hollows where the teeth should be, and the flesh hanging loose and flaccid on his cheek-bones; and what colour he had could have come only from exposure to that bitter night. But his eyes chiefly spoke of his extreme age. They were blue and deep, and filled with the wisdom of years; and when he turned them in my direction they appeared to look through me, beyond me, and back upon centuries of sorrow and the slow endurance of man, as if his immediate misfortune were but an inconsiderable item in a long list. They frightened me. Perhaps they conveyed a warning of that which I was to endure at their owner's hands. From compassion, I ordered the servants to take him to my wife, with word that I wished her to set food before him, and see that it passed his lips.

So much I did for this Stranger. Now learn how he rewarded me.

He has taken my youth from me, and the most of my substance, and the love of my wife.

From the hour when he tasted food in my house, he sat there without hint of going. Whether from design, or because age and his sufferings had really palsied him, he came back tediously to life and warmth, nor for many days professed himself able to stand erect. Meanwhile he lived on the best of our hospitality. My wife tended him, and my servants ran at his bidding; for he managed early to make them understand scraps of his language, though slow in acquiring ours — I believe out of

* B

calculation, lest someone should inquire his business (which was a mystery) or hint at his departure. I myself often visited the room he had appropriated, and would sit for an hour watching those fathomless eyes while I tried to make head or tail of his discourse. When we were alone, my wife and I used to speculate at times on his probable profession. Was he a merchant? —an aged mariner?—a tinker, tailor, beggarman, thief? We could never decide, and he never disclosed.

Then the awakening came. I sat one day in the chair beside his, wondering as usual. I had felt heavy of late, with a soreness and languor in my bones, as if a dead weight hung continually on my shoulders, and another rested on my heart. A warmer colour in the Stranger's cheek caught my attention; and I bent forward, peering under the pendulous lids. His eyes were livelier and less profound. The melancholy was passing from them as breath fades off a pane of glass. *He was growing younger.* Starting up, I ran across the room, to the mirror.

There were two white hairs in my forelock; and, at the corner of either eye, half a dozen radiating lines. I was an old man.

Turning, I regarded the Stranger. He sat phlegmatic as an Indian idol; and in my fancy I felt the young blood draining from my own heart, and saw it mantling in his cheeks. Minute by minute I watched the slow miracle—the old man beautified. As buds unfold, he put on a lovely youthfulness; and, drop by drop, left me winter.

I hurried from the room, and seeking my wife, laid the case before her. 'This is a ghoul,' I said, 'that we harbour: he is sucking my best blood, and the household is clean bewitched.' She laid aside the book in which she read, and laughed at me. Now my wife was well-looking, and her eyes were the light of my soul. Consider, then, how I felt as she laughed, taking the Stranger's part against me. When I left her, it was with a new suspicion in my heart. 'How shall it be,' I thought, 'if after stealing my youth, he go on to take the one thing that is better?'

In my room, day by day, I brooded upon this—hating my own alteration, and fearing worse. With the Stranger there was no longer any disguise. His head blossomed in curls; white teeth filled the hollows of his mouth; the pits in his cheeks were heaped full with roses, glowing under a transparent skin. It was Aeson renewed and thankless; and he sat on, devouring my substance.

Now, having probed my weakness, and being satisfied that I no longer dared to turn him out, he, who had half imposed his native tongue upon us, constraining the household to a hideous jargon, the bastard growth of two languages, condescended to jerk us back rudely into our own speech once more, mastering it with a readiness that proved his former dissimulation, and using it henceforward as the sole vehicle of his wishes. On his past life he remained silent; but took occasion to confide in me that he proposed embracing a military career, as soon as he should tire of the shelter of my roof.

And I groaned in my chamber; for that which I feared had come to pass. He was making open love to my wife. And the eyes with which he looked at her, and the lips with which he coaxed her, had been mine; and I was an old man. Judge now between me and this guest.

One morning I went to my wife; for the burden was past bearing, and I must satisfy myself. I found her tending the plants on her window-ledge; and when she turned, I saw that years had not taken from her comeliness one jot. And I was old.

So I taxed her on the matter of this Stranger, saying this and that, and how I had cause to believe he loved her.

'That is beyond doubt,' she answered, and smiled.

'By my head, I believe his fancy is returned!' I blurted out.

And her smile grew radiant, as, looking me in the face, she answered, 'By my soul, husband, it is.'

Then I went from her, down into my garden, where the day

grew hot and the flowers were beginning to droop. I stared upon them and could find no solution to the problem that worked in my heart. And then I glanced up, eastward, to the sun above the privet-hedge, and saw *him* coming across the flower-beds, treading them down in wantonness. He came with a light step and a smile, and I waited for him, leaning heavily on my stick.

'Give me your watch!' he called out, as he drew near.

'Why should I give you my watch?' I asked, while something worked in my throat.

'Because I wish it; because it is gold; because you are too old, and won't want it much longer.'

'Take it,' I cried, pulling the watch out and thrusting it into his hand. 'Take it—you who have taken all that is better! Strip me, spoil me——'

A soft laugh sounded above, and I turned. My wife was looking down on us from the window, and her eyes were both moist and glad.

'Pardon me,' she said, 'it is you who are spoiling the child.'

PSYCHE

'Among these million Suns how shall the strayed Soul find her way back to earth?'

THE man was an engine-driver, thick-set and heavy, with a short beard grizzled at the edge, and eyes perpetually screwed up, because his life had run for the most part in the teeth of the wind. The lashes, too, had been scorched off. If you penetrated the mask of oil and coal-dust that was part of his working suit, you found a reddish-brown phlegmatic face, and guessed its age at fifty. He brought the last down train into Lewminster station every night at 9.45, took her on five minutes later, and passed through Lewminster again at noon, on his way back with the Galloper, as the porters called it.

He had reached that point of skill at which a man knows every pound of metal in a locomotive; seemed to feel just what was in his engine the moment he took hold of the levers and started up; and was expecting promotion. While waiting for it, he hit on the idea of studying a more delicate machine, and married a wife. She was the daughter of a woman at whose house he lodged, and her age was less than half of his own. It is to be supposed he loved her.

A year after their marriage she fell into low health, and her husband took her off to Lewminster for fresher air. She was lodging alone at Lewminster, and the man was passing Lewminster station on his engine, twice a day, at the time when this tale begins.

People—especially those who live in the west of England— remember the great fire at the Lewminster theatre; how, in the second Act of the *Colleen Bawn*, a tongue of light shot from the wings over the actors' heads; how, even while the actors turned and ran, a sheet of fire swept out and on to the auditorium with a roaring wind, and the house was full of shrieks and blind death; how men and women were turned to a white ash as they rose from their seats, so fiercely the flames outstripped the smoke. These things were reported in the papers, with narratives and ghastly details, and for a week all England talked of Lewminster.

This engine-driver, as the 9.45 train neared Lewminster, saw the red in the sky. And when he rushed into the station and drew up, he saw that the country porters who stood about were white as corpses.

'What fire is that?' he asked one.

''Tis the theayter! There's a hundred burnt a'ready, and the rest treadin' each other's lives out while we stand talkin', to get 'pon the roof and pitch theirselves over!'

Now the engine-driver's wife was going to the play that night, and he knew it. She had met him at the station, and told him so, at mid-day.

But there was nobody to take the train on, if he stepped off the engine; for his fireman was a young hand, and had been learning his trade for less than three weeks.

So when the five minutes were up—or rather, ten, for the porters were bewildered that night—this man went on out of the station into the night. Just beyond the station the theatre was plain to see, above the hill on his left, and the flames were leaping from the roof; and he knew that his wife was there. But the train was never taken down more steadily, nor did a single passenger guess what manner of man was driving it.

At Drakeport, where his run ended, he stepped off the engine, walked from the railway-sheds to his mother-in-law's, where he still lodged, and went upstairs to his bed without alarming a soul.

In the morning, at the usual hour, he was down at the station again, washed and cleanly dressed. His fireman had the Galloper's engine polished, fired up, and ready to start.

'Mornin',' he nodded, and looking into his driver's eyes,

dropped the handful of dirty lint with which he had been polishing. After shuffling from foot to foot for a minute, he ended by climbing down on the far side of the engine.

'Oldster,' he said, ''tis mutiny p'raps; but s' help me, if I ride a mile 'longside that new face o' your'n!'

'Maybe you're right,' his superior answered wearily. 'You'd best go up to the office, and get somebody sent down i' my place. And while you're there, you might get me a third-class for Lewminster.'

So this man travelled up to Lewminster as passenger, and found his young wife's body among the two score stretched in a stable-yard behind the smoking theatre, waiting to be claimed. And the day after the funeral he left the railway company's service. He had saved a bit, enough to rent a small cottage two miles from the cemetery where his wife lay. Here he settled and tilled a small garden beside the high road.

Nothing seemed to be wrong with the man until the late summer, when he stood before the Lewminster magistrates charged with a violent and curiously wanton assault.

It appeared that one dim evening, late in August, a mild gentleman, with Leghorn hat, spectacles, and a green gauze net, came sauntering by the garden where the ex-engine-driver was pulling a basketful of scarlet runners: that the prisoner had suddenly dropped his beans, dashed out into the road, and catching the mild gentleman by the throat had wrenched the butterfly net from his hand and belaboured him with the handle till it broke.

There was no defence, nor any attempt at explanation. The mild gentleman was a stranger to the neighbourhood. The magistrates marvelled, and gave his assailant two months.

At the end of that time the man came out of jail and went quietly back to his cottage.

Early in the following April he conceived a wish to build a

small greenhouse at the foot of his garden, by the road, and spoke to the local mason about it. One Saturday afternoon the mason came over to look at the ground and discuss plans. It was bright weather, and while the two men talked a white butterfly floated past them—the first of the year.

Immediately the mason broke off his sentence and began to chase the butterfly round the garden: for in the west country there is a superstition that if a body neglect to kill the first butterfly he may see for the season, he will have ill luck throughout the year. So he dashed across the beds, hat in hand.

'I 'll hat 'en—I 'll hat 'en! No, fay! I 'll miss 'en, I b'lieve. Shan't be able to kill 'n if her 's wunce beyond th' gaate—stiddy, my son! Wo-op!'

Thus he yelled, waving his soft hat: and the next minute was lying stunned across a carrot-bed, with eight fingers gripping the back of his neck and two thumbs squeezing on his windpipe.

There was another assault case heard by the Lewminster bench; and this time the ex-engine-driver received four months. As before, he offered no defence: and again the magistrates were possessed with wonder.

Now the explanation is quite simple. This man's wits were sound, save on one point. He believed—why, God alone knows, who enabled him to drive that horrible journey without a tremor of the hand—that his wife's soul haunted him in the form of a white butterfly or moth. The superstition that spirits take this shape is not unknown in the west; and I suppose that as he steered his train out of the station, this fancy, by some odd freak of memory, leaped into his brain, and held it, hour after hour, while he and his engine flew forward and the burning theatre fell farther and farther behind. The truth was known a fortnight after his return from prison, which happened about the time of barley harvest.

A harvest-thanksgiving was held in the parish where he lived; and he went to it, being always a religious man. There were sheaves and baskets of vegetables in the chancel; fruit and flowers on the communion-table, with twenty-one tall candles burning above them; a processional hymn; and a long sermon. During the sermon, as the weather was hot and close, someone opened the door at the west end.

And when the preacher was just making up his mind to close the discourse, a large white moth fluttered in at the west door.

There was much light throughout the church; but the great blaze came, of course, from the twenty-one candles upon the altar. And towards this the moth slowly drifted, as if the candles sucked her nearer and nearer, up between the pillars of the nave, on a level with their capitals. Few of the congregation noticed her, for the sermon was a stirring one; only one or two children, perhaps, were interested—and the man I write of. He saw her pass over his head and float up into the chancel. He half rose from his chair.

'My brothers,' said the preacher, 'if two sparrows, that are sold for a farthing, are not too little for the care of this infinite Providence——'

A scream rang out and drowned the sentence. It was followed by a torrent of vile words, shouted by a man who had seen, now for the second time, the form that clothed his wife's soul shrivelled in unthinking flames. All that was left of the white moth lay on the altar-cloth among the fruit at the base of the tallest candlestick.

And because the man saw nothing but cruelty in the Providence of which the preacher spoke, he screamed and cursed, till they overpowered him and took him forth by the door. He was wholly mad from that hour.

THE WHITE MOTH

IF *a leaf rustled, she would start:*
   And yet she died a year ago.
How had so frail a thing the heart
   To journey where she trembled so?
And do they turn and turn in fright,
   Those little feet, in so much night?

The light above the poet's head
   Streamed on the page and on the cloth,
And twice and thrice there buffeted
   On the black pane a white-winged moth:
'Twas Annie's soul that beat outside
   And 'Open! open! open!' cried:

'I could not find the way to God:
   There were too many flaming suns
For signposts, and the fearful road
   Led over wastes where millions
Of tangled comets hissed and burned—
   I was bewildered, and I turned.

'Oh, it was easy then! I knew
   Your window and no star beside.
Look up, and take me back to you!'
   —He rose and thrust the window wide.
'Twas but because his head was hot
   With rhyming: for he heard her not.

But poets polishing a phrase
   Show anger over trivial things;
And as she blundered in the blaze
   Toward him, on ecstatic wings,
He raised a hand and smote her dead;
   Then wrote, '*That I had died instead!*'

A CAROL

Poem by "Q"

Set to Music by C. V. STANFORD

And choirs of view-less Che-ru-bin Shall guide you to that humble inn: Then sing, and rest you com-fort-ed,— "In ex-cel-sis glo-ri-a!" "And is it He that should be sent?" Three kings came from the o-ri-ent, A-ri-ding with the to-kens three, From Ind, Ca-thay, and A-ra-bye: Then sing, and rest you

THE PAUPERS

οὐ μὲν γὰρ τοῦ γε κρεῖσσον καὶ ἄρειον,
ἢ ὅθ᾽ ὁμοφρονέοντε νοήμασιν οἶκον ἔχητον
ἀνὴρ ἠδὲ γυνή.

I

ROUND the skirts of the plantation, and half-way down the hill, there runs a thick fringe of wild cherry-trees. Their white blossom makes, for three weeks in the year, a pretty contrast with the larches and Scotch firs that serrate the long ridge above; and close under their branches runs the line of oak rails that marks off the plantation from the meadow.

A labouring man came deliberately round the slope, as if following this line of rails. As a matter of fact, he was treading the little-used footpath that here runs close alongside the fence for fifty yards before diverging downhill towards the village. So narrow is this path that the man's boots were powdered to a rich gold by the buttercups they had brushed aside.

By and by he came to a standstill, looked over the fence, and listened. Up among the larches a faint chopping sound could just be heard, irregular but persistent. The man put a hand to his mouth, and hailed:

'Hi-i-i! Knock off! Stable clock's gone noo-oon!'

Came back no answer. But the chopping ceased at once; and this apparently satisfied the man, who leaned against the rail and waited, chewing a spear of brome-grass, and staring steadily, but incuriously, at his boots. Two minutes passed without stir or sound in this corner of the land. The human figure was motionless. The birds in the plantation were taking their noonday siesta. A brown butterfly rested, with spread wings, on the rail—so quietly, he might have been pinned there.

A cracked voice was suddenly lifted a dozen yards off, and within the plantation:

'Such a man as I be to work! Never heard a note o' that blessed clock, if you 'll believe me. Ab-sorbed, I s'pose.'

A thin withered man in a smock-frock emerged from among the cherry-trees with a bill-hook in his hand, and stooped to pass under the rail.

'Ewgh! The pains I suffer in that old back of mine you'll never believe, my son, not till the appointed time when you come to suffer 'em yousel'. Well-a-well! Says I just now, up among the larches, "Heigh, my sonny-boys. I can crow over you, anyways; for I was a man grown when Squire planted ye; and here I be, a lusty gaffer, markin' ye down for destruction." But hallo! where's the dinner?'

'There bain't none.'

'Hey?'

'There bain't none.'

'How's that? Damme! William Henry, dinner's dinner, an' don't you joke about it. Once you begin to make fun o' sacred things like meals and vittles——'

'And don't you flare up like that, at your time o' life. We're fashionists to-day: dining out. 'Quarter after nine this morning I was passing by the Green wi' the straw-cart, when old Jan Trueman calls after me, "Have 'ee heard the news?" "What news?" says I. "Why," says he, "me an' my missus be going into the House this afternoon—can't manage to pull along by ourselves no more," he says; "an' we wants you an' your father to drop in soon after noon an' take a bite wi' us, for old sake's sake. 'Tis our last taste o' free life, and we'm going to do the thing fittywise," he says.'

The old man bent a meditative look on the village roofs below.

'We'll pleasure 'en, of course,' he said slowly. 'So 'tis come round to Jan's turn? But a' was born in the year of Waterloo victory, ten year' afore me, so I s'pose he've kept his doom off longer than most.'

The two set off down the footpath. There is a stile at the foot of the meadow, and as he climbed it painfully, the old man spoke again.

'And his doorway, I reckon, 'll be locked for a little while, an' then opened by strangers; an' his nimble youth be forgot like a flower o' the field; an' fare thee well, Jan Trueman! Maria, too—I can mind her well as a nursing mother—a comely woman in her day. I'd no notion they'd got this in their mind.'

'Far as I can gather, they've been minded that way ever since their daughter Jane died, last fall.'

From the stile where they stood they could look down into the village street. And old Jan Trueman was plain to see, in clean linen and his Sunday suit, standing in the doorway and welcoming his guests.

'Come ye in—come ye in, good friends,' he called, as they approached. 'There's cold bekkon, an' cold sheep's liver, an' Dutch cheese, besides bread, an' a thimbleful o' gin-an'-water for every soul among ye, to make it a day of note in the parish.'

He looked back over his shoulder into the kitchen. A dozen men and women, all elderly, were already gathered there. They had brought their own chairs. Jan's wife wore her bonnet and shawl, ready to start at a moment's notice. Her luggage in a blue handkerchief lay on the table. As she moved about and supplied her guests, her old lips twitched nervously; but when she spoke it was with no unusual tremor of the voice.

'I wish, friends, I could ha' cooked ye a little something hot; but there'd be no time for the washing-up, an' I've ordained to leave the place tidy.'

One of the old women answered:

'There's nought to be pardoned, I'm sure. Never do I mind such a gay set-off for the journey. For the gin-an'-water is a little addition beyond experience. The vittles, no doubt, you begged up at the vicarage, sayin' you'd been a peck o' trouble to the family, but this was going to be the last time.'

'I did, I did,' assented Mr. Trueman.

'But the gin-an'-water—how on airth you contrived it is a riddle!'

The old man rubbed his hands together and looked around with genuine pride.

'There was old Miss Scantlebury,' said another guest, a smock-frocked gaffer of seventy, with a grizzled shock of hair. 'You remember Miss Scantlebury?'

'O' course, o' course.'

'Well, she did it better 'n anybody I 've heard tell of. When she fell into redooced circumstances she sold the eight-day clock that was the only thing o' value she had left. Brown o' Tregarrick made it, with a very curious brass dial, whereon he carved a full-rigged ship that rocked like a cradle, an' went down stern foremost when the hour struck. 'Twas worth walking a mile to see. Brown's grandson bought it off Miss Scantlebury for two guineas, he being proud of his grandfather's skill; an' the old lady drove into Tregarrick Work'us behind a pair o' greys wi' the proceeds. Over and above the carriage hire, she 'd enough left to adorn the horse wi' white favours an' give the rider a crown, large as my lord. Aye, an' at the Work'us door she said to the fellow, said she, "All my life I 've longed to ride in a bridal chariot; an' though my only lover died of a decline when I was scarce twenty-one, I 've done it at last," said she; "an' now heaven an' airth can't undo it!"'

A heavy silence followed this anecdote, and then one or two of the women vented small disapproving coughs. The reason was the speaker's loud mention of the Workhouse. A week, a day, a few hours before, its name might have been spoken in Mr. and Mrs. Trueman's presence. But now they had entered its shadow; they were 'going'—whether to the dim vale of Avilion, or with chariot and horses of fire to heaven, let nobody too curiously ask. If Mr. and Mrs. Trueman chose to speak definitely, it was another matter.

Old Jan bore no malice, however, but answered, 'That beats me, I own. Yet we shall drive, though it be upon two wheels an' behind a single horse. For Farmer Lear 's driving into Tregarrick in an hour's time, an' he 've a-promised us a lift.'

'But about that gin-an'-water? For real gin-an'-water it is, to sight an' taste.'

'Well, friends, I'll tell ye: for the trick may serve one of ye in the days when you come to follow me, tho' the new relieving officer may have learnt wisdom before then. You must know we've been considering of this step for some while; but hearing that old Jacobs was going to retire soon, I says to Maria, "We'll bide till the new officer comes, and if he's a green hand, we'll diddle 'en." Day before yesterday, as you know, was his first round at the work; so I goes up an' draws out my ha'af-crown same as usual, an' walks straight off for the "Four Lords" for a ha'af-crown's worth o' gin. Then back I goes, an' demands an admission order for me an' the missus. "Why, where's your ha'af-crown?" says he. "Gone in drink," says I. "Old man," says he, "you'm a scandal, an' the sooner you're put out o' the way o' drink, the better for you an' your poor wife." "Right you are," I says; an' I got my order. But there, I'm wasting time; for to be sure you've most of ye got kith or kin in the place where we'm going, and 'll be wanting to send 'em a word by us.'

It was less than an hour before Farmer Lear pulled up to the door in his red-wheeled spring-cart.

'Now, friends,' said Mrs. Trueman, as her ears caught the rattle of the wheels, 'I must trouble ye to step outside while I tidy up the floor.'

The women offered their help, but she declined it. Alone she put the small kitchen to rights, while they waited outside around the door. Then she stepped out with her bundle, locked the door after her, and slipped the key under an old flower-pot on the window-ledge. Her eyes were dry.

'Come'st along, Jan.'

There was a brief hand-shaking, and the paupers climbed up beside Farmer Lear.

'I've made a sort o' little plan in my head,' said old Jan at parting, 'of the order in which I shall see ye again, one by one.

'Twill be a great amusement to me, friends, to see how the fact fits in wi' my little plan.'

The guests raised three feeble cheers as the cart drove away, and hung about for several minutes after it had passed out of sight, gazing along the road as wistfully as more prosperous men look in through churchyard gates at the acres where their kinsfolk lie buried.

II

The first building passed by the westerly road as it descends into Tregarrick is a sombre pile of some eminence, having a gateway and lodge before it, and a high encircling wall. The sun lay warm on its long roof, and the slates flashed gaily there, as Farmer Lear came over the knap of the hill and looked down on it. He withdrew his eyes nervously to glance at the old couple beside him. At the same moment he reined up his dun-coloured mare.

'I reckoned,' he said timidly, 'I reckoned you'd be for stopping hereabouts an' getting down. You'd think it more seemly—that's what I reckoned: an' 'tis all downhill now.'

For ten seconds and more neither the man nor the woman gave a sign of having heard him. The spring-cart's oscillatory motion seemed to have entered into their spinal joints; and now that they were come to a halt, their heads continued to wag forward and back as they contemplated the haze of smoke spread, like a blue scarf, over the town, and the one long slate roof that rose from it as if to meet them. At length the old woman spoke, and with some viciousness, though her face remained as blank as the Workhouse door.

'The next time I go back up this hill, if ever I do, I'll be carried up feet first.'

'Maria,' said her husband, feebly reproachful, 'you tempt the Lord, that you do.'

'Thank 'ee, Farmer Lear,' she went on, paying no heed;

'you shall help us down, if you 've a mind to, an' drive on. We 'll make shift to trickly 'way down so far as the gate; for I 'd be main vexed if anybody that had known me in life should see us creep in. Come'st along, Jan.'

Farmer Lear alighted, and helped them out carefully. He was a clumsy man, but did his best to handle them gently. When they were set on their feet, side by side on the high road, he climbed back, and fell to arranging the reins, while he cast about for something to say.

'Well, folks, I s'pose I must be wishing 'ee good-bye.' He meant to speak cheerfully, but overacted, and was hilarious instead. Recognizing this, he blushed.

'We 'll meet in heaven, I dare say,' the woman answered. 'I put the door-key, as you saw, under the empty geranium-pot 'pon the window-ledge; an' whoever the new tenant's wife may be, she can eat off the floor, if she 's minded. Now drive along, that 's a good soul, and leave us to fend for ourselves.'

They watched him out of sight before either stirred. The last decisive step, the step across the Workhouse threshold, must be taken with none to witness. If they could not pass out of their small world by the more reputable mode of dying, they would at least depart with this amount of mystery. They had left the village in Farmer Lear's cart, and Farmer Lear had left them in the high road; and after that, nothing should be known.

'Shall we be moving on?' Jan asked at length. There was a gate beside the road just there, with a small triangle of green before it, and a granite roller half buried in dock leaves. Without making any answer, the woman seated herself on this, and pulling a handful of the leaves, dusted her shoes and skirt.

'Maria, you 'll take a chill that 'll carry you off, sitting 'pon that cold stone.'

'I don't care. 'Twon't carry me off afore I get inside; an' I 'm going in decent, or not at all. Come here, an' let me tittivate you.'

He sat down on the stone beside her, and submitted to be dusted.

'You'd as lief lower me as not in their eyes, I verily believe.'

'I always was one to gather dust.'

'An' a fresh spot o' bacon-fat 'pon your weskit, that I've kept the moths from since goodness knows when!'

Old Jan looked down over his waistcoat. It was of good West-of-England broadcloth, and he had worn it on the day when he married the woman at his side.

'I'm thinking——' he began nervously.

'Hey?'

'I'm thinking I'll find it hard to make friends in—in there. 'Tis such a pity, to my thinking, that by reggilations we'll be parted as soon as we get inside. You've a-got so used to my little ways an' cornders, an' we've a-got so many little secrets together an' old-fash'ned odds an' ends o' knowledge, that you can take my meaning almost afore I start to speak. An' that's a great comfort to a man o' my age. It'll be terrible hard, when I wants to talk, to begin at the beginning every time. There's that old yarn o' mine about Hambly's cow an' the lawn-mowing machine—I doubt that anybody'll enjoy it so much as you always do; an' I've so got out o' the way o' telling the beginning — which bain't extra funny, though needful to a stranger's understanding the whole joke—that I 'most forgets how it goes.'

'We'll see one another now an' then, they tell me. The sexes meet for Chris'mas-trees an' such-like.'

'I'm jealous that 'twon't be the same. You can't hold your triflin' confabs with a great Chris'mas-tree blazin' away in your face as important as a town afire.'

'Well, I'm going to start along,' the old woman decided, getting on her feet; 'or else someone'll be driving by and seeing us.'

Jan, too, stood up.

'We may so well make our congees here,' she went on, 'as under the porter's nose.'

An awkward silence fell between them for a minute, and these two old creatures, who for more than fifty years had felt no constraint in each other's presence, now looked into each other's eyes with a fearful diffidence. Jan cleared his throat, much as if he had to make a public speech.

'Maria,' he began in an unnatural voice, 'we 're bound for to part, and I can trewly swear, on leaving ye, that——'

'——that for two score year and twelve it 's never entered your head to consider whether I 've made 'ee a good wife or a bad. Kiss me, my old man; for I tell 'ee I wouldn' ha' wished it other. An' thank 'ee for trying to make that speech. What did it feel like?'

'Why, 't reminded me o' the time when I offered 'ee marriage.'

'It reminded me o' that, too,' the woman answered. 'Come'st along.'

They tottered down the hill towards the Workhouse gate. When they were but ten yards from it, however, they heard the sound of wheels on the road behind them, and walked bravely past, pretending to have no business at that portal. They had descended a good thirty yards beyond (such haste was put into them by dread of having their purpose guessed) before the vehicle overtook them—a four-wheeled dog-cart carrying a commercial traveller, who pulled up and offered them a lift into the town.

They declined.

Then, as soon as he passed out of sight, they turned, and began painfully to climb back towards the gate. Of the two, the woman had shown the less emotion. But all the way her lips were at work, and as she went she was praying a prayer. It was the only one she used night and morning, and she had never changed a word since she learned it as a chit of a child. Down to her seventieth year she had never found it absurd to beseech God to make her 'a good girl'; nor did she find it so as the Workhouse gate opened, and she began a new life.

LETTER TO MAARTEN MAARTENS

The Haven
Fowey, Cornwall
March 2nd 1894.

MY dear Mr. 'Maarten Maartens,'
When your letter reached me—and I think it was the pleasantest that ever came from an unknown friend—we were in great trouble here, by reason of the illness (fatal, as it turned out) of my wife's mother. I might have written you a polite note: but I wanted to send you much more than that: and had no heart to do it. Then I promised myself that I would write after reading *The Greater Glory*: but again the library has betrayed me by its delays: the three volumes have not yet arrived—country readers being neglected on principle—and I stand convicted of gross rudeness, unless you will understand my case and forgive it. As it is, I am ashamed to write, and yet cannot put off writing any longer.

I did not come to know your books as soon as I ought: but as soon as I knew them I wanted to know more, of them and of their author. It must be two years almost since Barrie and I talked of *God's Fool* throughout a long afternoon's walk. He was being taken out expressly to see the country round Fowey: but we clean forgot our purpose, and in the end I believe he might just as well have been walking along Oxford Street,— and this is as good a chance as any for saying that next time you visit England you must spend, if not less time in London, at any rate more in the country. As you know, from the *D. Duchy*, I do my piping in a corner: and the corner is a long way from London: but Dr. Nicoll may have told you that it is a beautiful spot. Moreover we have a prophet's chamber here, and, what-ever you may think of the invitation, it would be glad news to hear that you intended to spend a day or two with us. You could always collar Barrie in London and bring him along, to make sure of having good company. Tell him that he *must*, and he will come like a lamb: he knows that it is good for him. And, if you don't resent my saying it, it will be good for you, too, after long dinners and late hours in London, to come for a while to country fare, with claret and tobacco and much idleness in boats or by the harbourside, and bathing (if you like it) at the foot of the garden and ships going to and fro all the day long. I wish I could persuade you.

You speak too kindly of my books,—though I am not the less obliged to you for that. Or rather you see what they are trying for, instead of the poor work actually done. That's the best of a good word from an artist. The usual critic imagines one to be content (good Heavens!) with one's writings, and complacent. As if a man doesn't think fifty times of what he hopes to do to once of what he has done! And even if—as the chances are—all his trouble has only been a preparation for a feat that never comes off, why meanwhile he has been happy in his ignorance and happier for the encouragement. I cannot tell you how much your letter has cheered me. Some day I hope you will let me tell you face to face. Meanwhile we are all cultivating our gardens: and if mine is a narrow one, I shall none the less be happy in your success, and perhaps send you a flower from time to time as tribute.

Believe me

sincerely yours

'Q.'

THE LOOE DIE-HARDS

CAPTAIN POND, of the East and West Looe Volunteer Artillery (familiarly known as the Looe Die-hards), put his air-cushion to his lips and blew. This gave his face a very choleric and martial expression.

Nevertheless, above his suffused and distended cheeks his eyes preserved a pensive melancholy as they dwelt upon his Die-hards gathered in the rain below him on the long-shore, or Church-end, wall. At this date (November 3, 1809) the company numbered seventy, besides Captain Pond and his two subalterns; and of this force four were out in the boat just now, mooring the practice-mark—a barrel with a small red flag stuck on top; one, the bugler, had been sent up the hill to the nine-pounder battery, to watch and sound a call as soon as the target was ready; a sixth, Sergeant Fugler, lay at home in bed, with the senior lieutenant (who happened also to be the local doctor) in attendance. Captain Pond clapped a thumb over the orifice of his air-cushion, and heaved a sigh as he thought of Sergeant Fugler. The remaining sixty-four Die-hards, with their fire-locks under their great-coats, and their collars turned up against the rain, lounged by the embrasures of the shore-wall, and gossiped dejectedly, or eyed in silence the blurred boat bobbing up and down in the grey blur of the sea.

'Such coarse weather I hardly remember to have met with for years,' said Uncle Israel Spettigew, a cheerful sexagenarian who ranked as efficient on the strength of his remarkable eye-sight, which was keener than most boys'. 'The sweep from over to Polperro was cleanin' my chimbley this mornin', and he told me in his humorous way that with all this rain 'tis so much as he can do to keep his face dirty—hee-hee!'

Nobody smiled. 'If you let yourself give way to the enjoyment of little things like that,' observed a younger gunner gloomily, 'one o' these days you 'll find yourself in a better land like the snuff of a candle. 'Tis a year since the Company's been allowed to move in double time, and all because you can't manage a step o' thirty-six inches 'ithout getting the palpitations.'

'Well-a-well, 'tis but for a brief while longer—a few fleeting weeks, an' us Die-hards shall be as though we had never been. So why not be cheerful? For my part, I mind back in 'seventy-nine, when the fleets o' France an' Spain assembled an' come up agen' us—sixty-six sail o' the line, my sonnies, besides frigates an' corvettes to the amount o' twenty-five or thirty, all as plain as the nose on your face: an' the alarm guns goin', up to Plymouth, an' the signals hoisted at Maker Tower—a bloody flag at the pole an' two blue 'uns at the outriggers. Four days they laid to, an' I mind the first time I seed mun, from this very place as it might be where we 'm standin' at this moment, I said "Well, 'tis all over with East Looe this time!" I said: "an' when 'tis over, 'tis over, as Joan said by her weddin'." An' then I spoke them verses by royal Solomon—Wisdom two, six to nine. "Let us fill oursel's wi' costly wine an' ointments," I said: "an' let no flower o' the spring pass by us. Let us crown oursel's wi' rosebuds, afore they be withered: let none of us go without his due part of our voluptuousness"——'

'Why, you old adage, that 's what Solomon makes th' *ungodly* say!' interrupted young Gunner Oke, who had recently been appointed parish clerk, and happened to know.

'As it happens,' Uncle Issy retorted, with sudden dignity—'as it happens, I *was* ungodly in them days. The time I 'm talkin' about was August 'seventy-nine; an' if I don't mistake, your father an' mother, John Oke, were courtin' just then, an' 'most too shy to confide in each other about havin' a parish clerk for a son.'

'Times hev' marvellously altered in the meanwhile, to be sure,' put in Sergeant Pengelly of the Sloop Inn.

'Well, then,' Uncle Issy continued, without pressing his

triumph, "''Tis all over with East Looe," I said, "an' this is a black day for King Gearge," an' then I spoke them verses o' Solomon. "Let none of us," I said, "go without his due part of our voluptuousness"; and with that I went home and dined on tatties an' bacon. It hardly seems a thing to be believed at this distance o' time, but I never relished tatties an' bacon better in my life than that day—an' yet not meanin' the laste disrespect to King Gearge. Disrespect? If his Majesty only knew it, he 've no better friend in the world than Israel Spettigew. God save the King!'

And with this Uncle Issy pulled off his cap and waved it round his head, thereby shedding a *moulinet* of raindrops full in the faces of his comrades around.

This was observed by Captain Pond, standing on the platform above, beside Thundering Meg, the big 24-pounder, which with four 18-pounders on the shore-wall formed the lower defences of the haven.

'Mr. Clogg,' he called to his junior lieutenant, 'tell Gunner Spettigew to put on his hat at once. Ask him what he means by taking his death and disgracing the company.'

The junior lieutenant—a small farmer from Talland parish—touched his cap, spread his hand suddenly over his face and sneezed.

'Hallo! You 've got a cold.'

'No, sir. I often sneezes like that, and no reason for it whatever.'

'I 've never noticed it before.'

'No, sir. I keeps it under so well as I can. A great deal can be done sometimes by pressing your thumb on the upper lip.'

'Ah, well! So long as it 's not a cold——' returned the Captain, and broke off to arrange his air-cushion over the depressed muzzle of Thundering Meg. Hereupon he took his seat, adjusted the lapels of his great-coat over his knees, and gave way to gloomy reflection.

Sergeant Fugler was at the bottom of it. Sergeant Fugler,

the best marksman in the Company, was a hard drinker, with a hobnailed liver. He lay now in bed with that hobnailed liver and the Doctor said it was only a question of days. But why should this so extraordinarily discompose Captain Pond, who had no particular affection for Fugler, and knew, besides, that all men—and especially hard drinkers—are mortal?

The answer is that the East and West Looe Volunteer Artillery was no ordinary Company. When, on the 16th of May, 1803, King George told his faithful subjects, who had been expecting the announcement for some time, that the Treaty of Amiens was no better than waste paper, public feeling in the two Looes rose to a very painful pitch. The inhabitants used to assemble before the post office, to hear the French bulletins read out; and though it was generally concluded that they held much falsehood, yet everybody felt misfortune in the air. Rumours flew about that a diversion would be made by sending an army into the Duchy to draw the troops thither while the invaders directed their main strength upon London. Quiet villagers, therefore, dwelt for the while in a constant apprehension, fearing to go to bed lest they should awake at the sound of the trumpet, or in the midst of the French troops; scarcely venturing beyond sight of home lest, returning, they should find the homestead smoking and desolate. Each man had laid down the plan he should pursue. Some were to drive off the cattle, others to fire the corn. While the men worked in the fields, their woman-kind—young maids and grandmothers, and all that could be spared from domestic work—encamped above the cliffs, wearing red cloaks to scare the Frenchmen, and by night kept big bon-fires burning continually. Amid this painful disquietude of the public mind 'the great and united Spirit of the British People armed itself for the support of their ancient Glory and Inde-pendence against the unprincipled Ambition of the French Government.' In other words, the Volunteer movement began. In the Duchy alone no less than 8,362 men enrolled themselves in thirty Companies of foot, horse, and artillery, as well out of

enthusiasm as to escape the general levy that seemed probable
—so mixed are all human actions.

Of these the Looe Company was neither the greatest nor the
least. It had neither the numerical strength of the Royal
Stannary Artillery (1,115 men and officers) nor the numerical
eccentricity of the St. Germans Cavalry, which consisted of
forty troopers, all told, and eleven officers, and hunted the fox
thrice a week during the winter months under Lord Eliot,
Captain and M.F.H. The Looe Volunteers, however, started
well in the matter of dress, which consisted of a dark-blue coat
and pantaloons, with red facings and yellow wings and tassels,
and a white waistcoat. The officers' sword-hilts were adorned
with prodigious red and blue tassels, and the blade of Captain
Pond's, in particular, bore the inscription, '*My Life's Blood for
the Two Looes!*'—a legend which we must admit to be touching,
even while we reflect that the purpose of the weapon was not
to draw its owner's life-blood.

As a matter of mere history, this devoted blade had drawn
nobody's blood; since, in the six years that followed their
enlistment, the Looe Die-hards had never been given an opportunity for a brush with their country's hereditary foes. How,
then, did they acquire their proud title?

It was the Doctor's discovery; and perhaps, in the beginning,
professional pride may have had something to do with it; but
his enthusiasm was quickly caught up by Captain Pond and
communicated to the entire Company.

'Has it ever occurred to you, Pond,' the Doctor began, one
evening in the late summer of 1808, as the two strolled homeward from parade, 'to reflect on the rate of mortality in this
Company of yours? Have you considered that in all these five
years since their establishment not a single man has died?'

'Why the deuce should he?'

'But look here: I've worked it out on paper, and the mean
age of your men is thirty-four years, or some five years more
than the mean age of the entire population of East and West

Looe. You see, on the one hand, you enlist no children, and on the other, you 've enlisted several men of ripe age, because you 're accustomed to them and know their ways—which is a great help in commanding a Company. But this makes the case still more remarkable. Take any collection of seventy souls the sum of whose ages, divided by seventy, shall be thirty-four, and by all the laws of probability three, at least, ought to die in the course of a year. I speak, for the moment, of civilians. In the military profession,' the Doctor continued, with perfect seriousness, 'especially in time of war, the death-rate will be enormously heightened. But'—with a flourish of the hand—'I waive that. I waive even the real, if uncertainly estimated, risk of handling, twice or thrice a week and without timidity or particular caution, the combustibles and explosives supplied us by Government. And still I say that we might with equanimity have beheld our ranks thinned during these five years by the loss of fifteen men. And we have not lost a single one! It is wonderful!'

'War is a fearful thing,' commented Captain Pond, whose mind moved less nimbly than the Doctor's.

'Dash it all, Pond! Can't you see that I 'm putting the argument on a *peace* footing? I tell you that in five years of *peace* any ordinary Company of the same size would have lost at least fifteen men.'

'Then all I can say is that peace is a fearful thing, too.'

'But don't you see that at this moment you 're commanding the most remarkable Company in the Duchy, if not in the whole of England?'

'I do,' answered Captain Pond, flushing. 'It 's a responsibility, though. It makes a man feel proud; but, all the same, I almost wish you hadn't told me.'

Indeed at first the weight of his responsibility counteracted the Captain's natural elation. It lifted, however, at the next Corporation dinner, when the Doctor made public announcement of his discovery in a glowing speech, supporting his rhetoric by extracts from a handful of statistics and calculations, and ending, 'Gentlemen, we know the motto of the East and West Looe Volunteer Artillery to be *"Never Say Die!"* but seeing, after five years' trial of them, that they never *do* die, what man (I ask) will not rejoice to belong to such a Company? What man would not be proud *to command it?*'

After this, could Captain Pond lag behind? His health was drunk amid thunders of applause. He rose: he cast timidity to the winds: he spoke, and while he spoke, wondered at his own enthusiasm. Scarcely had he made an end before his fellow-townsmen caught him off his feet and carried him shoulder high through the town by the light of torches. There were many aching heads in the two Looes next morning; but nobody died: and from that night Captain Pond's Company wore the name of 'The Die-hards.'

All went well at first; for the autumn closed mildly. But with November came a spell of north-easterly gales, breeding bronchial discomfort among the aged; and Black Care began to dog the Commander. He caught himself regretting the admission of so many gunners of riper years, although the majority of these had served in His Majesty's Navy, and were by consequence the best marksmen. They weathered the winter, however; and a slight epidemic of whooping-cough, which broke out in the early spring, affected none of the Die-hards except the small bugler, and he took it in the mildest form. The men, following the Doctor's lead, began to talk more boastfully than ever. Only the Captain shook his head, and his eyes wore a wistful look, as though he listened continually for the footsteps of Nemesis—as, indeed, he did. The strain was breaking him. And in August, when word came from headquarters that, all danger of invasion being now at an end, the Looe Volunteer Artillery would be disbanded at the close of the year, he tried in vain to grieve. A year ago he would have wept in secret over the news. Now he went about with a solemn face and a bounding heart. A few months more and then——

And then, almost within sight of goal, Sergeant Fugler had broken down. Every one knew that Fugler drank prodigiously; but so had his father and grandfather, and each of them had reached eighty. The fellow had always carried his liquor well enough, too. Captain Pond looked upon it almost as a betrayal.

'I don't know what folks' constitutions are coming to in these days,' he kept muttering, on this morning of November the 3rd, as he sat on the muzzle of Thundering Meg and dangled his legs.

And then, glancing up, he saw the Doctor coming from the town along the shore-wall, and read evil news at once. For many of the Die-hards stopped the Doctor to question him, and stood gloomy as he passed on. It was popularly said in the two Looes, that 'if the Doctor gave a man up, that man might as well curl up his toes then and there.'

Catching sight of his Captain on the platform, the Doctor bent his steps thither, and they were slow and inelastic.

'Tell me the worst,' said Captain Pond.

'The worst is that he's no better; no, the worst of all is that he knows he's no better. My friend, between ourselves, it's only a question of a day or two.'

Silence followed for half a minute, the two officers avoiding each other's eyes.

'He has a curious wish,' the Doctor resumed, still with his face averted and his gaze directed on the dull outline of Looe Island, a mile away. 'He says he knows he's disgracing the Company: but he's anxious, all the same, to have a military funeral: says if you can promise this, he'll feel in a way that he's forgiven.'

'He shall have it, of course.'

'Ah, but that's not all. You remember, a couple of years back, when they had us down to Pendennis Castle for a week's drill, there was a funeral of a Sergeant-Major in the Loyal Meneage; and how the band played a sort of burial tune ahead of the body? Well, Fugler asked me if you couldn't manage this Dead March, as he calls it, as well. He can whistle the tune if you want to know it. It seems it made a great impression on him.'

'Then the man must be wandering! How the dickens can we manage a Dead March without a band?—and we haven't even a fife and drum!'

'That's what I told him. I suppose we couldn't do anything with the church musicians.'

'There's only one man in the Company who belongs to the gallery, and that's Uncle Issy Spettigew: and he plays the bass-viol. I doubt if you can play the Dead March on a bass-viol, and I'm morally certain you can't play it and walk with it too. I suppose we can't borrow a band from another Company?'

'What, and be the mock of the Duchy?—after all our pride! I fancy I see you going over to Troy and asking Browne for the loan of his band. "Hallo!" he'd say, "I thought you never had such a thing as a funeral over at Looe!" I can hear the fellow chuckle. But I wish something could be done, all the same. A trifle of pomp would draw folks' attention off our disappointment.'

Captain Pond sighed and rose from the gun; for the bugle was sounding from the upper battery.

'Fall in, gentlemen, if you please!' he shouted. His politeness in addressing his Company might be envied even by the 'Blues.'

The Doctor formed them up and told them off along the sea-wall, as if for inspection. 'Or-der arms!' 'Fix bayonets!' 'Shoul-der arms!' Then with a glance of inquiry at his Captain, who had fallen into a brown study, 'Rear rank, take open order!'

'No, no,' interposed the Captain, waking up and taking a guess at the sun's altitude in the grey heavens. 'We're late this morning: better march 'em up to the battery at once.'

Then, quickly re-forming them, he gave the word, 'By the

* C

left! Quick march!' and the Die-hards swung steadily up the hill towards the platform where the four nine-pounders grinned defiance to the ships of France.

As a matter of fact, this battery stood out of reach of harm, with the compensating disadvantage of being able to inflict none. The reef below would infallibly wreck any ship that tried to approach within the point-blank range of some 270 yards, and its extreme range of ten times that distance was no protection to the haven, which lay round a sharp corner of the cliff. But the engineer's blunder was never a check upon the alacrity of the Die-hards, who cleaned, loaded, rammed home, primed, sighted, and blazed away with the precision of clock-work and the ardour of Britons, as though aware that the true strength of a nation lay not so much in the construction of her fortresses as in the spirit of her sons.

Captain Pond halted, re-formed his men upon the platform, and, drawing a key from his pocket, ordered Lieutenant Clogg to the store-hut, with Uncle Issy in attendance, to serve out the ammunition, rammers, sponges, water-buckets, etc.

'But the door's unlocked, sir,' announced the lieutenant, with something like dismay.

'Unlocked!' echoed the Doctor.

The Captain blushed.

'I could have sworn, Doctor, I turned the key in the lock before leaving last Thursday. I think my head must be going. I've been sleeping badly of late—it's this worry about Fugler. However, I don't suppose anybody——'

A yell interrupted him. It came from Uncle Issy, who had entered the store-hut, and now emerged from it as if projected from a gun.

'THE FRENCH! THE FRENCH!'

For two terrible seconds the Die-hards eyed one another. Then someone in the rear rank whispered, 'An ambush!' The two ranks began to waver—to melt. Uncle Issy, with head down and shoulders arched, was already stumbling down the slope towards the town. In another ten seconds the whole Company would be at his heels.

The Doctor saved their reputation. He was as pale as the rest; but a hasty remembrance of the cubic capacity of the store-hut told him that the number of Frenchmen in ambush there could hardly be more than half a dozen.

'Halt!' he shouted; and Captain Pond shouted 'Halt!' too, adding, 'There'll be heaps of time to run when we find out what's the matter.'

The Die-hards hung, still wavering, upon the edge of the platform.

'For my part,' the Doctor declared, 'I don't believe there's anybody inside.'

'But there *is*, Doctor! for I saw him myself just as Uncle Issy called out,' said the second lieutenant.

'Was it only *one* man that you saw?' demanded Captain Pond.

'That's all. You see, it was this way: Uncle Issy stepped fore, with me a couple of paces behind him thinking of nothing so little as bloodshed and danger. If you'll believe me, these things was the very last in my thoughts. Uncle Issy rolls aside the powder-cask, and what do I behold but a man ducking down behind it! "He's firing the powder," thinks I, "and here endeth William George Clogg!" So I shut my eyes, not willing to see my gay life whisked away in little portions; though I feared it must come. And then I felt Uncle Issy flee past me like the wind. But I kept my eyes tight till I heard the Doctor here saying there wasn't anybody inside. If you ask me what I think about the whole matter, I say, putting one thing with another, that 'tis most likely some poor chap taking shelter from the rain.'

Captain Pond unsheathed his sword and advanced to the door of the hut. 'Whoever you be,' he called aloud and firmly, 'you've got no business there; so come out of it, in the name of King George!'

At once there appeared in the doorway a little round-headed man in tattered and mud-soiled garments of blue cloth. His hair and beard were alike short, black, and stubbly; his eyes large and feverish, his features smeared with powder and a trifle pinched and pale. In his left hand he carried a small bundle, wrapped in a knotted blue kerchief: his right he waved submissively towards Captain Pond.

'See now,' he began, 'I give up. I am taken. Look you.'

'I think you must be a Frenchman,' said Captain Pond.

'Right. It is war: you have taken a Frenchman. Yes?'

'A spy?' the Captain demanded more severely.

'An escaped prisoner, more like,' suggested the Doctor; 'broken out of Dartmoor, and hiding there for a chance to slip across.'

'Monsieur le Lieutenant has guessed,' the little man answered, turning affably to the Doctor. 'A spy? No. It is not on purpose that I find me near your fortifications—oh, not a bit! A prisoner more like, as Monsieur says. It is three days that I was a prisoner, and now look here, a prisoner again. Alas! will Monsieur le Capitaine do me the honour to confide the name of his corps so gallant?'

'The Two Looes.'

'*La Toulouse!* But it is singular that we also have a Toulouse——'

'Hey?' broke in Second Lieutenant Clogg.

'I assure Monsieur that I say the truth.'

'Well, go on; only it don't sound natural.'

'Not that I have seen it'—('Ha!' commented Mr. Clogg)—'for it lies in the south, and I am from the north: Jean Alphonse Marie Trinquier, instructor of music, rue de la Madeleine quatr'-vingt-neuf, Dieppe.'

'Instructor of music?' echoed Captain Pond and the Doctor quickly and simultaneously, and their eyes met.

'And *Directeur des Fêtes Périodiques* to the Municipality of Dieppe. All the Sundays, you comprehend, upon the sands—

poum poum! while the citizens *se promènent sur la plage.* But all is not gay in this world. Last winter a terrible misfortune befell me. I lost my wife—my adored Philomène. I was desolated, inconsolable. For two months I could not take up my *cornet-à-piston.* Always when I blew—pouf!—the tears came also. Ah, what memories! Hippolyte, my—what you call it—my *beau-frère,* came to me and said, "Jean Alphonse, you must forget." I say, "Hippolyte, you ask that which is impossible." "I will teach you," says Hippolyte: "To-morrow night I sail for Jersey, and from Jersey I cross to Dartmouth, in England, and you shall come with me." Hippolyte made his living by what you call the Free Trade. This was far down the coast for him, but he said the business with Rye and Deal was too dangerous for a time. Next night we sailed. It was his last voyage. With the morning the wind changed, and we drove into a fog. When we could see again, *peste!*—there was an English frigate. She sent down her cutter and took the rest of us; but not Hippolyte—poor Hippolyte was shot in the spine of his back. Him they cast into the sea, but the rest of us they take to Plymouth, and then the War Prison on the moor. This was in May, and there I rest until three days ago. Then I break out—*je me sauve.* How? It is my affair: for I foresee, Messieurs, I shall now have to do it over again. I am *sot.* I gain the coast here at night. I am weary, *je n'en puis plus.* I find this *cassine* here: the door is open: I enter *pour faire un petit somme.* Before day I will creep down to the shore. A comrade in the prison said to me, "Go to Looe. I know a good Cornishman there——"'

'And you overslept yourself,' Captain Paul briskly interrupted, alert as ever to protect the credit of his Company. He was aware that several of the Die-hards, in extra-military hours, took an occasional trip across to Guernsey: and Guernsey is a good deal more than half-way to France.

'The point is,' observed the Doctor, 'that you play the cornet.'

'It is certain that I do so, monsieur; but how that can be the point——'

'And instruct in music?'

'Decidedly!'

'Do you know the Dead March?'

M. Trinquier was unfeignedly bewildered.

Said Captain Pond: 'Listen while I explain. You are my prisoner, and it becomes my duty to send you back to Dartmoor under escort. But you are exhausted; and notwithstanding my detestation of that infernal tyrant, your master, I am a humane man. At all events, I'm not going to expose two of my Die-hards to the risks of a tramp to Dartmoor just now—I wouldn't turn out a dog in such weather. It remains a question what I am to do with you in the meanwhile. I propose that you give me your parole that you will make no attempt to escape, let us say, for a month: and on receiving it I will at once escort you to my house, and see that you are suitably clothed, fed, and entertained.'

'I give it willingly, Monsieur le Capitaine. But how am I to thank you?'

'By playing the Dead March upon the *cornet-à-piston* and teaching others to do the like.'

'That seems a singular way of showing one's gratitude. But why the Dead March, monsieur? And, excuse me, there is more than one Dead March. I myself, *par exemple*, composed one to the memory of my adored Philomène but a week before Hippolyte came with his so sad proposition.'

'I doubt if that will do. You see,' said Captain Pond, lifting his voice for the benefit of the Die-hards, who by this time were quite as sorely puzzled as their prisoner, 'we are about to bury one of our Company, Sergeant Fugler——'

'Ah! he is dead?'

'He is dying,' Captain Pond pursued, the more quickly since he now guessed, not without reason, that Fugler was the 'good Cornishman' to whose door M. Trinquier had been directed.

'He is dying of a hobnailed liver. It is his wish to have the Dead March played at his burying.'

'He whistled the tune over to me,' said the Doctor; 'but plague take me if I can whistle it to you. I 've no ear: but I 'd know it again if I heard it. Dismal isn't the word for it.'

'It will be Handel. I am sure it will be Handel—the Dead March in his *Saul.*'

'In his what?'

'In his oratorio of *Saul.* Listen—*poum, poum, prrr, poum*——'

'Be dashed, but you 've got it!' cried the Doctor, delighted; 'though you do give it a sort of foreign accent. But I dare say that won't be so noticeable on the key-bugle.'

'But about this key-bugle, monsieur? And the other instruments?—not to mention the players.'

'I 've been thinking of that,' said Captain Pond. 'There 's Butcher Tregaskis has a key-bugle. He plays *Rule, Britannia!* upon it when he goes round with the suet. He 'll lend you that till we can get one down from Plymouth. A drum, too, you shall have. Hockaday's trader calls here to-morrow on her way to Plymouth; she shall bring both instruments back with her. Then we have the church musicians—Peter Tweedy, first fiddle; Matthew John Ede, second ditto; Thomas Tripconey, scorpion——'

'Serpent,' the Doctor corrected.

'Well, it 's a filthy thing to look at, anyway. Israel Spettigew, bass-viol; William Henry Phippin, flute; and William Henry Phippin's eldest boy Archelaus to tap the triangle at the right moment. That boy, sir, will play the triangle almost as well as a man grown.'

'Then, monsieur, take me to your house. Give me a little food and drink, pen, ink, and paper, and in three hours you shall have *la partition.*'

Said the Doctor, 'That 's all very well, Pond, but the church musicianers can't march with their music, as you told me just now.'

'I've thought of that, too. We'll have Miller Penrose's covered three-horse wagon to march ahead of the coffin. Hang it in black and go slow, and all the musicianers can sit around inside and play away as merry as grigs.'

'The cover 'll give the music a sort of muffly sound; but that,' Lieutenant Clogg suggested, 'will be all the more fitty for a funeral.'

'So it will, Clogg; so it will. But we're wasting time. I suppose you won't object, sir, to be marched down to my house by the Company? It's the regular thing in case of taking a prisoner, and you'll be left to yourself as soon as you get to my door.'

'Not at all,' said M. Trinquier amiably.

'Then, gentlemen, fall in! The practice is put off. And when you get home, mind you change your stockings, all of you. We're in luck's way this morning, but that's no reason for recklessness.'

So M. Trinquier, some time Director of Periodical Festivities to the Municipality of Dieppe, was marched down into East Looe, to the wonder and delight of the inhabitants, who had just recovered from the shock of Gunner Spettigew's false alarm, and were in a condition to be pleased with trifles. As the Company tramped along the street, Captain Pond pointed out the Town Hall to his prisoner.

'That will be the most convenient place to hold your practices. And that is Fugler's house, just opposite.'

'But we cannot practise without making a noise.'

'I hope not, indeed. Didn't I promise you a big drum?'

'But in that case the sick man will hear. It will disturb his last moments.'

'Confound the fellow, he can't have everything! If he'd asked for peace and quiet, he should have had it. But he didn't: he asked for a Dead March. Don't trouble about Fugler. He's not an unreasonable man. The only question is, if the Doctor here can keep him going until you're perfect with the tune.'

And this was the question upon which the men of Looe, and especially the Die-hards, hung breathless for the next few days. M. Trinquier produced his score; the musicianers came forward eagerly; Miller Penrose promised his wagon; the big drum arrived from Plymouth in the trader *Good Intent*, and was discharged upon the quay amid enthusiasm. The same afternoon, at four o'clock, M. Trinquier opened his first practice in the Town Hall, by playing over the air of the 'Dead Marching Soul'—(to this the popular mouth had converted the name)—upon his cornet, just to give his pupils a general notion of it.

The day had been a fine one, with just that suspicion of frost in the air which indicates winter on the warm south-western coast. While the musicians were assembling the Doctor stepped across the street to see how the invalid would take it. Fugler —a sharp-featured man of about fifty, good-looking, with blue eyes and a tinge of red in his hair—lay on his bed with his mouth firmly set and his eyes resting, wistfully almost, on the last wintry sunbeam that floated in by the geraniums on the window-ledge. He had not heard the news. For five days now he expected nothing but the end, and lay and waited for it stoically and with calm good temper.

The Doctor took a seat by the bed-side, and put a question or two. They were answered by Mrs. Fugler, who moved about the small room quietly, removing, dusting and replacing the china ornaments on the chimneypiece. The sick man lay still, with his eyes upon the sunbeam.

And then very quietly and distinctly the notes of M. Trinquier's key-bugle rose outside on the frosty air.

The sick man started, and made as if to raise himself on his elbow, but quickly sank back again—perhaps from weakness, perhaps because he caught the Doctor's eye and the Doctor's reassuring nod. While he lay back and listened, a faint flush crept into his face, as though the blood ran quicker in his weak limbs; and his blue eyes took a new light altogether.

'That 's the tune, hey?' the Doctor asked.

'That's the tune.'

'Dismal, ain't it?'

'Ay, it's that.' His fingers were beating time on the counterpane.

'That's our new bandmaster. He's got to teach it to the rest, and you've got to hold out till they pick it up. Whew! I'd no idea music could be so dismal.'

'Hush 'ee, Doctor, do! till he've a-done. 'Tis like rain on blossom.' The last notes fell. 'Go you down, Doctor, and say my duty and will he please play it over once more, and Fugler 'll gi'e 'em a run for their money.'

The Doctor went back to the Town Hall and delivered this encore, and M. Trinquier played his solo again; and in the middle of it Mr. Fugler dropped off into an easy sleep.

After this the musicians met every evening, Sundays and weekdays, and by the third evening the Doctor was able to predict with confidence that Fugler would last out. Indeed, the patient was strong enough to be propped up into a sitting posture during the hour of practice, and not only listened with pleasure to the concerted piece, but beat time with his fingers while each instrument went over its part, delivering, at the close of each performance, his opinion of it to Mrs. Fugler or the Doctor: 'Tripconey's breath's failin'. He don't do no sort o' justice by that sarpint.' Or: 'There's Uncle Issy agen! He always do come to grief juss there! I reckon a man of sixty-odd ought to give up the bass-viol. He ha'n't got the agility.'

On the fifth evening Mrs. Fugler was sent across to the Town Hall to ask why the triangle had as yet no share in the performance, and to suggest that William Henry Phippin's eldest boy, Archelaus, played that instrument 'to the life.' M. Trinquier replied that it was unusual to seek the aid of the triangle in rendering the Dead March in *Saul*. Mr. Fugler sent back word that, 'if you came to *that*, the whole thing was unusual, from start to finish.' To this M. Trinquier discovered no answer; and the triangle was included, to the extreme delight of Archelaus Phippin, whose young life had been clouded for a week past.

On the sixth evening, Mr. Fugler announced a sudden fancy to 'touch pipe.'

'Hey?' said the Doctor, opening his eyes.

'I'd like to tetch pipe. An' let me light the brimstone mysel'. I likes to see the little blue flame turn yellow, a-dancin' on the baccy.'

'Get 'n his pipe and baccy, missis,' the Doctor commanded. 'He may kill himself clean-off now: the band'll be ready by the funeral, anyway.'

On the three following evenings Mr. Fugler sat up and smoked during band practice, the Doctor observing him with a new interest. The tenth day, the Doctor was called away to attend a child-birth at Downderry. At the conclusion of the cornet solo, with which M. Trinquier regularly opened practice, the sick man said:

'Wife, get me out my clothes.'

'WHAT!'

'Get me out my clothes.'

'You're mad! It'll be your death.'

'I don't care: the band's ready. Uncle Issy got his part perfect las' night, an' that's more'n I ever prayed to hear. Get me out my clothes an' help me downstairs.'

The Doctor was far away. Mrs. Fugler was forced to give in. Weeping, and with shaking hands, she dressed him and helped him to the foot of the stairs, where she threw open the parlour door.

'No,' he said, 'I'm not goin' in there. I'll be steppin' across to the Town Hall. Gi'e me your arm.'

Thomas Tripconey was rehearsing upon the serpent when the door of the Town Hall opened: and the music he made died away in a wail, as of a dog whose foot has been trodden on. William Henry Phippin's eldest son Archelaus cast his triangle down and shrieked 'Ghosts, ghosts!' Uncle Issy cowered behind his bass-viol and put a hand over his eyes. M. Trinquier spun round to face the intruder, baton in one hand, cornet in the other.

'Thank 'ee, friends,' said Mr. Fugler, dropping into a seat by the door, and catching breath: 'you 've got it very suent. 'Tis a beautiful tune: an' I 'm ha'f ashamed to tell 'ee that I bain't a-goin' to die, this time.'

Nor did he.

The East and West Looe Volunteer Artillery was disbanded a few weeks later, on the last day of the year 1809. The Corporations of the Two Boroughs entertained the heroes that evening to a complimentary banquet in the East Looe Town Hall, and Sergeant Fugler had recovered sufficiently to attend, though not to partake. The Doctor made a speech over him, proving him by statistics to be the most wonderful member of the most wonderful corps in the world. The Doctor granted, however—at such a moment the Company could make concessions—that the Die-hards had been singularly fortunate in the one foeman whom they had been called upon to face. Had it not been for a gentleman of France the death-roll of the Company had assuredly not stood at zero. He, their surgeon, readily admitted this, and gave them a toast, 'The Power of Music,' associating with this the name of Monsieur Jean Alphonse Marie Trinquier, Director of Periodic Festivities to the Municipality of Dieppe. The toast was drunk with acclamation. M. Trinquier responded, expressing his confident belief that two so gallant nations as England and France could not long be restrained from flinging down their own arms and rushing into each other's. And then followed Captain Pond, who, having moved his audience to tears, pronounced the Looe Die-hards disbanded. Thereupon, with a gesture full of tragic inspiration, he cast his naked blade upon the board. As it clanged amid the dishes and glasses, M. Trinquier lifted his arms, and the band crashed out the 'Dead Marching Soul,' following it with *God Save the King* as the clock announced midnight and the birth of the New Year.

'But hallo!' exclaimed Captain Pond, sinking back in his chair, and turning towards M. Trinquier. 'I had clean forgot that you are our prisoner, and should be sent back to Dartmoor! And now the Company is disbanded, and I have no one to send as escort.'

'Monsieur also forgets that my parole expired a fortnight since, and that my service from that hour has been a service of love!'

M. Trinquier did not return to Dartmoor. For it happened, one dark night early in the following February, that Mr. Fugler (now restored to health) set sail for the island of Guernsey upon a matter of business. And on the morrow the music-master of Dieppe had become but a pleasing memory to the inhabitants of the Two Looes.

And now, should you take up Mr. Thomas Bond's *History of East and West Looe,* and read of the Looe Volunteers that 'not a single man of the Company died during the six years, which is certainly very remarkable,' you will be not utterly incredulous; for you will know how it came about. Still, when one comes to reflect, it does seem an odd boast for a company of warriors.

ALMA MATER

[OXFORD]

KNOW you her secret none can utter?
   Hers of the Book, the tripled Crown?
Still on the spire the pigeons flutter,
   Still by the gateway flits the gown;
Still on the street, from corbel and gutter,
   Faces of stone look down.

Faces of stone, and stonier faces—
   Some from library windows wan
Forth on her gardens, her green spaces,
   Peer and turn to their books anon.
Hence, my Muse, from the green oases
   Gather the tent, begone!

Nay, should she by the pavement linger
   Under the rooms where once she played,
Who from the feast would rise to fling her
   One poor *sou* for her serenade?
One short laugh for the antic finger
   Thrumming a lute-string frayed?

Once, my dear—but the world was young then—
   Magdalen elms and Trinity limes—
Lissom the blades and the backs that swung then,
   Eight good men in the good old times—
Careless we, and the chorus flung then
   Under St. Mary's chimes!

Reins lay loose and the ways led random—
   Christ Church meadow and Iffley track,
'Idleness horrid and dog-cart' (tandem),
   Aylesbury grind and Bicester pack—
Pleasant our lines, and faith! we scanned 'em:
   Having that artless knack.

Come, old limmer, the times grow colder;
   Leaves of the creeper redden and fall.
Was it a hand then clapped my shoulder?—
   Only the wind by the chapel wall!
Dead leaves drift on the lute . . . So, fold her
   Under the faded shawl.

Never we wince, though none deplore us,
   We who go reaping that we sowed;
Cities at cock-crow wake before us—
   Hey, for the lilt of the London road!
One look back, and a rousing chorus!
   Never a palinode!

Still on her spire the pigeons hover;
   Still by her gateway haunts the gown.
Ah! but her secret?   You, young lover,
   Drumming her old ones forth from town,
Know you the secret none discover?
   Tell it—when *you* go down.

Yet if at length you seek her, prove her,
   Lean to her whispers never so nigh;
Yet if at last, not less her lover,
   You in your hansom leave the High;
Down from her towers a ray shall hover—
   Touch you, a passer-by!

ODE

I

O PASTORAL heart of England! like a psalm
    Of green days telling with a quiet beat—
O wave into the sunset flowing calm!
   O tirèd lark descending on the wheat!
Lies it all peace beyond that western fold
   Where now the lingering shepherd sees his star
Rise upon Malvern?   Paints an Age of Gold
     Yon cloud with prophecies of linkèd ease—
      Lulling this land, with hills drawn up like knees,
   To drowse beside her implements of war?

II

Man shall outlast his battles.   They have swept
   Avon from Naseby Field to Severn Ham;
And Evesham's dedicated stones have stepped
   Down to the dust with Montfort's oriflamme.
Nor the red tear nor the reflected tower
   Abides; but yet these eloquent grooves remain
Worn in the sandstone parapet hour by hour
     By labouring bargemen where they shifted ropes.
     E'en so shall man turn back from violent hopes
   To Adam's cheer, and toil with spade again.

III

Ay, and his mother Nature, to whose lap
  Like a repentant child at length he hies,
Not in the whirlwind or the thunder-clap
  Proclaims her more tremendous mysteries:
But when in winter's grave, bereft of light,
  With still, small voice divinelier whispering
—Lifting the green head of the aconite,
    Feeding with sap of hope the hazel-shoot—
    She feels God's finger active at the root,
  Turns in her sleep, and murmurs of the Spring.

DOLOR OOGO

THIRTEEN men by Ruan Shore,
    —Dolor Oogo, Dolor Oogo—
Drownèd men since 'eighty-four,
    Down in Dolor Oogo:
On the cliff against the sky,
Ailsa, wife of Malachi—
    That cold woman—
Sits and knits eternally.

By her silent husband's side
    —Dolor Oogo, Dolor Oogo—
Stretched awake, she hears the tide
    Moan in Dolor Oogo:
Till athwart the easter gale
Hark! the merry dead men hail—
    'Thou cold woman,
Take the lantern from the nail!'

Rising in her chilly sark
    —Dolor Oogo, Dolor Oogo—
Forth she fares by Behan Parc,
    Out to Dolor Oogo:
Kneeling there above the brink,
Lets her long red tresses sink
    —That cold woman—
For the sailor-men to drink.

Then the sailor men beneath
        —Dolor Oogo, Dolor Oogo—
Take the ends between their teeth,
        Deep in Dolor Oogo.
      'Lusty blood is this to quaff:
      (So the merry dead men laugh)
        O, cold woman,
      Hath thy man as good by half?'

'Drownèd men by Ruan Shore
        —Dolor Oogo, Dolor Oogo—
Lost aboard the *Elsinore*
        Down by Dolor Oogo—
      If the gulls behind the share
      Yesterday had called 'Beware,
        Thy cold woman!'
      Paler now had been my hair.

'Socks I knit you each a pair
        —Dolor Oogo, Dolor Oogo—
Half of yarn and half of hair,
        Over Dolor Oogo.'
      'Dripping, dripping on the tide,
      What red dye thy hair hath dyed,
        Thou cold woman?'
      'It hath brushed upon his side.'

Knitting with her double thread
        —Dolor Oogo, Dolor Oogo—
Half of black and half of red—
        Over Dolor Oogo,
      On the cliff against the sky,
      Ailsa, wife of Malachi,
        That cold woman,
      Wipes her hands incessantly.

THE PLANTED HEEL

BY Talland Church as I did go,
I passed my kindred all in a row;

Straight and silent there by the spade
Each in his narrow chamber laid.

While I passed, each kinsman's clay
Stole some virtue of mine away:

Till my shoes on the muddy road
Left not a print, so light they trod.

Back I went to the Bearers' Lane,
Begged the dead for my own again.

Answered the eldest one of my line—
'Thy heart was no one's heart but mine.'

The second claimed my working skill,
The third my wit, the fourth my will:

The fifth one said, 'Thy feet I gave;
But want no fleetness here in the grave.'

'For feet a man need have no care,
If they no weight of his own may bear.

'If I own naught by separate birth,
What binds my heel e'en now to the earth?'

The dead together answered back—
'Naught but the wealth in thy knapsack.'

'Nay, then,' said I, 'that's quick to unload':
And strewed my few pence out on the road.

'O kinsmen, now be quick, resume
Each rag of me to its rightful tomb!'

The dead were silent then for a space.
Still I stood upright in my place.

Said one, 'Some strength he will yet conceal.
Belike 'tis pride of a planted heel?

'Man has but one perduring pride:
Of knowledge alone he is justified.

'Lie down, lie down by us in the sod:
Thou shalt be wise in the ways of God.'

'Nay, so I stand upright in the dust,
I'll take God's purposes all on trust.

'An inch of heel for a yard of spine,—
So give me again the goods that are mine!'

I planted my heel by their headstones,
And wrestled an hour with my kinsmen's bones.

I shook their dust thrice into a sieve,
And gathered all that they had to give.

I winnowed knowledge out of the heap:
'Take it,' I said, 'to warm your sleep.'

I cast their knowledge back on the sod,
And went on my journey, praising God.

Of all their knowledge I thought me rid:
But one little grain in my pack had hid.—

Now, as I go, myself I tell,
'On a planted heel man wrestles well.'

But that little grain keeps whispering me—
'Better, perhaps, on a planted knee.'

SONNET

ISLES OF SCILLY

I SAW Narcissus in a portico
   Leaning his ear toward the yellow bells
  Of his own flower, festooned, that from the shells
Voluted on the pavement, caught the low
Long echoes of an Archipelago
   Afar, beyond the pillared parallels
   Wherein a soft wind wound, and nothing else,
Between his shoulder and the afterglow.

Figure of bronze!   Thou listenest alway:
   Ever for thee that lazy song beguiles.
But I must wake, and toil again, and pray;
   And yet will come but rarely, and at whiles,
The shout and vision of the sea-gods grey,
   Stampeding by the lone Scillonian isles.

THE FAMOUS BALLAD OF THE
JUBILEE CUP

YOU may lift me up in your arms, lad, and turn my face
to the sun,
For a last look back at the dear old track where the Jubilee Cup
was won;
And draw your chair to my side, lad—no, thank ye, I feel no
pain—
For I'm going out with the tide, lad, but I'll tell you the tale
again.

I'm seventy-nine, or nearly, and my head it has long turned
grey,
But it all comes back as clearly as though it was yesterday—
The dust, and the bookies shouting around the clerk of the scales,
And the clerk of the course, and the nobs in force, and His
Highness, the Pr*nce of W*les.

'Twas a nine-hole thresh to wind'ard, but none of us cared for
that,
With a straight run home to the service tee, and a finish along
the flat.
'Stiff?' Ah, well you may say it! Spot-barred, and at five-
stone-ten!
But at two and a bisque I'd ha' run the risk; for I was a green-
horn then.

So we stripped to the B. Race signal, the old red swallow-tail—
There was young Ben Bolt, and the Portland Colt, and Aston
Villa, and Yale;
And W. G., and Steinitz, Leander, and The Saint,
And the German Emperor's Meteor, a-looking as fresh as paint;

64

John Roberts (scratch), and Safety Match, The Lascar, and
    Lorna Doone,
Oom Paul (a bye), and Romany Rye, and me upon Wooden
    Spoon;
And some of us cut for partners, and some of us strung to
    baulk,
And some of us tossed for stations—But there, what use
    to talk?

Three-quarter-back on the Kingsclere crack was station enough
    for me,
With a fresh jackyarder blowing and the Vicarage goal a-lee!
And I leaned and patted her centre-bit, and eased the quid in
    her cheek,
With a 'Soh, my lass!' and a 'Woa, you brute!'—for she could
    do all but speak.

She was geared a thought too high, perhaps; she was trained a
    trifle fine;
But she had the grand reach forward! *I* never saw such a line!
Smooth-bored, clean-run, from her fiddle head with its dainty
    ear half-cock,
Hard-bit, *pur sang*, from her overhang to the heel of her off
    hind sock.

Sir Robert he walked beside me as I worked her down to the
    mark;
'There's money on this, my lad,' said he, 'and most of 'em's
    running dark;
But ease the sheet if you're bunkered, and pack the scrimmages
    tight,
And use your slide at the distance, and we'll drink to your health
    to-night!'

D

But I bent and tightened my stretcher.   Said I to myself, said I,—
'John Jones, this here is the Jubilee Cup, and you have to do
    or die.'
And the words weren't hardly spoken when the umpire shouted
    'Play!'
And we all kicked off from the Gasworks end with a 'Yoicks!'
    and a 'Gone away!'

And at first I thought of nothing, as the clay flew by in lumps,
But stuck to the old Ruy Lopez, and wondered who'd call for
    trumps,
And luffed her close to the cushion, and watched each one as
    it broke,
And in triple file up the Rowley mile we went like a trail of smoke.

The Lascar made the running: but he didn't amount to much,
For old Oom Paul was quick on the ball, and headed it back to
    touch;
And the whole first flight led off with the right, as The Saint
    took up the pace,
And drove it clean to the putting green and holed it there with
    an ace.

John Roberts had given a miss in baulk, but Villa cleared with
    a punt;
And keeping her service hard and low The Meteor forged to
    the front,
With Romany Rye to windward at dormy and two to play,
And Yale close up—but a Jubilee Cup isn't run for every day.

We laid our course for the Warner—I tell you the pace was hot!
And again off Tattenham Corner a blanket covered the lot.
Check side!   Check side!   Now steer her wide! and barely an
    inch of room,
With The Lascar's tail over our lee rail, and brushing Leander's
    boom!

We were running as strong as ever—eight knots—but it couldn't last;

For the spray and the bails were flying, the whole field tailing fast;

And the Portland colt had shot his bolt, and Yale was bumped at the Doves,

And The Lascar resigned to Steinitz, stale-mated in fifteen moves.

It was bellows to mend with Roberts—starred three for a penalty kick:

But he chalked his cue and gave 'em the butt, and Oom Paul scored the trick—

'Off-side—no-ball—and at fourteen all! Mark cock! and two for his nob!'—

When W. G. ran clean through his lee, and beat him twice with a lob.

He yorked him twice on a crumbling pitch, and wiped his eye with a brace,

But his guy-rope split with the strain of it, and he dropped back out of the race;

And I drew a bead on The Meteor's lead, and challenging none too soon,

Bent over and patted her garboard strake, and called upon Wooden Spoon.

She was all of a shiver forward, the spoondrift thick on her flanks,

But I'd brought her an easy gambit, and nursed her over the banks;

She answered her helm—the darling!—and woke up now with a rush,

While The Meteor's jock he sat like a rock—he knew we rode for his brush!

There was no one else left in it.   The Saint was using his
    whip,
And Safety Match, with a lofting catch, was pocketed deep at
    slip;
And young Ben Bolt with his niblick took miss at Leander's
    lunge,
But topped the net with the ricochet, and Steinitz threw up the
    sponge.

But none of the lot could stop the rot—nay, don't ask *me* to
    stop!—
The Villa had called for lemons, Oom Paul had taken his
    drop,
And both were kicking the referee.   Poor fellow! he done his
    best;
But, being in doubt, he 'd ruled them out—which he always did
    when pressed.

So, inch by inch, I tightened the winch, and chucked the sand-
    bags out—
I heard the nursery cannons pop, I heard the bookies shout:
'The Meteor wins!' 'No, Wooden Spoon!' 'Check!' 'Van-
    tage!' 'Leg before!'
'Last lap!'   'Pass Nap!'   At his saddle-flap I put up the helm
    and wore.

You may overflap at the saddle-flap, and yet be loo'd on the
    tape:
And it all depends upon changing ends, how a seven-year-old
    will shape;
It was tack and tack to the Lepe and back—a fair ding-dong
    to the Ridge,
And he led by his forward canvas yet as we shot 'neath Hammer-
    smith Bridge.

He led by his forward canvas—he led from his strongest suit—
But along we went on a roaring scent, and at Fawley I gained
    a foot.
He fisted off from the throttle, and gave me his wash—too late!
Deuce—vantage—check!   By neck and neck, we rounded into
    the straight.

I could hear the 'Conquering 'Ero' a-crashing on Godfrey's band,
And my hopes fell sudden to zero, just there with the race in
    hand—
In sight of the Turf's Blue Ribbon, in sight of the umpire's tape,
As I felt the tack of her spinnaker crack, as I heard the steam
    escape!

Had I lost at that awful juncture my presence of mind? . . .
    but no!
I leaned and felt for the puncture, and plugged it there with
    my toe . . .
Hand over hand by the Members' Stand I lifted and eased her up,
Shot—clean and fair—to the crossbar there, and landed the
    Jubilee Cup!

'The odd by a head, and leg before,' so the Judge he gave the
    word:
And the Umpire shouted 'Over!' but I neither spoke nor stirred.
They crowded round: for there on the ground I lay in a dead-
    cold swoon,
Pitched neck and crop on the turf atop of my beautiful Wooden
    Spoon.

Her dewlap tire was punctured, her bearings all red-hot;
She 'd a lolling tongue, and her bowsprit sprung, and her running
    gear in a knot;
And amid the sobs of her backers, Sir Robert loosened her girth
And led her away to the knacker's.   She had raced her last on
    earth!

But I mind me well of the tear that fell from the eye of our noble
Pr*nce,

And the things he said as he tucked me in bed—and I 've lain
there ever since;

Tho' it all gets mixed up queerly that happened before my spill,—

But I draw my thousand yearly: it 'll pay for the doctor's bill.

I 'm going out with the tide, lad—You 'll dig me a humble grave,

And whiles you will bring your bride, lad, and your sons (if
sons you have),

And there, when the dews are weeping, and the echoes murmur
'Peace!'

And the salt, salt tide comes creeping and covers the popping-
crease,

In the hour when the ducks deposit their eggs with a boasted
force,

They 'll look and whisper 'How was it?' and you 'll take them
over the course,

And your voice will break as you try to speak of the glorious
first of June,

When the Jubilee Cup, with John Jones up, was won upon
Wooden Spoon.

CHANT ROYAL OF HIGH VIRTUE

WHO lives in suit of armour pent
  And hides himself behind a wall,
For him is not the great event,
  The garland nor the Capitol.
And is God's guerdon less than they?
Nay, moral man, I tell thee Nay:
Nor shall the flaming forts be won
By sneaking negatives alone,
  By Lenten fast or Ramazàn;
But by the challenge proudly thrown—
  Virtue is that becrowns a Man!

God, in His Palace resident
  Of Bliss, beheld our sinful ball,
And charged His own Son innocent
  Us to redeem from Adam's fall.
'Yet must it be that men Thee slay.'
'Yea, tho' it must, must I obey,'
Said Christ; and came, His royal Son,
To die, and dying to atone
  For harlot, thief, and publican.
Read on that rood He died upon—
  Virtue is that becrowns a Man!

Beneath that rood where He was bent
  I saw the world's great captains all
Pass riding home from tournament
  Adown the road from Roncesvalles—
Lord Charlemagne, in one array
Lords Caesar, Cyrus, Attila,
Lord Alisaundre of Macedon . . .
With flame on lance and habergeon
  They passed, and to the rataplan
Of drums gave salutation—
  'Virtue is that becrowns a Man!'

Had tall Achilles lounged in tent
   For aye, and Xanthus neigh'd in stall,
The towers of Troy had ne'er been shent,
   Nor stay'd the dance in Priam's hall.
Bend o'er thy book till thou be grey,
Read, mark, perpend, digest, survey,
Instruct thee deep as Solomon,
One only chapter thou shalt con,
   One lesson learn, one sentence scan,
One title and one colophon—
   Virtue is that becrowns a Man!

High Virtue's hest is eloquent
   With spur and not with martingall:
Swear not to her thou 'rt continent:
   BE COURTEOUS, BRAVE, AND LIBERAL.
God fashion'd thee of chosen clay
For service, nor did ever say,
'Deny thee this,' 'Abstain from yon,'
But to inure thee, thew and bone,
   To be confirmèd of the clan
That made immortal Marathon—
   Virtue is that becrowns a Man!

ENVOY

Young Knight, the lists are set to-day!
Hereafter shall be time to pray
In sepulture, with hands of stone.
Ride, then! outride the bugle blown!
   And gaily dinging down the van
Charge with a cheer—'*Set on! Set on!*
   Virtue is that becrowns a Man!'

A NEW BALLAD OF SIR PATRICK SPENS

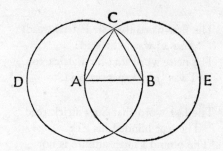

THE King sits in Dunfermline toun
    Drinking the blude-red wine:
'O wha will rear me an equilateral triangle
    Upon a given straight line?'

O up and spake an eldern knight,
    Sat at the King's right knee—
'Of a' the clerks by Granta side
    Sir Patrick bears the gree.

''Tis he was taught by the Tod-huntére
    Tho' not at the tod-hunting;
Yet gif that he be given a line,
    He 'll do as brave a thing.'

Our King has written a braid letter
    To Cambrigge or thereby,
And there it found Sir Patrick Spens
    Evaluating π.

He hadna warked his quotient
    A point but barely three,
There stepped to him a little foot-page
    And louted on his knee.

The first word that Sir Patrick read,
    '*Plus x*' was a' he said:
The neist word that Sir Patrick read,
    'Twas '*plus* expenses paid.'

The last word that Sir Patrick read,
    The tear blinded his e'e:
'The pound I most admire is not
    In Scottish currencie.'

Stately stepped he east the wa',
    And stately stepped he north:
He fetched a compass frae his ha'
    And stood beside the Forth.

Then gurly grew the waves o' Forth,
    And gurlier by-and-by—
'O never yet was sic a storm,
    Yet it isna sic as I!'

Syne he has crost the Firth o' Forth
    Until Dunfermline toun;
And tho' he came with a kittle wame
    Fu' low he louted doun.

'A line, a line, a gude straight line,
    O King, purvey me quick!
And see it be of thilka kind
    That 's neither braid nor thick.'

'Nor thick nor braid?' King Jamie said,
　'I 'll eat my gude hat-band
If arra line as ye define
　Be found in our Scotland.'

'Tho' there be nane in a' thy rule,
　It sall be ruled by me';
And lichtly with his little pencil
　He 's ruled the line A B.

Stately stepped he east the wa',
　And stately stepped he west;
'Ye touch the button,' Sir Patrick said,
　'And I sall do the rest.'

And he has set his compass foot
　Untill the centre A,
From A to B he 's stretched it oot—
　'Ye Scottish carles, give way!'

Syne he has moved his compass foot
　Untill the centre B,
From B to A he 's stretched it oot,
　And drawn it viz-a-vee.

The tane circle was B C D,
　And A C E the tither:
'I rede ye well,' Sir Patrick said,
　'They interseck ilk ither.

'See here, and whaur they interseck—
　To wit, with yon point C—
Ye 'll just obsairve that I conneck
　The twa points A and B.

'And there ye have a little triangle
  As bonny as e'er was seen;
The whilk is not isosceles,
  Nor yet it is scalene.'

'The proof! the proof!' King Jamie cried:
  'The how and eke the why!'
Sir Patrick laughed within his beard—
  ''Tis *ex hypothesi*—

'When I ligg'd in my mither's wame,
  I learn'd it frae my mither,
That things was equal to the same,
  Was equal ane to t'ither.

'Sith in the circle first I drew
  The lines B A, B C,
Be radii true, I wit to you
  The baith maun equal be.

'Likewise and in the second circle,
  Whilk I drew widdershins,
It is nae skaith the radii baith,
  A B, A C, be twins.

'And sith of three a pair agree
  That ilk suld equal ane,
By certes they maun equal be
  Ilk unto ilk by-lane.'

'Now by my faith!' King Jamie saith,
  'What *plane* geometrie!
If only Potts had written in Scots,
  How loocid Potts wad be!'

'Now wow's my life!' said Jamie the King,
  And the Scots lords said the same,
For but it was that envious knicht,
  Sir Hughie o' the Graeme.

'Flim-flam, flim-flam!' and 'Ho indeed?'
  Quod Hughie o' the Graeme;
''Tis I could better upon my heid
  This prabblin prablem-game.'

Sir Patrick Spens was nothing laith
  When as he heard 'flim-flam,'
But syne he's ta'en a silken claith
  And wiped his diagram.

'Gif my small feat may better'd be,
  Sir Hew, by thy big head,
What I hae done with an A B C
  Do thou with X Y Z.'

Then sairly sairly swore Sir Hew,
  And loudly laucht the King;
But Sir Patrick tuk the pipes and blew,
  And *played* that eldritch thing!

He's play'd it reel, he's played it jig,
  And the baith alternative;
And he's danced Sir Hew to the Asses' Brigg,
  That's Proposetion Five.

And there they've met, and there they've fet,
  Forenenst the Asses' Brigg,
And waefu', waefu', was the fate
  That gar'd them there to ligg.

For there Sir Patrick 's slain Sir Hew,
   And Sir Hew Sir Patrick Spens—
Now wasna' that a fine to-do
   For Euclid's Elemen's?

But let us sing Long live the King!
   And his foes the Deil attend 'em:
For he has gotten his little triangle
   Quod erat faciendum!

LAYING UP THE BOAT

THERE arrives a day towards the end of October—or with luck we may tide over into November—when the wind in the mainsail suddenly takes a winter force, and we begin to talk of laying up the boat. Hitherto we have kept a silent compact and ignored all change in the season. We have watched the blue afternoons shortening, fading through lilac into grey, and let pass their scarcely perceptible warnings. One afternoon a few kittiwakes appeared. A week later the swallows fell to stringing themselves like beads along the coastguard's telephone-wire on the hill. They vanished, and we pretended not to miss them. When our hands grew chill with steering we rubbed them by stealth or stuck them nonchalantly in our pockets. But this vicious unmistakable winter gust breaks the spell. We take one look around the harbour, at the desolate buoys awash and tossing; we cast another seaward at the thick weather through which, in a week at latest, will come looming the earliest of the Baltic merchantmen, our November visitors—bluff vessels with red-painted channels, green deckhouses, white top-strakes, wooden davits overhanging astern, and the Danish flag fluttering aloft in the haze. Then we find speech; and with us, as with the swallows, the move into winter quarters is not long delayed when once it comes into discussion. We have dissembled too long; and know, as we go through the form of debating it, that our date must be the next spring-tides.

This ritual of laying up the boat is our way of bidding farewell to summer; and we go through it, when the day comes, in ceremonial silence. *Favete linguis!* The hour helps us, for the spring-tides at this season reach their height a little after night-fall, and it is on an already slackening flood that we cast off our moorings and head up the river with our backs to the waning sunset. Since we tow a dinghy astern and are ourselves

79

towed by the silent yachtsman, you may call it a procession. She has been stripped, during the last two days, of sails, rigging, and all spars but the mainmast.   Now we bring her alongside the town quay and beneath the shears—the abhorrèd shears— which lift this too out of its step, dislocated with a creak as poignant as the cry of Polydorus.   We lower it, lay it along the deck, and resume our way; past quay doors and windows where already the townsfolk are beginning to light their lamps; and so by the jetties where foreign crews rest with elbows on bulwarks and stare down upon us idly through the dusk.   She is after all but a little cutter of six tons, and we might well apologize, like the Athenian, for so diminutive a corpse.   But she is our own; and they never saw her with jackyarder spread, or spinnaker or jib-topsail delicate as samite—those heavenly wings!—nor felt her gallant spirit straining to beat her own record before a tense northerly breeze.   Yet even to them her form, in pure white with gilt fillet, might tell of no common obsequies.

For in every good ship the miracle of Galatea is renewed; and the shipwright who sent this keel down the ways to her element surely beheld the birth of a goddess.   He still speaks of her with pride, but the conditions of his work keep him a modest man; for he goes about it under the concentred gaze of half a dozen old mariners hauled ashore, who haunt his yard uninvited, slow of speech but deadly critical.   Nor has the language a word for their appalling candour.   Often, admiring how cheerfully he tolerates them, I have wondered what it would feel like to compose a novel under the eyes of half a dozen reviewers.   But to him, as to his critics, the ship was a framework only until the terrible moment when with baptism she took life.   Did he in the rapture, the brief ecstasy of creation, realize that she had passed from him?   Ere the local artillery band had finished *Rule, Britannia!* and while his friends were still shaking his hands and drinking to him, did he know his loss in his triumph?   His fate is to improve the world, not to possess; to chase perfection, knowing that under the final mastering touch it must pass from his hand; to lose his works and anchor himself upon the workmanship, the immaterial function. For of art this is the cross and crown in one; and he, modest man, was born to the sad eminence.

She is ours now by purchase, but ours, too, by something better. Like a slave's her beautiful untaught body came to us; but it was we who gave wings to her, and with wings a soul, and a law to its grace, and discipline to its vital impulses. She is ours, too, by our gratitude, since the delicate machine

> Has like a woman given up its joy;

and by memories of her helpfulness in such modest perils as we tempt, of her sweet companionship through long days empty of annoyance—land left behind with its striving crowds, its short views, its idols of the market-place, its sordid worries; the breast flung wide to the horizon, swept by wholesome salt airs, void perhaps, but so beatifically clean! Then it was that we learned her worth, drinking in the knowledge without effort, lulled hour after hour by her whisperings which asked for no answer, by the pulse of her tiller soft against the palm. Patter of reef-points, creak of cordage, hum of wind, hiss of brine— I think at times that she has found a human language. Who that has ever steered for hours together cannot report of a mysterious voice 'breaking the silence of the seas,' as though a friend were standing and speaking astern? or has not turned his head to the confident inexplicable call? The fishermen fable of drowned sailors 'hailing their names.' But the voice is of a single speaker; it bears no likeness to the hollow tones of the dead; it calls no name; it utters no particular word. It merely speaks. Sometimes, ashamed at being tricked by an illusion so absurd, I steal a glance at the yachtsman forward. He is smoking, placidly staring at the clouds. Patently he was not the speaker, and patently he has heard nothing. Was it Cynthia, my dearer shipmate? She, too, knows the voice; even answered it one day, supposing it mine, and in her confusion I surprised our common secret. But we never hear it together. She is seated now on the lee side of the cockpit, her hands folded on the coaming, her chin rested on them, and her eyes gazing out beneath the sail and across the sea from which they surely have drawn their wine-coloured glooms. She has not stirred for many minutes. No, it was not Cynthia. Then either it must be the wild, obedient spirit who carries us, straining at the impassable bar of speech, to break through and be at one with her master, or else—Can it have been Ariel, perched aloft in the shrouds, with mischievous harp?

> That was the chirp of Ariel
> You heard, as overhead it flew,
> The farther going more to dwell
> And wing our green to wed our blue;
> But whether note of joy or knell
> Not his own Father-singer knew;
> Nor yet can any mortal tell,
> Save only how it shivers through;
> The breast of us a sounded shell,
> The blood of us a lighted dew.

Perhaps; but for my part I believe it was the ship; and if you deride my belief, I shall guess you one of those who need a figure-head to remind them of a vessel's sex. There are minds which find a certain romance in figure-heads. To me they seem a frigid, unintelligent device, not to say idolatrous. I have known a crew to set so much store by one that they kept a tinsel locket and pair of ear-rings in the forecastle and duly adorned their darling when in port. But this is materialism. The true personality of a ship resides in no prefiguring lump of wood with a sightless smile to which all seas come alike and all weathers. Lay your open palm on the mast, rather, and feel life pulsing beneath it, trembling through and along every nerve of her. Are you converted? That life is yours to control. Take the tiller, then, and for an hour be a god! For indeed you shall be a god, and of the very earliest. The centuries shall run out with the chain as you slip moorings—run out and drop from you, plumb, and leave you free, winged!   Or if you cannot forget in a moment the times to which you were born, each wave shall turn back a page as it rolls past to break on the shore towards which you revert no glance.   Even the romance of it shall fade with the murmur of that coast.

> Sails of silk and ropes of sendal,
>   Such as gleam in ancient lore,
> And the singing of the sailor,
>   And the answer from the shore—

these shall pass and leave you younger than romance—a child open-eyed and curious, pleased to meet a sea-parrot or a rolling porpoise, or to watch the gannets diving—

> As Noah saw them dive
> O'er sunken Ararat.

Yes, and sunset shall bring you, a god, to the gates of a kingdom I must pause to describe for you, though when you reach it you will forget my description and imagine yourself its first discoverer.   But that is a part of its charm.

Walter Pater, reading the *Odyssey*, was brought up (as we say) 'with a round turn' by a passage wherein Homer describes briefly and with accuracy how some mariners came to harbour, took down sail, and stepped ashore.   It filled him with wonder that so simple an incident—nor to say ordinary—could be made so poetical; and, having pondered it, he divided the credit between the poet and his fortunate age—a time (said he) in which one could hardly have spoken at all without ideal effect, or the sailors pulled down their sail without making a picture 'in the great style' against a sky charged with marvels.

You will discover, when you reach the river-mouth of which I am telling, and are swept over the rolling bar into quiet water —you will discover (and with ease, being a god) that Mr. Pater was entirely mistaken, and the credit belongs neither to Homer nor to his fortunate age. For here are woods with woodlanders, and fields with ploughmen, and beaches with fishermen hauling nets; and all these men, as they go about their work, contrive to make pictures 'in the great style' against a sky charged with marvels, obviously without any assistance from Homer, and quite as if nothing had happened for, say, the last three thousand years. That the immemorial craft of seafaring has no specially 'heroic age'—or that, if it have, that age is yours—you will discover by watching your own yachtsman as he moves about lowering foresail and preparing to drop anchor.

It is a river of gradual golden sunsets, such as Wilson painted —a broad-bosomed flood between deep and tranquil woods, the main banks holding here and there a village as in an arm maternally crook'd, but opening into creeks where the oaks dip their branches in the high tides, where the stars are glassed all night long without a ripple, and where you may spend whole days with no company but herons and sandpipers. Even by the main river each separate figure—the fisherman on the shore, the ploughman on the upland, the ferryman crossing between them—moves slowly upon a large landscape, while, permeating all, 'the essential silence cheers and blesses.' After a week at anchor in the heart of this silence Cynthia and I compared notes, and set down the total population at fifty souls; and even so she would have it that I had included the owls. Lo! the next morning an unaccustomed rocking awoke us in our berths, and, raising the flap of our dew-drenched awning, we 'descried at sunrise an emerging prow' of a peculiarly hideous excursion steamboat. She blew no whistle, and we were preparing to laugh at her grotesque temerity when we became aware of a score of boats putting out towards her from the shadowy banks. Like spectres they approached, reached her, and discharged their complements, until at last a hundred and fifty passengers crowded her deck. In silence—or in such silence as a paddle-boat can achieve—she backed, turned, and bore them away: on what festal errand we never discovered. We never saw them return.

They raised no cheer; no band accompanied them; they passed without even the faint hum of conversation. In five minutes at most the apparition had vanished around the river-bend seawards and out of sight. We stared at the gently heaving water, turned, and caught sight of Euergetes, his head and red cap above the forecastle hatch. (I call our yachtsman Euergetes because it is so unlike his real name that neither he nor his family will recognize it.) 'Why, Euergetes,' exclaimed Cynthia, 'wherever did they all come from?' 'I 'm sure I can't tell you, ma'am,' he answered, 'unless 'twas from the woods'—giving us to picture these ardent holiday-makers roosting all night in the trees while we slumbered. But the odd thing was that the labourers manned the fields that day, the fishermen the beach that evening, in undiminished numbers. We landed, and could detect no depletion in the village. We landed on subsequent days, and discovered no increase. And the inference, though easy, was startling.

I suppose that 'in the great style' could hardly be predicated of our housekeeping on these excursions; and yet it achieves, in our enthusiastic opinion, a primitive elegance not often recaptured by mortals since the passing of the Golden Age. We cook for ourselves, but bring a fine spirit of emulation both to cuisine and service. We dine frugally, but the claret is sound. From the moment when Euergetes awakes us by washing down the deck, and the sound of water rushing through the scuppers calls me forth to discuss the weather with him, method rules the early hours, that we may be free to use the later as we list. First the cockpit beneath the awning must be prepared as a dressing-room for Cynthia; next Euergetes summoned on deck to valet me with the simple bucket. And when I am dressed and tingling from the douche, and sit me down on the cabin top, barefooted and whistling, to clean the boots, and Euergetes has been sent ashore for milk and eggs, bread and clotted cream, there follows a peaceful half-hour until Cynthia flings back a corner of the awning and, emerging, confirms the dawn. Then begins the business, orderly and thorough, of redding up the cabin, stowing the beds, washing out the lower deck, folding away the awning, and transforming the cockpit into a breakfast-room, with table neatly set forth. Meanwhile Euergetes has returned, and from the forecastle comes the sputter of red mullet cooking. Cynthia clatters the cups and saucers, while in the well by the cabin door I perform some acquired tricks with the new-laid eggs. There is plenty to be done on board a small boat, but it is all simple enough. Only, you must not let it overtake you. Woe to you if it fall into arrears!

By ten o'clock or thereabouts we have breakfasted, my pipe is lit, and a free day lies before us:

> All the wood to ransack,
> All the wave explore.

We take the dinghy and quest after adventures. The nearest railway lies six miles off, and is likely to deposit no one in whom we have the least concern. The woods are deep, we carry our lunch-basket and may roam independent of taverns. If the wind invite, we can hoist our small sail; if not, we can recline and drift and stare at the heavens, or land and bathe, or search in vain for curlews' or kingfishers' nests, or in more energetic moods seek out a fisherman and hire him to shoot his seine. Seventy red mullet have I seen fetched at one haul out of those delectable waters, remote and enchanted as the lake whence the fisherman at the genie's orders drew fish for the young king of the Black Isles. But such days as these require no filling, and why should I teach you how to fill them?

Best hour of all perhaps is that before bed-time, when the awning has been spread once more, and after long hours in the open our world narrows to the circle of the reading-lamp in the cockpit. Our cabin is prepared. Through the open door we see its red curtain warm in the light of the swinging lamp, the beds laid, the white sheets turned back. Still we grudge these moments to sleep. Outside we hear the tide streaming seawards, light airs play beneath the awning, above it rides the host of heaven. And here, gathered into a few square feet, we have home—larder, cellar, library, tables, and cupboards; life's small appliances with the human comradeship they serve, chosen for their service after severely practical discussion, yet ultimately by the heart's true nesting instinct. We are isolated, bound even to this strange river-bed by a few fathoms of chain only. To-morrow we can lift anchor and spread wing; but we carry home with us.

> I will make you brooches and toys for your delight
> Of bird-song at morning and star-shine at night;
> I will make a palace fit for you and me
> Of green days in forests and blue days at sea.
>
> I will make my kitchen and you shall keep your room
> Where white flows the river and bright blows the broom;
> And you shall wash your linen and keep your body white
> In rainfall at morning and dewfall at night.

You see now what memories we lay up with the boat. Will you think it ridiculous that after such royal days of summer, her inconspicuous obsequies have before now put me in mind of Turner's 'Fighting *Téméraire*'? I declare, at any rate, that the fault lies not with me, but with our country's painters and poets for providing no work of art nearer to my mood. We English have a great seafaring and a great poetical past. Yet the magic of the sea and shipping has rarely touched our poetry, and for its finest expression we must still turn to an art in which as a race we are less expert, and stand before that picture of Turner's in the National Gallery. The late Mr. Froude believed in a good time coming when the sea-captains of Elizabeth are to find their bard and sit enshrined in 'a great English national epic as grand as the *Odyssey*.' It may be, but as yet our poets have achieved but a few sea-fights, marine adventures, and occasional pieces, which wear a spirited but accidental look, and suggest

the excursionist.   On me, at any rate, no poem in our language
—not even *The Ancient Mariner*—binds as that picture binds, the

> Mystic spell,
> Which none but sailors know or feel,
> And none but they can tell—

if indeed they *can* tell.   In it Turner seized and rolled together
in one triumphant moment the emotional effect of noble shipping
and a sentiment as ancient and profound as the sea itself—human
regret for transitory human glory.   The great warship, glimmering in her Mediterranean fighting-paint, moving like a queen
to execution; the pert and ignoble tug, itself an emblem of the
new order, eager, pushing, ugly, and impatient of the slow
loveliness it supersedes; the sunset hour, closing man's labour;
the fading river-reach—you may call these things obvious, but
all art's greatest effects are obvious when once genius has discovered them.   I should know well enough by this time what
is coming when I draw near that picture, and yet my heart never
fails to leap with the old wild wonder.   There are usually one
or two men standing before it—I observe that it affects women
less—and I glance at them furtively to see how *they* take it.
If ever I surprise one with tears in his eyes, I believe we shall
shake hands.   And why not?   For the moment we are not
strangers, but men subdued by the wonder and sadness of our
common destiny: 'we feel that we are greater than we know.'
We are two Englishmen, in one moment realizing the glories
of our blood and state.   We are alone together, gazing upon
a new Pacific, 'silent, upon a peak in Darien.'

For—and here lies his subtlety—in the very flush of amazement the painter flatters you by whispering that for *you* has his
full meaning been reserved.   The *Téméraire* goes to her doom
unattended, twilit, obscure, with no pause in the dingy bustle
of the river.   You alone have eyes for the passing of greatness,
and a heart to feel it.

> There's a far bell ringing,

but you alone hear it tolling to evensong, to the close of day, the end of deeds.

So, as we near the beach where she is to lie, a sense of proud exclusiveness mingles with our high regret. Astern the jetty-men and stevedores are wrangling over their latest job; trains are shunting, cranes working, trucks discharging their cargoes amid clouds of dust. We and we only assist at the passing of a goddess. Euergetes rests on his oars, the tow-rope slackens, she glides into the deep shadow of the shore, and with a soft grating noise—ah, the eloquence of it!—takes ground. Silently we carry her chain out and noose it about a monster elm; silently we slip the legs under her channels, lift and make fast her stern moorings, lash the tiller for the last time, tie the coverings over cabin top and well; anxiously, with closed lips, praetermitting no due rite. An hour, perhaps, passes, and November darkness has settled on the river ere we push off our boat, in a last farewell committing her—our treasure 'locked up, not lost'—to a winter over which Jove shall reign genially

Et fratres Helenae, lucida sidera.

As we thread our dim way homeward among the riding-lights flickering on the black water, the last pale vision of her alone and lightless follows and reminds me of the dull winter ahead, the short days, the long nights. She is haunting me yet as I land on the wet slip strewn with dead leaves to the tide's edge. She follows me up the hill, and even to my library door. I throw it open, and lo! a bright fire burning, and, smiling over against the blaze of it, cheerful, companionable, my books have been awaiting me.

THE HARBOUR OF FOWEY

O THE Harbour of Fowey
 Is a beautiful spot,
And it 's there I enjowey
 To sail in a yot;
Or to race in a yacht
 Round a mark or a buoy—
Such a beautiful spacht
 Is the Harbour of Fuoy!

When her anchor is weighed
 And the water she ploughs,
Upon neat lemoneighed
 O it 's then I caroughs;
And I take Watts's hymns
 And I sing them aloud
When it 's homeward she skymns
 O'er the waters she ploud.

But the wave mountain-high,
 And the violent storm,
Do I risk them? Not Igh!
 But prefer to sit worm
With a book on my knees
 By the library fire,
While I list to the brees
 Rising hire and hire.

And so, whether I weigh
 Up the anchor or not,
I am happy each deigh
 In my home or my yot;
Every care I resign,
 Every comfort enjoy,
In this cottage of mign
 By the Harbour of Foy.

And my leisure 's addressed
    To composing of verse
Which, if hardly the bessed,
    Might be easily werse.
And, the spelling I use
    Should the critics condemn,
Why, I have my own vuse
    And I don't think of themn.

Yes, I have my own views:
    But the teachers I follow
Are the Lyrical Miews
    And the Delphic Apollow.
Unto them I am debtor
    For spelling and rhyme,
And I 'm doing it bebtor
    And bebtor each thyme.

THE ROOM OF MIRRORS

A STORY OF HATE, TOLD BY THE PURSUER

A LATE hansom came swinging round the corner into
Lennox Gardens, cutting it so fine that the near wheel
ground against the kerb and jolted the driver in his little seat.
The jingle of bells might have warned me; but the horse's hoofs
came noiselessly on the half-frozen snow, which lay just deep
enough to hide where the pavement ended and the road began;
and, moreover, I was listening to the violins behind the first-
floor windows of the house opposite. They were playing the
Wiener Blut.

As it was, I had time enough and no more to skip back and
get my toes out of the way. The cabby cursed me. I cursed
him back so promptly and effectively that he had to turn in his
seat for another shot. The windows of the house opposite let
fall their light across his red and astonished face. I laughed,
and gave him another volley. My head was hot, though my
feet and hands were cold; and I felt equal to cursing down any
cabman within the four-mile radius. That second volley
finished him. He turned to his reins again and was borne
away defeated; the red eyes of his lamps peering back at me
like an angry ferret's.

Up in the lighted room shadows of men and women crossed
the blinds, and still the *Wiener Blut* went forward.

The devil was in that waltz. He had hold of the violins and
was weaving the air with scents and visions—visions of Ascot
and Henley; green lawns, gay sunshades, midsummer heat, cool
rivers flowing, muslins rippled by light breezes; running horses
and silken jackets; white tables heaped with roses and set with
silver and crystal, jewelled fingers moving in the soft candle-
light, bare necks bending, diamonds, odours, bubbles in the
wine; blue water and white foam beneath the leaning shadow

of sails; hot air flickering over stretches of moorland; blue again—Mediterranean blue—long façades, the din of bands and King Carnival parading beneath showers of blossom:—and all this noise and warmth and scent and dazzle flung out into the frozen street for a beggar's portion. I had gone under.

The door of the house opposite had been free to me once— and not six months ago; freer to me perhaps than to any other. Did I long to pass behind it again? I thrust both hands into my pockets for warmth, and my right hand knocked against something hard. Yes . . . just once. . . .

Suddenly the door opened. A man stood on the threshold for a moment while the butler behind him arranged the collar of his fur overcoat. The high light in the portico flung the shadows of both down the crimson carpet laid on the entrance steps. Snow had fallen and covered the edges of the carpet, which divided it like a cascade of blood pouring from the hall into the street. And still overhead the *Wiener Blut* went forward.

The man paused in the bright portico, his patent-leather boots twinkling under the lamp's rays on that comfortable carpet. I waited, expecting him to whistle for a hansom. But he turned, gave an order to the butler, and stepping briskly down into the street, made off eastwards. The door closed behind him. He was the man I most hated in the world. If I had longed to cross the threshold a while back it was to seek him, and for no other reason.

I started to follow him, my hands still in my pockets. The snow muffled our footfalls completely, for as yet the slight north-east wind had frozen but the thinnest crust of it. He was walking briskly, as men do in such weather, but with no appearance of hurry. At the corner of Sloane Street he halted under a lamp, pulled out his watch, consulted it, and lit a cigarette; then set off again up the street towards Knightsbridge.

This halt of his had let me up within twenty paces of him. He never turned his head; but went on, presenting me his back, a target not to be missed. Why not do it now? Better now and here than in a crowded thoroughfare. My right hand gripped the revolver more tightly. No, there was plenty of time: and I was curious to know what had brought Gervase out at this hour: why he had left his guests, or his wife's guests, to take care of themselves: why he chose to be trudging afoot through this infernally unpleasant snow.

The roadway in Sloane Street was churned into a brown mass like chocolate, but the last bus had rolled home and left it to freeze in peace. Half-way up the street I saw Gervase meet and pass a policeman, and altered my own pace to a lagging walk. Even so, the fellow eyed me suspiciously as I went by—or so I thought: and guessing that he kept a watch on me, I dropped still farther behind my man. But the lamps were bright at the end of the street, and I saw him turn to the right by the great drapery shop at the corner.

Once past this corner I was able to put on a spurt. He crossed the roadway by the Albert Gate, and by the time he reached the Park railings the old distance separated us once more. Half-way up the slope he came to a halt, by the stone drinking-trough: and flattening myself against the railings, I saw him try the thin ice in the trough with his finger-tips, but in a hesitating way, as if his thoughts ran on something else and he scarcely knew what he did or why he did it. It must have been half a minute before he recovered himself with a shrug of his shoulders, and plunging both hands deep in his pockets, resumed his pace.

As we passed Hyde Park Corner I glanced up at the clock there: the time was between a quarter and ten minutes to one. At the entrance of Down Street he turned aside again, and began to lead me a zigzag dance through the quiet thoroughfare: and I followed, still to the tune of the *Wiener Blut*.

But now, at the corner of Charles Street, I blundered against another policeman, who flashed his lantern in my face, stared after Gervase, and asked me what my game was. I demanded innocently enough to be shown the nearest way to Oxford Street, and the fellow, after pausing a moment to chew his suspicions, walked with me slowly to the south-west corner of Berkeley Square, and pointed northwards.

'That's your road,' he growled, 'straight on. And don't you forget it!'

He stood and watched me on my way. Nor did I dare to turn aside until well clear of the square. At the crossing of Davies and Grosvenor Streets, however, I supposed myself safe, and halted for a moment.

From the shadow of a porch at my elbow a thin voice accosted me.

'Kind gentleman——'

'Heh?' I spun round on her sharply: for it was a woman, stretching out one skinny hand and gathering her rags together with the other.

'Kind gentleman, spare a copper! I've known better days —I have indeed.'

'Well,' said I, 'as it happens, I'm in the same case. And they couldn't be much worse, could they?'

She drew a shuddering breath back through her teeth, but still held out her hand. I felt for my last coin, and her fingers closed on it so sharply that their long nails scraped the back of mine.

'Kind gentleman——'

'Ay, they are kind, are they not?'

She stared at me, and in a nerveless note let one horrible oath escape her.

'There'll be one less before morning,' said I, 'if that's any consolation to you. Good night!' Setting off at a shuffling run, I doubled back along Grosvenor Street and Bond Street to the point where I hoped to pick up the trail again. And just there, at the issue of Bruton Street, two constables stood ready for me.

'I thought as much,' said the one who set me on my way.

'Hi, you! Wait a moment, please'; then to the other, 'Best turn his pockets out, Jim.'

'If you dare to try——' I began, with my hand in my pocket; the next moment I found myself sprawling face downward on the sharp crust of snow.

'Hallo, constables!' said a voice. 'What's the row?' It was Gervase. He had turned leisurely back from the slope of Conduit Street, and came strolling down the road with his hands in his pockets.

'This fellow, sir—we have reason to think he was followin' you.'

'Quite right,' Gervase answered cheerfully. 'Of course he was.'

'Oh, if you knew it, sir——'

'Certainly I knew it. In fact, he was following at my invitation.'

'What for did he tell me a lie, then?' grumbled the constable, chapfallen.

I had picked myself up by this time and was wiping my face. 'Look here,' I put in, 'I asked you the way to Oxford Street, that and nothing else.' And I went on to summarize my opinion of him.

'Oh! it's you can swear a bit,' he growled. 'I heard you just now.'

'Yes,' Gervase interposed suavely, drawing the glove from his right hand and letting flash a diamond finger-ring in the lamp-light. 'He *is* a bit of a beast, policeman, and it's not for the pleasure of it that I want his company.'

A sovereign passed from hand to hand. The other constable had discreetly drawn off a pace or two.

'All the same, it's a rum go.'

'Yes, isn't it?' Gervase assented in his heartiest tone. 'Here is my card, in case you're not satisfied.'

'If *you're* satisfied, sir——'

'Quite so. Good night!' Gervase thrust both hands into

his pockets again and strode off. I followed him, with a heart hotter than ever—followed him like a whipped cur, as they say. Yes, that was just it. He who had already robbed me of everything else had now kicked even the pedestal from under me as a figure of tragedy. Five minutes ago I had been the implacable avenger tracking my unconscious victim across the city. Heaven knows how small an excuse it was for self-respect; but one who has lost character may yet chance to catch a dignity from circumstances; and to tell the truth, for all my desperate earnestness I had allowed my vanity to take some artistic satisfaction in the sinister chase. It had struck me—shall I say?—as an effective ending, nor had I failed to note that the snow lent it a romantic touch.

And behold, the unconscious victim knew all about it, and had politely interfered when a couple of unromantic Bobbies threatened the performance by tumbling the stalking avenger into the gutter! They had knocked my tragedy into harlequinade as easily as you might bash in a hat; and my enemy had refined the cruelty of it by coming to the rescue and ironically restarting the poor play on lines of comedy. I saw too late that I ought to have refused his help, to have assaulted the constable and been hauled to the police station. Not an impressive wind-up, to be sure; but less humiliating than this! Even so, Gervase might have trumped the poor card by following with a gracious offer to bail me out!

As it was, I had put the whip into his hand, and must follow him like a cur. The distance he kept assured me that the similitude had not escaped him. He strode on without deigning a single glance behind, still in cold derision presenting me his broad back and silently challenging me to shoot. And I followed, hating him worse than ever, swearing that the last five minutes should not be forgotten, but charged for royally when the reckoning came to be paid.

I followed thus up Conduit Street, up Regent Street, and across the Circus. The frost had deepened and the mud in the

E

roadway crackled under our feet.   At the Circus I began to
guess, and when Gervase struck off into Great Portland Street,
and thence by half a dozen turnings northwards by east, I knew
to what house he was leading me.

At the entrance of the side street in which it stood he halted
and motioned me to come close.

'I forget,' he said with a jerk of his thumb, 'if you still have
the entry.   These people are not particular, to be sure.'

'I have not,' I answered, and felt my cheeks burning.   He
could not see this, nor could I see the lift of his eyebrows as
he answered:

'Ah?   I hadn't heard of it. . . . You'd better step round
by the mews, then.   You know the window, the one which
opens into the passage leading to Pollox Street.   Wait there.
It may be ten minutes before I can open.'

I nodded.   The house was a corner one, between the street
and a by-lane tenanted mostly by cabmen; and at the back of
it ran the mews where they stabled their horses.   Half-way
down this mews a narrow alley cut across it at right angles: a
passage unfrequented by traffic, known only to the stablemen,
and in the daytime used only by their children, who played hop-
scotch on the flagged pavement, where no one interrupted them.
You wondered at its survival—from end to end it must have
measured a good fifty yards—in a district where every square
foot of ground fetched money; until you learned that the house
had belonged, in the twenties, to a nobleman who left a name
for eccentric profligacy, and who, as owner of the land, could
afford to indulge his humours.   The estate since his death was
in no position to afford money for alterations, and the present
tenants of the house found the passage convenient enough.

My footsteps disturbed no one in the sleeping mews; and
doubling back noiselessly through the passage, I took up my
station beside the one low window which opened upon it from
the blank back premises of the house.   Even with the glimmer
of snow to help me, I had to grope for the window-sill to make

sure of my bearings. The minutes crawled by, and the only sound came from a stall where one of the horses had kicked through his thin straw bedding and was shuffling an uneasy hoof upon the cobbles. Then, just as I too had begun to shuffle my frozen feet, I heard a scratching sound, the unbolting of a shutter, and Gervase drew up the sash softly.

'Nip inside!' he whispered. 'No more noise than you can help. I have sent off the night porter. He tells me the bank is still going in the front of the house—half a dozen playing, perhaps.'

I hoisted myself over the sill, and dropped inside. The wall of this annexe—which had no upper floor, and invited you to mistake it for a harmless studio—was merely a sheath, so to speak. Within, a corridor divided it from the true wall of the room: and this room had no window or top-light, though a handsome one in the roof—a dummy—beguiled the eyes of its neighbours.

There was but one room: an apartment of really fine proportions, never used by the tenants of the house, and known but to a few curious ones among its frequenters.

The story went that the late owner, Earl C——, had reason to believe himself persistently cheated at cards by his best friends, and in particular by a Duke of the Blood Royal, who could hardly be accused to his face. The Earl's sense of honour forbade him to accuse any meaner man while the big culprit went unrebuked. Therefore he continued to lose magnificently while he devised a new room for play: the room into which I now followed Gervase.

I had stood in it once before and admired the courtly and costly thoroughness of the Earl's rebuke. I had imagined him conducting his expectant guests to the door, ushering them in with a wave of the hand, and taking his seat tranquilly amid the dead, embarrassed silence: had imagined him facing the Royal Duke and asking: 'Shall we cut?' with a voice of the politest inflection.

For the room was a sheet of mirrors. Mirrors panelled the walls, the doors, the very backs of the shutters. The tables had mirrors for tops: the whole ceiling was one vast mirror. From it depended three great candelabra of cut-glass, set with reflectors here, there, and everywhere.

I had heard that even the floor was originally of polished brass. If so, later owners must have ripped up the plates and sold them: for now a few cheap oriental rugs carpeted the unpolished boards. The place was abominably dusty: the striped yellow curtains had lost half their rings and drooped askew from their soiled valances. Across one of the wall-panels ran an ugly scar. A smell of rat pervaded the air. The present occupiers had no use for a room so obviously unsuitable to games of chance, as they understood chance: and I doubt if a servant entered it once a month. Gervase had ordered candles and a fire: but the chimney was out of practice, and the smoke wreathed itself slowly about us as we stood surrounded by the ghostly company of our reflected selves.

'We shall not be disturbed,' said Gervase. 'I told the man I was expecting a friend, that our business was private, and that until he called I wished to be alone. I did not explain by what entrance I expected him. The people in the front cannot hear us. Have a cigar?' He pushed the open case towards me. Then, as I drew back: 'You 've no need to be scrupulous,' he added, 'seeing that they were bought with your money.'

'If that 's so, I will,' said I; and having chosen one struck a match. Glancing round, I saw a hundred small flames spurt up, and a hundred men hold them to a hundred glowing cigar-tips.

'After you with the match.' Gervase took it from me with a steady hand. He, too, glanced about him while he puffed. 'Ugh!' He blew a long cloud, and shivered within his furred overcoat. 'What a gang!'

'It takes all sorts to make a world,' said I fatuously, for lack of anything better.

'Don't be an infernal idiot!' he answered, flicking the dust off one of the gilt chairs, and afterwards cleaning a space for his elbow on the looking-glass table. 'It takes only two sorts to make the world we 've lived in, and that 's you and me.' He gazed slowly round the walls. 'You and me, and a few fellows like us—not to mention the women, who don't count.'

'Well,' said I, 'as far as the world goes—if you must discuss it—I always found it a good enough place.'

'Because you started as an unconsidering fool: and because, afterwards, when we came to grips, you were the under-dog, and I gave you no time. My word—how I have hustled you!'

I yawned. 'All right: I can wait. Only if you suppose I came here to listen to your moral reflections——'

He pulled the cigar from between his teeth and looked at me along it.

'I know perfectly well why you came here,' he said slowly, and paused. 'Hadn't we better have it out—with the cards on the table?' He drew a small revolver from his pocket and laid it with a light clink on the table before him. I hesitated for a moment, then followed his example, and the silent men around us did the same.

A smile curled his thin lips as he observed this multiplied gesture. 'Yes,' he said, as if to himself, 'that is what it all comes to.'

'And now,' said I, 'since you know my purpose here, perhaps you will tell me yours.'

'That is just what I am trying to explain. Only you are so impatient, and it—well, it 's a trifle complicated.' He puffed for a moment in silence. 'Roughly, it might be enough to say that I saw you standing outside my house a while ago; that I needed a talk with you alone, in some private place; that I guessed, if you saw me, you would follow with no more invitation; and that, so reasoning, I led you here, where no one is likely to interrupt us.'

'Well,' I admitted, 'all that seems plain sailing.'

'Quite so; but it's at this point the thing grows complicated.' He rose, and walking to the fire-place, turned his back on me and spread his palms to the blaze. 'Well,' he asked, after a moment, gazing into the mirror before him, 'why don't you shoot?'

I thrust my hands into my trouser-pockets and leaned back staring—I dare say sulkily enough—at the two revolvers within grasp. 'I've got my code,' I muttered.

'The code of — these mirrors. You don't do the thing because it's not the thing to do; because these fellows'—he waved a hand and the ghosts waved back at him—'don't do such things, and you haven't the nerve to sin off your own bat. Come'—he strolled back to his seat and leaned towards me across the table—'it's not much to boast of, but at this eleventh hour we must snatch what poor credit we can. You are, I suppose, a more decent fellow for not having fired: and I—— By the way, you did feel the temptation?'

I nodded. 'You may put your money on that. I never see you without wanting to kill you. What's more, I'm going to do it.'

'And I,' he said, 'knew the temptation and risked it. No: let's be honest about it. There was no risk: because, my good sir, I know you to a hair.'

'There was,' I growled.

'Pardon me, there was none. I came here having a word to say to you, and these mirrors have taught me how to say it. Take a look at them—the world we are leaving—that's it: and a cursed second-hand, second-class one at that.'

He paced slowly round on it, slewing his body in the chair.

'I say a second-class one,' he resumed, 'because, my dear Reggie, when all's said and done, we are second class, the pair of us, and pretty bad second class. I met you first at ——. Our fathers had money: they wished us to be gentlemen without well understanding what it meant: and with unlimited pocket-money and his wits about him any boy can make himself a power in a big school. That is what we did: towards the end we even set the fashion for a certain set; and a rank bad fashion it was. But, in truth, we had no business there: on every point of breeding we were outsiders. I suspect it was a glimmering consciousness of this that made us hate each other from the first. We understood one another too well. Oh, there's no mistake about it! Whatever we've missed in life, you and I have hated.'

He paused, eyeing me queerly. I kept my hands in my pockets. 'Go on,' I said.

'From —— we went to College—the same business over again. We drifted, of course, into the same set; for already we had become necessary to each other. We set the pace of that set—were its apparent leaders. But in truth we were alone —you and I—as utterly alone as two shipwrecked men on a raft. The others were shadows to us: we followed their code because we had to be gentlemen, but we did not understand it in the least. For, after all, the roots of that code lay in the breeding and tradition of honour, with which we had no concern. To each other you and I were intelligible and real; but as concerned that code and the men who followed it by right of birth and nature, we were looking-glass men imitating— imitating—imitating.'

'We set the pace,' said I. 'You've allowed that.'

'To be sure we did. We even modified the code a bit —to its hurt; though as conscious outsiders we could dare very little. For instance, the talk of our associates about women—and no doubt their thoughts, too—grew sensibly baser. The sanctity of gambling debts, on the other hand, we did nothing to impair: because we had money. I recall your virtuous indignation at the amount of paper floated by poor W—— towards the end of the great baccarat term. Poor devil! He paid up—or his father did—and took his name off the books. He's in Ceylon now, I believe. At length you have earned a partial right to sympathize: or would have, if only you had paid up.'

'Take care, Gervase!'

'My good sir, don't miss my point. Wasn't I just as indignant with W——? If I 'd been warned off Newmarket Heath, if I 'd been shown the door of the hell we 're sitting in, shouldn't I feel just as you are feeling? Try to understand!'

'You forget Elaine, I think.'

'No: I do not forget Elaine. We left College: I to add money to money in my father's office; you to display your accomplishments in spending what your father had earned. That was the extent of the difference. To both of us, money and the indulgence it buys meant everything in life. All I can boast of is the longer sight. The office-hours were a nuisance, I admit: but I was clever enough to keep my hold on the old set; and then, after office-hours, I met you constantly, and studied and hated you—studied you because I hated you. Elaine came between us. You fell in love with her. That I, too, should fall in love with her was no coincidence, but the severest of logic. Given such a woman and two such men, no other course of fate is conceivable. She made it necessary for me to put hate into practice. If she had not offered herself, why, then it would have been somebody else: that 's all. Good Lord!' he rapped the table, and his voice rose for the first time above its level tone of exposition: 'You don't suppose all my study—all my years of education—were to be wasted!'

He checked himself, eyed me again, and resumed in his old voice:

'You wanted money by this time. I was a solicitor—your old college friend—and you came to me. I knew you would come, as surely as I knew you would not fire that pistol just now. For years I had trained myself to look into your mind and anticipate its working. Don't I tell you that from the first you were the only real creature this world held for me? You were my only book, and I had to learn you: at first without fixed purpose, then deliberately. And when the time came I put into practice what I knew: just that and no more. My dear Reggie, you never had a chance.'

'Elaine?' I muttered again.

'Elaine was the girl for you—or for me: just that again and no more.'

'By George!' said I, letting out a laugh. 'If I thought that!'

'What?'

'Why, that after ruining me, you have missed being happy!'

He sighed impatiently, and his eyes, though he kept them fastened on mine, seemed to be tiring. 'I thought,' he said, 'I could time your intelligence over any fence. But to-night there's something wrong. Either I'm out of practice or your brain has been going to the deuce. What, man! You're shying at every bank! Is it drink, hey? Or hunger?'

'It might be a little of both,' I answered. 'But stay a moment and let me get things straight. I stood between you and Elaine—no, give me time—between you and your aims, whatever they were. Very well. You trod over me; or, rather, you pulled me up by the roots and pitched me into outer darkness to rot. And now it seems that, after all, you are not content. In the devil's name, why?'

'Why? Oh, cannot you see? . . . Take a look at these mirrors again—our world, I tell you. See—you and I—you and I—always you and I! Man, I pitched you into darkness as you say, and then I woke and knew the truth—that you were necessary to me.'

'Hey?'

'*I can't do without you!*' It broke from him in a cry. 'So help me God, Reggie, it is the truth!'

I stared in his face for half a minute maybe, and broke out laughing. 'Jeshurun waxed fat and—turned sentimental! A nice copy-book job you make of it, too!

> Oh, send my brother back to me—
> I cannot play alone!

* E

Perhaps you 'd like me to buy a broom and hire the crossing in Lennox Gardens?   Then you 'd be able to contemplate me all day long, and nourish your fine fat soul with delicate eating. Pah!   You make me sick.'

'It 's the truth,' said he quietly.

'It may be.   To me it looks a sight more like *foie gras*. Can't do without me, can't you?   Well, I can jolly well do without you, and I 'm going to.'

'I warn you,' he said: 'I have done you an injury or two in my time, but by George if I stand up and let you shoot me —well, I hate you badly enough, but I won't let you do it without fair warning.'

'I 'll risk it anyway,' said I.

'Very well.'   He stood up, and folded his arms.   'Shoot, then, and be hanged!'

I put out my hand to the revolver, hesitated, and with-drew it.

'That 's not the way,' I said.   'I 've got my code, as I told you before.'

'Does the code forbid suicide?' he asked.

'That 's a different thing.'

'Not at all.   The man who commits suicide kills an unarmed man.'

'But the unarmed man happens to be himself.'

'Suppose that in this instance your distinction won't work? Look here,' he went on, as I pushed back my chair impatiently, 'I have one truth more for you.   I swear I believe that what we have hated, we two, is not each other, but ourselves or our own likeness.   I swear I believe we two have so shared natures in hate that no power can untwist and separate them to render each his own.   But I swear also I believe that if you lift that revolver to kill, you will take aim, not at me, but by instinct at a worse enemy—yourself, vital in my heart.'

'You have some pretty theories to-night,' I sneered.   'Per-haps you 'll go on to tell me which of us two had been Elaine's husband, feeding daintily in Lennox Gardens, clothed in purple and fine linen, while the other——'

He interrupted me by picking up his revolver and striding to the fire-place again.

'So be it, since you will have it so. Kill me,' he added, with a queer look, 'and perhaps you may go back to Lennox Gardens and enjoy all these things in my place.'

I took my station. Both revolvers were levelled now. I took sight along mine at his detested face. It was white but curiously eager—hopeful even. I lowered my arm, scanning his face still; and still scanning it, set my weapon down on the table.

'I believe you are mad,' said I slowly. 'But one thing I see —that, mad or not, you 're in earnest. For some reason you want me to kill you; therefore that shall wait. For some reason it is torture to you to live and do without me: well, I 'll try you with that. It will do me good to hurt you a bit.' I slipped the revolver into my pocket and tapped it. 'Though I don't understand them, I won't quarrel with your sentiments so long as you suffer for them. When that fails, I 'll find another opportunity for this. Good night.' I stepped to the door.

'Reggie!'

I shut the door on his cry: crossed the corridor, and climbing out through the window, let myself drop into the lane.

As my feet touched the snow a revolver-shot rang out in the room behind me.

I caught at the frozen sill to steady myself: and crouching there, listened. Surely the report must have alarmed the house! I waited for the sound of footsteps: waited for three minutes— perhaps longer. None came. To be sure, the room stood well apart from the house: but it was incredible that the report should have awakened no one! My own ears still rang with it.

Still no footsteps came. The horse in the stable close by was still shuffling his hoof on the cobbles, no other sound. . . .

Very stealthily I hoisted myself up on the sill again, listened, dropped inside, and tiptoed my way to the door. The candles were still burning in the Room of Mirrors. And by the light of them, as I entered, Gervase stepped to meet me.

'Ah, it's you,' I stammered. 'I heard—that is, I thought——'

And with that I saw—recognized with a catch of the breath —that the figure I spoke to was not Gervase, but my own reflected image, stepping forward with pale face and ghastly from a mirror. Yet a moment before I could have sworn it was Gervase.

Gervase lay stretched on the hearthrug with his hand towards the fire. I caught up a candle, and bent over him. His features were not to be recognized.

As I straightened myself up, with the candle in my hand, for an instant those features, obliterated in the flesh, gazed at me in a ring, a hundred times repeated behind a hundred candles. And again, at a second glance, I saw that the face was not Gervase's but my own.

I set down the candle and made off, closing the door behind me. The horror of it held me by the hair, but I flung it off and pelted down the lane and through the mews. Once in the street I breathed again, pulled myself together, and set off at a rapid walk, southwards, but not clearly knowing whither.

As a matter of fact, I took the line by which I had come: with the single difference that I made straight into Berkeley Square through Bruton Street. I had, I say, no clear purpose in following this line rather than another. I had none for taking Lennox Gardens on the way to my squalid lodgings in Chelsea. I had a purpose, no doubt; but will swear it only grew definite as I came in sight of the lamp still burning beneath Gervase's portico.

There was a figure, too, under the lamp—the butler— bending there and rolling up the strip of red carpet. As he pulled its edges from the frozen snow I came on him suddenly.

'Oh, it's you, sir!' He stood erect, and with the air of a man infinitely relieved.

'Gervase!'

The door opened wide and there stood Elaine in her ball-gown, a-glitter with diamonds.

'Gervase, dear, where have you been? We have been terribly anxious——'

She said it, looking straight down on me—on me—who stood in my tattered clothes in the full glare of the lamp. And then I heard the butler catch his breath, and suddenly her voice trailed off in wonder and pitiful disappointment.

'It's not Gervase! It's Reg—Mr. Travers. I beg your pardon. I thought——'

But I passed up the steps and stood before her: and said, as she drew back:

'There has been an accident. Gervase has shot himself.' I turned to the butler. 'You had better run to the police station. Stay: take this revolver. It won't count anything as evidence: but I ask you to examine it and make sure all the chambers are loaded.'

A thud in the hall interrupted me. I ran in and knelt beside Elaine, and as I stooped to lift her—as my hand touched her hair—this was the jealous question on my lips:

'What has *she* to do with it. It is *I* who cannot do without him—who must miss him always!'

THE COLLABORATORS

OR, THE COMEDY THAT WROTE ITSELF: AS RELATED BY
G. A. RICHARDSON

I

> How pleasant it is to have money, heigho!
> How pleasant it is to have money!

sings (I think) Clough. Well, I had money, and more of it
than I felt any desire to spend; which is as much as any
reasonable man can want. My age was five-and-twenty, my
health good, my conscience moderately clean, and my appetite
excellent: I had fame in some degree, and a fair prospect of
adding to it: and I was unmarried. In later life a man may
seek marriage for its own sake, but at five-and-twenty he
marries against his will—because he has fallen in love with a
woman; and this had not yet happened to me. I was a bachelor,
and content to remain one.

To come to smaller matters—The month was early June, the
weather perfect, the solitude of my own choosing, and my
posture comfortable enough to invite drowsiness. I had bathed
and, stretched supine in the shade of a high sand-bank, was
smoking the day's first cigarette. Behind me lay Ambleteuse;
before me the sea. On the edge of it, their shrill challenges
softened by the distance to music, a score of children played
with spades and buckets, innocently composing a hundred pretty
groups of brown legs, fluttered hair, bright frocks and jerseys,
and innocently conspiring with morning to put a spirit of youth
into the whole picture. Beyond them the blue sea flashed with
its own smiles, and the blue heaven over them with the glancing
wings of gulls. On this showing it is evident that I, George
Anthony Richardson, ought to have been happy; whereas, in
fact, Richardson was cheerful enough, but George Anthony
restless and ill-content: by reason that Richardson, remembering

the past, enjoyed by contrast the present, and knew himself to be jolly well off; while George Anthony, likewise remembering the past, felt gravely concerned for the future.

Let me explain. A year ago I had been a clerk in the Office of the Local Government Board—a detested calling with a derisory stipend. It was all that a University education (a second in Moderations and a third in *Literae Humaniores*) had enabled me to win, and I stuck to it because I possessed no patrimony and had no 'prospects' save one, which stood precariously on the favour of an uncle—my mother's brother, Major-General Allan McIntosh, C.B. Now the General could not be called an indulgent man. He had retired from active service to concentrate upon his kinsfolk those military gifts which even on the wide plains of Hindostan had kept him the terror of his country's foes and the bugbear of his own soldiery. He had an iron sense of discipline and a passion for it; he detested all forms of amusement; in religion he belonged to the sect of the Peculiar People; and he owned a gloomy house near the western end of the Cromwell Road, where he dwelt and had for butler, valet, and factotum a Peculiar Person named Trewlove.

In those days I found my chief recreation in the theatre; and by and by, when I essayed to write for it, and began to pester managers with curtain-raisers, small vaudevilles, comic libretti and the like, you will guess that in common prudence I called myself by a *nom de guerre*. Dropping the 'Richardson,' I signed my productions 'George Anthony,' and as 'George Anthony' the playgoing public now discusses me. For some while, I will confess, the precaution was superfluous, the managers having apparently entered into league to ensure me as much obscurity as I had any use for. But at length in an unguarded moment the manager of the Duke of Cornwall's Theatre (formerly the Euterpe) accepted a three-act farce. It was poorly acted, yet for some reason it took the town. '*Larks in Aspic*, a Farcical Comedy by George Anthony,' ran for a solid three hundred nights; and before it ceased my unsuspecting uncle had closed his earthly career, leaving me with seventy thousand pounds (the bulk of it invested in India Government stock), the house in the Cromwell Road, and, lastly, in sacred trust, his faithful body-servant, William John Trewlove.

Here let me pause to deplore man's weakness and the allurement of splendid possessions. I had been happy enough in my lodgings in Jermyn Street, and, thanks to *Larks in Aspic*, they were decently furnished. At the prompting, surely, of some malignant spirit, I exchanged them for a house too large for me in a street too long for life, for my uncle's furniture (of the Great Exhibition period), and for the unnecessary and detested services of Trewlove.

This man enjoyed, by my uncle's will, an annuity of fifty pounds. He had the look, too, of one who denied himself small pleasures, not only on religious grounds, but because they cost money. Somehow, I never doubted that he owned a balance at the bank, or that, after a brief interval spent in demonstrating that our ways were uncongenial, he would retire on a competence and await translation to join my uncle in an equal sky—equal, that is, within the fence of the elect. But not a bit of it! I had been adjured in the will to look after him: and at first I supposed that he clung to me against inclination, from a conscientious resolve to give me every chance. By and by, however, I grew aware of a change in him; or, rather, of some internal disquiet, suppressed but volcanic, working towards a change. Once or twice he staggered me by answering some casual question in a tone which, to say the least of it, suggested an ungainly attempt at facetiousness. A look at his sepulchral face would reassure me, but did not clear up the mystery. Something was amiss with Trewlove.

The horrid truth broke upon me one day as we discussed the conduct of one of my two housemaids. Trewlove, returning one evening (as I gathered) from a small *réunion* of his fellow-sectarians in the Earl's Court Road, had caught her in the act of exchanging railleries from an upper window with a trooper in the 2nd Life Guards, and had reported her.

'Most unbecoming,' said I.

'Unwomanly,' said Trewlove, with a sudden contortion of the face; 'unwomanly, sir!—but ah, how like a woman!'

I stared at him for one wild moment, and turned abruptly to the window. The rascal had flung a quotation at me—out of *Larks in Aspic*! He knew, then! He had penetrated the disguise of 'George Anthony,' and, worse still, he meant to forgive it. His eye had conveyed a dreadful promise of complicity. Almost—I would have given worlds to know, and yet dared not face it—almost it had been essaying a wink!

I dismissed him with instructions—not very coherent, I fear —to give the girl a talking-to, and sat down to think. How long had he known?—that was my first question, and in justice to him it had to be considered: since, had he known and kept the secret in my uncle's lifetime, beyond a doubt, and unpleasant as the thought might be, I was enormously his debtor. That stern warrior's attitude towards the playhouse had ever been uncompromising. Stalls, pit, and circles—the very names suggested Dantesque images and provided illustrations for many a discourse. Themselves verbose, these discourses indicated A Short Way with State-players, and it stood in no doubt that the authorship of *Larks in Aspic* had only to be disclosed to him to provide me with the shortest possible cut out of seventy thousand pounds.

I might, and did, mentally consign Trewlove to all manner of painful places, as, for instance, the bottom of the sea; but I could not will away this obligation. After cogitating for a while I rang for him.

'Trewlove,' said I, 'you know, it seems, that I have written a play.'

'Yessir! *Larks in Aspic*, sir.'

I winced. 'Since when have you known this?'

The dog, I am sure, took the bearings of this question at

once. But he laid his head on one side, and while he pulled one whisker, as if ringing up the information, his eyes grew dull and seemed to be withdrawing into visions of a far-away past. 'I have been many times to see it, Mr. George, and would be hard put to it to specify the first occasion. But it was a mattinay.'

'That is not what I asked, Trewlove. I want to know when you first suspected or satisfied yourself that I was the author.'

'Oh, at once, sir! The style, if I may say so, was un-mistakable: *in*-nimitable, sir, if I may take the libbaty.'

'Excuse me,' I began, but he did not hear. He had passed for the moment beyond decorum, and his eyes began to roll in a manner expressive of inward rapture, but not pretty to watch.

'I had not listened to your talk, sir, in private life—I had not, as one might say, imbibed it—for nothink. The General, sir—your lamented uncle—had a flow: he would, if allowed, and meaning no disrespect, talk the hind leg off a jackass; but I found him lacking in 'umour. Now you, Mr. George, 'ave 'umour. You 'ave not your uncle's flow, sir—the Lord forbid! But in give-and-take, as one might say, you are igstreamly droll. On many occasions, sir, when you were extra sparkling I do assure you it required pressure not to explode.'

'I thank you, Trewlove,' said I coldly. 'But will you, please, waive these unsolicited testimonials and answer my question? Let me put it in another form. Was it in my uncle's lifetime that you first witnessed my play?'

Trewlove's eyes ceased to roll, and, meeting mine, withdrew themselves politely behind impenetrable mists. 'The General sir, was opposed to theatre-going *in toto*; anathemum was no word for what he thought of it. And if it had come to *Larks in Aspic*, with your permission I will only say "Great Scot!"'

'I may take it then that you did not see the play and surprise my secret until after his death?'

Trewlove drew himself up with fine reserve and dignity. 'There is such a thing, sir, I 'ope, as Libbaty of Conscience.'

With that I let him go. The colloquy had not only done me no service, but had positively emboldened him—or so I seemed to perceive as the weeks went on—in his efforts to cast off his old slough and become a travesty of me, as he had been a travesty of my uncle. I am willing to believe that they caused him pain. A crust of habit so inveterate as his cannot be rent without throes, to the severity of which his facial contortions bore witness whenever he attempted a witticism.—Warned by them, I would sometimes admonish him.

'Mirth without vulgarity, Trewlove!'

'Yessir,' he would answer, and add with a sigh: 'It's the best sort, sir—*ad*mittedly.'

But if painful to him, this metamorphosis was torture to my nerves. I should explain that, flushed with the success of *Larks in Aspic*, I had cheerfully engaged myself to provide the Duke of Cornwall's with a play to succeed it. At the moment of signing the contract, my bosom's lord had sat lightly on its throne, for I felt my head to be humming with ideas. But affluence, or the air of the Cromwell Road, seemed uncongenial to the Muse.

Three months had slipped away. I had not written a line. My ideas, which had seemed on the point of precipitation, surrendering to some strange centrifugal eddy, slipped one by one beyond grasp. I suppose every writer of experience knows these vacant terrifying intervals; but they were strange to me then, and I had not learnt the virtue of waiting. I grew flurried, and saw myself doomed to be the writer of one play.

In this infirmity the daily presence of Trewlove became intolerable. There arrived an evening when I found myself toying with the knives at dinner, and wondering where precisely lay the level of his fifth rib at the back of my chair.

I dropped the weapon and pushed forward my glass to be refilled. 'Trewlove,' said I, 'you shall pack for me to-morrow, and send off the servants on board wages. I need a holiday. I—I trust this will not be inconvenient to you?'

'I thank you, sir; not in the least.'   He coughed, and I bent my head, some instinct forewarning me.

'I shall be away for three months at least,' I put in quickly. (Five minutes before I had not dreamed of leaving home.)

But the stroke was not to be averted.   For months it had been preparing.

'As for inconvenience, sir—if I may remind you—the course of Trewlove never did——'

'For three months at least,' I repeated, rapping sharply on the table.

Next day I crossed the Channel and found myself at Ambleteuse.

II

I chose Ambleteuse because it was there that I had written the greater part of *Larks in Aspic*.   I went again to my old quarters at Madame Peyron's.   As before, I eschewed company, excursions, all forms of violent exercise.   I bathed, ate, drank, slept, rambled along the sands, or lay on my back and stared at the sky, smoking and inviting my soul.   In short, I reproduced all the old conditions.   But in vain!   At Ambleteuse, no less than in London, the Muse either retreated before my advances, or, when I sat still and waited, kept her distance, declining to be coaxed.

Matters were really growing serious.   Three weeks had drifted by with not a line and scarcely an idea to show for them; and the morning's post had brought me a letter from Cozens, of the Duke of Cornwall's, begging for (at least) a scenario of the new piece.   My play (he said) would easily last this season out; but he must reopen in the autumn with a new one, and—in short, weren't we beginning to run some risk?

I groaned, crushed the letter into my pocket, and by an effort of will put the tormenting question from me until after my morning bath.   But now the time was come to face it.   I began weakly by asking myself why the dickens I—with enough for my needs—had bound myself to write this thing within a given time, at the risk of turning out inferior work. For that matter, why should I write a comedy at all if I didn't want to? These were reasonable questions, and yet they missed the point. The point was that I had given my promise to Cozens, and that Cozens depended on it. Useless to ask now why I had given it! At the time I could have promised cheerfully to write him three plays within as many months.

So full my head was then, and so empty now! A grotesque and dreadful suspicion took me. While Trewlove tortured himself to my model, was I, by painful degrees, exchanging brains with him? I laughed; but I was unhinged. I had been smoking too many cigarettes during these three weeks, and the vampire thought continued to flit obscenely between me and the pure seascape. I saw myself the inheritor of Trewlove's cast-off personality, his inelegancies of movement, his religious opinions, his bagginess at the knees, his mournful, pensile whiskers——

This would never do! I must concentrate my mind on the play. Let me see—— The title can wait. Two married couples have just been examined at Dunmow, and awarded the 'historic' flitch for conjugal happiness. Call them A and Mrs. A, B and Mrs. B. On returning to the hotel with their trophies, it is discovered that B and Mrs. A are old flames, while each finds a mistaken reason to suspect that A and Mrs. B have also met years before, and at least dallied with courtship. Thus while their spouses alternately rage with suspicion and invent devices to conceal their own defaults, A and Mrs. B sit innocently nursing their illusions and their symbolical flitches. The situation holds plenty of comedy, and the main motive begins to explain itself. Now then for anagnorisis, comic peripeteia, division into acts, and the rest of the wallet!

I smoked another two cigarettes and flung away a third in despair. Useless! The plaguy thing refused to take shape. I sprang up and paced the sands, dogged by an invisible Cozens piping thin reproaches above the hum of the breakers.

Suddenly I came to a halt. Why *this* play? Why expend vain efforts on this particular complication when in a drawer at home lay two acts of a comedy ready written, and the third and final act sketched out? The burden of months broke its straps and fell from me as I pondered. *My Tenant* was the name of the thing, and I had thrust it aside only when the idea of *Larks in Aspic* occurred to me—not in any disgust. And really, now, what I remembered of it seemed to me astonishingly good!

I pulled out my watch; and as I did so there flashed on me—in that sudden freakish way which the best ideas affect—a new and brilliant idea for the plot of *My Tenant*. The whole of the third and concluding act spread itself instantaneously before me. I knew then and there why the play had been laid aside. It had waited for this, and it wanted only this. I held the thing now, compact and tight, within my five fingers: as tight and compact as the mechanism of the watch in my hand.

But why had I pulled out the watch? Because the manuscript of *My Tenant* lay in the drawer of my writing-table in the Cromwell Road, and I was calculating how quickly a telegram would reach Trewlove with instructions to find and forward it. Then I bethought me that the lock was a patent one, and that I carried the key with me on my private key-chain. Why should I not cross from Calais by the next boat and recover my treasure? It would be the sooner in my possession. I might be reading it again that very night in my own home and testing my discovery. I might return with it on the morrow—that is, if I desired to return. After all, Ambleteuse had failed me. In London I could shut myself up and work at white heat. In London, too, I should be near Cozens: a telegram would fetch him out to South Kensington within the hour, to listen and approve. (I had no doubt of his approval.) In London I should renew relations with the real Trewlove—the familiar, the absurd. I will not swear that for the moment I thought of Trewlove at all: but he remained at the back of my mind, and at Calais I began the process of precipitating him (so to speak) by a telegram advertising him of my return, and requesting that my room might be prepared.

I had missed the midday boat, and reached Dover by the later and slower one as the June night began to descend. From Victoria I drove straight to my club, and snatched a supper of cold meats in its half-lit dining-room. Twenty minutes later I was in my hansom again and swiftly bowling westward— I say 'bowling' because it is the usual word, and I was in far too fierce a hurry to think of a better.

I had dropped back upon London in the fastest whirl of the season, and at the hour when all the world rolls homeward from the theatres. Two hansoms raced with mine, and red lights by the score dotted the noble slope of Piccadilly. To the left the street-lamps flung splashes of theatrical green on the sombre boughs of the Green Park. In one of the porticoes to the right half a dozen guests lingered for a moment and laughed together before taking their leave. One of them stood on the topmost steps, lighting a cigarette: he carried his silk-lined Inverness over his arm—so sultry the night was—and the ladies wore but the slightest of wraps over their bright frocks and jewels. One of them as we passed stepped forward, and I saw her dismissing her brougham. A night for walking, thought the party: and a fine night for sleeping out of doors, thought the road-watchman close by, watching them and meditatively smoking behind his barricade hung with danger - lanterns. Overhead rode the round moon.

It is the fashion to cry down London, and I have taken my part in the chorus; but always—be the absence never so short —I come back to her with the same lift of the heart. Why did I ever leave her? What had I gone a-seeking in Amble- teuse?—a place where a man leaves his room only to carry his writing-desk with him and plant it by the sea. London offered the only true recreation. In London a man might turn the key on himself and work for so long as it pleased him. But let him emerge, and—pf!—the jostle of the streets shook his head clear of the whole stuffy business. No; decidedly I would not return to Madame Peyron's. London for me, until my comedy should be written, down to the last word on the last page!

We were half-way down the Cromwell Road when I took this resolution, and at once I was aware of a gathering of carriages drawn up in a line ahead and close beside the pavement. At intervals the carriages moved forward a few paces and the line closed up; but it stretched so far that I soon began to wonder which of my neighbours could be entertaining on a scale so magnificent.

'What number did you say, sir?' the cabman asked through his trap.

'Number 402,' I called up.

'Blest if I can get alongside the pavement then,' he grumbled. He was a surly man.

'Never mind that. Pull up opposite Number 402 and I'll slip between. I've only my bag to carry.'

'Didn't know folks was so gay in these outlyin' parts,' he commented sourly, and closed the trap, but presently opened it again. His horse had dropped to a walk. 'Did you say four-nought-two?' he asked.

'Oh, confound it—yes!' I was growing impatient.

He pulled up and began to turn the horse's head.

'Hi! What are you doing?'

'Goin' back to the end of the line—back to take our bloomin' turn,' he answered wearily. 'Four-nought-two, you said, didn't you?'

'Yes, yes; are you deaf? What have I to do with this crowd?'

'I hain't deaf, but I got eyes. Four-nought-two's where the horning's up, that's all.'

'The horning? What's that?'

'Oh, I'm tired of egsplanations. A horning's a horning, what they put up when they gives a party; leastways,' he added reflectively, '*Hi* don't.'

'But there's no party at Number 402,' I insisted. 'The thing's impossible.'

'Very well, then; I'm a liar, and that ends it.' He wheeled again and began to walk his horse sullenly forward. ''Oo's blind this time?' he demanded, coming to a standstill in front of the house.

An awning stretched down from the front door and across the pavement, where two policemen guarded the alighting guests from pressure by a small but highly curious crowd. Overhead, the first-floor windows had been flung wide; the rooms within were aflame with light; and, as I grasped the rail of the splash-board, and, straightening myself up, gazed over the cab-roof with a wild surmise into the driver's face, a powerful but invisible string band struck up the 'Country Girl' Lancers!

''Oo's a liar now?' He jerked his whip towards the number '402' staring down at me from the illuminated pane above the awning.

'But it's my own house!' I gasped.

'Hoh?' said he. 'Well, it *may* be. *I* don't conteraddict.'

'Here, give me my bag!' I fumbled in my pocket for his fare.

'Cook giving a party? Well, you're handy for the Wild West out here—good old Earl's Court!' He jerked his whip again towards the awning as a North American Indian in full war-paint passed up the steps and into the house, followed by the applause of the crowd.

I must have overpaid the man extravagantly, for his tone changed suddenly as he examined the coins in his hand. 'Look here, guvnor, if you want any little 'elp, I was barman one time at the "Elephant"——'

But I caught up my bag, swung off the step, and, squeezing between a horse's wet nose and the back of a brougham, gained the pavement, where a red baize carpet divided the ranks of the crowd.

'Hallo!' One of the policemen put out a hand to detain me.

'It's all right,' I assured him, 'I belong to the house.' It seemed a safer explanation than that the house belonged to me.

'Is it the ices?' he asked.

But I ran up the porchway, eager to get to grips with Trewlove.

On the threshold a young and extremely elegant footman confronted me.

'Where is Trewlove?' I demanded.

The footman was glorious in a tasselled coat and knee-breeches, both of bright blue. He wore his hair in powder, and eyed me with suspicion if not with absolute disfavour.

'Where is Trewlove?' I repeated, dwelling fiercely on each syllable.

The ass became lightly satirical. 'Well we may wonder,' said he; 'search the wide world over! But reely and truly you've come to the wrong 'ouse this time. Here, stand to one side!' he commanded, as a lady in the costume of the Pompadour, followed by an Old English Gentleman with an anachronistic Hebrew nose, swept past me into the hall. He bowed deferentially while he mastered their names, 'Mr. and Mrs. Levi-Levy!' he cried, and a second footman came forward to escort them up the stairs. To convince myself that this was my own house I stared hard at a bust of Havelock—my late uncle's chief, and for religious as well as military reasons his beau ideal of a British warrior.

The young footman resumed. 'When you've had a good look round and seen all you want to see——'

'I am Mr. Richardson,' I interrupted; 'and up to a few minutes ago I supposed myself to be the owner of this house. Here—if you wish to assure yourself—is my card.'

His face fell instantly, fell so completely and woefully that I could not help feeling sorry for him. 'I beg pardon, sir—most 'umbly, I do indeed. You will do me the justice, sir—I had no idea, as *per* description, sir, being led to expect a different kind of gentleman altogether.'

'You had my telegram, then?'

'Telegram, sir?' He hesitated, searching his memory.

'Certainly—a telegram sent by me at one o'clock this afternoon, or thereabouts——'

Here, with an apology, he left me to attend to a new arrival —a Yellow Dwarf with a decidedly music-hall manner, who nudged him in the stomach and fell upon his neck exclaiming: 'My long-lost brother!'

'Cert'nly, sir. You will find the *company* upstairs, sir.' The young man disengaged himself with admirable dignity and turned again to me. 'A telegram did you say——'

'Addressed to "Trewlove, 402, Cromwell Road."'

'William!' He summoned another footman forward. 'This gentleman is inquiring for a telegram sent here this afternoon, addressed "Trewlove."'

'There was such a telegram,' said William. 'I heard Mr. Horrex a-discussing of it in the pantry. The mistress took the name for a telegraphic address, and sent it back to the office, saying there must be some mistake.'

'But I sent it myself!'

'Indeed, sir?'

'It contained an order to get my room ready.'

'This gentleman is Mr. Richardson,' explained the younger footman.

'Indeed, sir?' William's face brightened. 'In that case there's no 'arm done, for your room is ready, and I laid out your dress myself. Mr. 'Erbert gave particular instructions before going out.'

'Mr. Herbert?' I gazed around me blankly. Who in the name of wonder was Mr. Herbert?

'If you will allow me, sir,' suggested William, taking my bag, while the other went back to his post.

'Thank you,' said I, 'but I know my own room, I hope.'

He shook his head. 'The mistress made some alterations at the last moment, and you're on the fourth floor over the street.

Mr. 'Erbert's last words were that if you arrived before him I was to 'ope you didn't mind being so near the roof.'

Well, of one thing at least I could be sure: I was in my own house. For the rest, I might be Rip Van Winkle or the Sleeper Awakened. Who was this lady called 'the mistress'? Who was Mr. Herbert? How came they here? And—deepest mystery of all—how came they to be expecting *me*? Some villainy of Trewlove's must be the clue of this tangle; and, holding to this clue, I resolved to follow whither fate might lead.

III

William lifted my bag and led the way. On the first landing, where the doors stood open and the music went merrily to the last figure of the Lancers, we had to pick our way through a fantastic crowd which eyed me with polite curiosity. Couples seated on the next flight drew aside to let us pass. But the second landing was empty, and I halted for a moment at the door of my own workroom, within which lay my precious manuscript.

'This room is unoccupied?'

'Indeed, no, sir. The mistress considers it the cheerfullest in the 'ouse.'

'Our tastes agree, then.'

'She had her bed moved in there the very first night.'

'Indeed?' I swung round on him hastily. 'By the by, what is your mistress's name?'

He drew back a pace and eyed me with some embarrassment. 'You'll excuse me, sir, but that ain't quite a fair question as between you and me.'

'No? I should have thought it innocent enough.'

'Of course, it's a hopen secret, and you're only askin' it to try me. But so long as the mistress fancies a hincog——'

'Lead on,' said I. 'You are an exemplary young man, and I, too, am playing the game to the best of my lights.'

'Yes, sir.' He led me up to a room prepared for me—with candles lit, hot water ready, and bed neatly turned down. On the bed lay the full costume of a Punchinello: striped stockings, breeches with rosettes, tinselled coat with protuberant stomach and hump, cocked hat, and all proper accessories—even to a false nose.

'Am I expected to get into these things?' I asked.

'If I can be of any assistance, sir——'

'Thank you: no.' I handed him the key of my bag, flung off coat and waistcoat, and sat down to unlace my boots. 'Your mistress is in the drawing-room, I suppose, with her guests?'

'She is, sir.'

'And Mr. Herbert?'

'Mr. 'Erbert was to have been 'ome by ten-thirty. He is— as you know, sir—a little irregilar. But youth'—William arranged my brushes carefully—'youth must 'ave its fling. Oh, he's a caution!' A chuckle escaped him; he checked it and was instantly demure. Almost, indeed, he eyed me with a look of rebuke. 'Anything more, sir?'

'Nothing more, thank you.'

He withdrew. I thrust my feet into the dressing slippers he had set out for me, and, dropping into an arm-chair, began to take stock of the situation. 'The one thing certain,' I told myself, 'is that Trewlove in my absence has let my house. Therefore Trewlove is certainly an impudent scoundrel, and any grand jury would bring in a true bill against him for a swindler. My tenants are a lady whose servants may not reveal her name, and a young man—her husband perhaps—described as "a little irregular." They are giving a large fancy-dress ball below—which seems to prove that, at any rate, they don't fear publicity. And, further, although entire strangers to me, they are expecting my arrival and have prepared a room. Now, why?'

Here lay the real puzzle, and for some minutes I could make nothing of it. Then I remembered my telegram. According to William it had been referred back to the post office. But

William on his own admission had but retailed pantry gossip caught up from Mr. Horrex (presumably the butler). Had the telegram been sent back *unopened*? William's statement left this in doubt. Now supposing these people to be in league with Trewlove, they might have opened the telegram, and, finding to their consternation that I was already on the road and an exposure inevitable, have ordered my room to be prepared, trusting to throw themselves on my forgiveness, while Trewlove lay in hiding or was fleeing from vengeance across the high seas. Here was a possible explanation; but I will admit that it seemed, on second thoughts, an unlikely one. An irate landlord, returning unexpectedly and finding his house in possession of unauthorized tenants—catching them, moreover, in the act of turning it upside-down with a fancy-dress ball— would naturally begin to be nasty on the doorstep. The idea of placating him by a bedroom near the roof and the costume of a Punchinello was too bold altogether, and relied too much on his unproved fund of good nature. Moreover, Mr. Herbert (whoever he might be) would not have treated the situation so cavalierly. At the least (and however 'irregilar'), Mr. Herbert would have been waiting to deprecate vengeance. A wild suspicion occurred to me that 'Mr. Herbert' might be another name for Trewlove, and that Trewlove under that name was gaining a short start from justice. But no: William had alluded to Mr. Herbert as to a youth sowing his wild oats. Impossible to contemplate Trewlove under this guise! Where then did Trewlove come in? Was he, perchance, 'Mr. Horrex,' the butler?

I gave it up and began thoughtfully, and not without difficulty, to case myself in the disguise of Punchinello. I resolved to see this thing through. The costume had evidently not been made to my measure, and in the process of enduing it I paused once or twice to speculate on the eccentricities of the figure to which it had been shaped or the abstract anatomical knowledge of the tailor who had shaped it. I declare that the hump seemed the one normal thing about it. But by this time my detective-hunger—not to call it a thirst for vengeance—was asserting itself above petty vanity. I squeezed myself into the costume; and then, clapping on the false nose, stood arrayed—as queer a figure, surely, as ever was assumed by retributive Justice.

So, with a heart hardened by indignation and prepared for the severest measures, I descended to the drawing-room landing. Two doors opened upon it—that of the drawing-room itself, which faced over a terrace roofing the kitchens and across it to a garden in the rear of the house, and that of a room overlooking the street and scarcely less spacious. This had been the deceased General's bedroom, and in indolence rather than impiety I had left it unused with all its hideous furniture—including the camp-bed which his martial habits affected. And this was the apartment I entered, curious to learn how it had been converted into a reception-room for the throng which now filled it.

I recognized only the wall-paper. The furniture had been removed, the carpet taken up, the boards waxed to a high degree of slipperiness; and across the far end stretched a buffet-table presided over by a venerable person in black, with white hair, a high clear complexion, and a deportment which hit a nice mean between the military and the episcopal.

I had scarcely time to tell myself that this must be Mr. Horrex, before he looked up and caught sight of me. His features underwent a sudden and astonishing change; and almost dropping a bottle of champagne in his flurry, he came swiftly round the end of the buffet towards me.

I knew not how to interpret his expression: surprise was in it, and eagerness, and suppressed agitation, and an appeal for secrecy, and at the same time (if I mistook not) a deep relief.

'I beg your pardon, sir,' he began, in a sort of confidential whisper, very quick and low, 'but I was not aware you had arrived.'

I gazed at him with stern inquiry.

'You *are* Mr. Richardson, are you not?' he asked. There could be no doubt of his agitation.

'I am; and I have been in this, my house, for some three-quarters of an hour.'

'They never told me!' he groaned. 'And I left particular instructions—— But perhaps you have already seen the mistress?'

'I have not. May I ask you to take me to her—since I have not the pleasure of her acquaintance?'

'Cert'nly, sir. Oh, at once! She is in the drawing-room putting the best face on it. Twice she has sent in to know if you have arrived, and I sent word, "No, not yet," though it cut me to the 'eart.'

'She is anxious to see me?'

'Desprit, sir.'

'She thinks to avoid exposure, then?' said I darkly, keeping a set face.

'She 'opes, sir: she devoutly 'opes.' He groaned and led the way. 'It may, after all, be a lesson to Mr. 'Erbert,' he muttered as we reached the landing.

'I fancy it's going to be a lesson to several of you.'

'The things we've 'ad to keep dark, sir—the goings-on!'

'I can well believe it.'

'I was in some doubts about you, sir—begging your pardon: but in spite of the dress, sir—which gives a larky appearance, if I may say it—and doubtless is so meant—you reassure me, sir: you do indeed. I feel the worst is over. We can put ourselves in your 'ands.'

'You have certainly done that,' said I. 'As for the worst being over——'

We were within the drawing-room by this time, and he plucked me by the sleeve in his excitement, yet deferentially. 'Yonder is the mistress, sir—in the yellow h'Empire satin—talking with the gentleman in sky-blue rationals. Ah, she sees you!'

She did. And I read at once in her beautiful eyes that while talking with her partner she had been watching the door for me. She came towards me with an eager catch of the breath—one so very like a cry of relief that in the act of holding out her hand she had to turn to the nearest guests and explain.

'It's Mr. Richardson—"George Anthony," you know—who wrote *Larks in Aspic*! I had set my heart on his coming, and had almost given him up. Why are you so cruelly late?' she demanded, turning her eyes on mine.

Her hand was still held out to me. I had meant to hold myself up stiffly and decline it; but somehow I could not. She was a woman, after all, and her look told me—and me only—that she was in trouble. Also I knew her by face and by report. I had seen her acting in more than one exceedingly stupid musical comedy, and wondered why 'Clara Joy' condescended to waste herself upon such inanities. I recalled certain notes in her voice, certain moments when, in the midst of the service of folly, she had seemed to isolate herself and stand watching, aloof from the audience and her fellow-actors, almost pathetically alone. Report said, too, that she was good, and that she had domestic troubles, though it had not reached me what these troubles were. Certainly she appeared altogether too good for these third-rate guests—for third rate they were to the most casual eye. And the trouble, which signalled to me now in her look, clearly and to my astonishment included no remorse for having walked into a stranger's house and turned it upside-down without so much as a by-your-leave. She claimed my goodwill confidently, without any appeal to be forgiven. I held my feelings under rein and took her hand.

As I released it she motioned me to give her my arm. 'I must find you supper at once,' she said quietly, in a tone that warned me not to decline. 'Not—not in there; we will try the library downstairs.'

Down to the library I led her accordingly, and somehow was aware—by that supernumerary sense which works at times in

F

the back of a man's head—of Horrex discreetly following us. At the library door she turned to him. 'When I ring,' she said. He bowed and withdrew.

The room was empty and dark. She switched on the light and nodded to me to close the door.

'Take that off, please,' she commanded.

'I beg your pardon? . . . Ah, to be sure: I had forgotten my false nose.'

'How did Herbert pick up with you?' she asked musingly. 'His friends are not usually so—so——'

'Respectable?' I suggested.

'I think I meant to say "presentable." They are never respectable by any chance.'

'Then, happily, it still remains to be proved that I am one of them.'

'He seems, at any rate, to reckon you high amongst them, since he gave your name.'

'Gave my name? To whom?'

'Oh, I don't know—to the magistrate—or the policeman—or whoever it is. I have never been in a police cell myself,' she added, with a small smile.

'Is Herbert, then, in a police cell?'

She nodded. 'At Vine Street. He wants to be bailed out.'

'What amount?'

'Himself in ten pounds and a friend in another ten. He gave your name; and the policeman is waiting for the answer.'

'I see,' said I. 'But excuse me if I fail to see why, being apparently so impatient to bail him out, you have waited for me. To be sure (for reasons which are dark to me) he appears to have given my name to the police; but we will put that riddle aside for the moment. Any respectable citizen would have served, with the money to back him. Why not have sent Horrex, for example?'

'But I thought the—the——'

'Surety?' I suggested.

'I thought he must be a householder. No,' she cried, as I turned away with a slight shrug of the shoulder, 'that was not the real reason! Herbert is—oh, why will you force me to say it?'

'I beg your pardon,' said I. 'He is at certain times not too tractable; Horrex, in particular, cannot be trusted to manage him; and—and in short you wish him released as soon as possible, but not brought home to this house until your guests have taken leave?'

She nodded at me with swimming eyes. She was passing beautiful, more beautiful than I had thought.

'Yes, yes; you understand! And I thought that—as his friend—and with your influence over him——'

I pulled out my watch. 'Has Horrex a hansom in waiting?'

'A four-wheeler,' she corrected me. Our eyes met, and with a great pity I read in hers that she knew only too well the kind of cab suitable.

'Then let us have in the policeman. A four-wheeler will be better, as you suggest, since with your leave I am going to take Horrex with me. The fact is, I am a little in doubt as to my influence: for to tell you the plain truth, I have never to my knowledge set eyes on your husband.'

'My husband?' She paused with her hand on the bell-pull, and gazed at me blankly. 'My husband?' She began to laugh softly, uncannily, in a way that tore my heart. 'Herbert is my brother.'

'Oh!' said I, feeling pretty much of a fool.

'But what gave you—what do you mean——'

'Lord knows,' I interrupted her; 'but if you will tell Horrex to get himself and the policeman into the cab, I will run upstairs, dress, and join them in five minutes.'

IV

In five minutes I had donned my ordinary clothes again and, descending through the pack of guests to the front door, found a four-wheeler waiting, with Horrex inside and a policeman whom, as I guessed, he had been drugging with strong waters for an hour past in some secluded chamber of the house. The fellow was somnolent, and in sepulchral silence we journeyed to Vine Street. There I chose to be conducted to the cell alone, and Mr. Horrex, hearing my decision, said fervently, 'May you be rewarded for your goodness to me and mine!'

I discovered afterwards that he had a growing family of six dependent on him, and think this must explain a gratefulness which puzzled me at the time.

'He's quieter this last half-hour,' said the police sergeant, unlocking the cell and opening the door with extreme caution.

The light fell and my eyes rested on a sandy-haired youth with a receding chin, a black eye, a crumpled shirt-front smeared with blood, and a dress-suit split and soiled with much rolling in the dust.

'Friend of yours, sir, to bail you out,' announced the sergeant

'I have no friends,' answered the prisoner in hollow tones. 'Who's this Johnny?'

'My name is Richardson,' I began.

'From the Grampian Hills? Al'ri', old man; what can I do for you?'

'Well, if you've no objection, I've come to bail you out.'

'Norra a bit of it. Go 'way: I want t' other Richardson, good old larks-in-aspic! Sergeant——'

'Yessir.'

'I protest—you hear?—protest in sacred name of law; case of mish—case of mistaken 'dentity. Not this Richardson— take him away! Don't blame you: common name. Richardson *I* want has whiskers down to here, tiddy-fol-ol; calls 'em "Piccadilly weepers." Can't mistake him. If at first you don't succeed, try, try again.'

'Look here,' said I, 'just you listen to this; I'm Richardson, and I'm here to bail you out.'

'Can't do it, old man; mean well, no doubt, but can't do it. One may lead a horse to the water—twenty can't bail him out. Go 'way and don't fuss.'

I glanced at the sergeant. 'You 'll let me deal with him as I like?' I asked.

He grinned. 'Bless you, sir, we 're used to it. *I* ain't listening.'

'Thank you.' I turned to the prisoner. 'Now, then, you drunken little hog, stand up and walk,' said I, taking him by the ear and keeping my left ready.

I suppose that the drink suddenly left him weak, for he stood up at once.

'There 's some ho—horrible mistake,' he began to whimper. 'But if the worst comes to the worst, you 'll *adopt* me, won't you?'

Still holding him by the ear, I led him forth and flung him into the cab, in a corner of which the trembling Horrex had already huddled himself. He fell, indeed, across Horrex's knees, and at once screamed aloud.

'Softly, softly, Master 'Erbert,' whispered the poor man soothingly. 'It 's only poor old Horrex, that you 've known since a boy.'

'Horrex?' Master Herbert straightened himself up. 'Do I understand you to say, sir, that your name is Horrex? Then allow me to tell you, Horrex, that you are no gentleman. You hear?' He spoke with anxious lucidity, leaning forward and tapping the butler on the knee. 'No gentleman.'

'No, sir,' assented Horrex.

'That being the case, we 'll say no more about it. I decline to argue with you. If you 're waking, call me early—there 's many a black, black eye, Horrex, but none so black as mine. Call me at eleven-fifteen, bringing with you this gentleman's blood in a bottle—*an*' don't forget soda. Goo'-night, go bye-bye. . . .'

By the fleeting light of a street-lamp I saw his head drop forward, and a minute later he was gently snoring.

It was agreed that on reaching home Master Herbert must be smuggled into the basement of No. 402 and put to rest on

Horrex's own bed; also that, to avoid the line of carriages waiting in the Cromwell Road for the departing guests, the cab should take us round to the gardens at the back. I carried on my chain a key which would admit us to these and unlock the small gate between them and the kitchens. This plan of action so delighted Horrex that for a moment I feared he was going to clasp my hands.

'If it wasn't irreverent, sir, I could almost say you had dropped on me from heaven!'

'You may alter your opinion,' said I grimly, 'before I've done dropping.'

At the garden entrance we paid and dismissed the cab. I took Master Herbert's shoulders and Horrex his heels, and between us we carried his limp body across the turf—a procession so suggestive of dark and secret tragedy that I blessed our luck for protecting us from the casual intrusive policeman. Our entrance by the kitchen passage, however, was not so fortunate. Stealthily as we trod, our footsteps reached the ears in the servants' hall, and we were met by William and a small but compact body of female servants urging him to armed resistance. A kitchen-maid fainted away as soon as we were recognized, and the strain of terror relaxed.

I saw at once that Master Herbert's condition caused them no surprise. We carried him to the servants' hall and laid him in an arm-chair, to rest our arms, while the motherly cook lifted his unconscious head to lay a pillow beneath it.

As she did so, a bell jangled furiously on the wall above.

'Good Lord!' Horrex turned a scared face up at it. 'The library!'

'What's the matter in the library?'

But he was gone: to reappear, a minute later, with a face whiter than ever.

'The mistress wants you at on'st, sir, if you'll follow me. William, run out and see if you can raise another cab—four-wheeler.'

'What, at this time of night?' answered William. 'Get along with you!'

'Do your best, lad.' Mr. Horrex appealed gently but with pathetic dignity. 'If there's miracles indoors there may be miracles outside. This way, sir!'

He led me to the library door, knocked softly, opened it, and stood aside for me to enter.

Within stood his mistress, confronting—another policeman!

Her hands rested on the back of a library chair: and though she stood up bravely and held herself erect with her finger-tips pressed hard into the leather, I saw that she was swaying on the verge of hysterics, and I had the sense to speak sharply.

'What's the meaning of this?' I demanded.

'This one—comes from Marlborough Street!' she gasped.

I stepped back to the door, opened it, and, as I expected, discovered Horrex listening.

'A bottle of champagne and a glass at once,' I commanded, and he sped. 'And now, Miss Joy, if you please, the constable and I will do the talking. What's your business, constable?'

'Prisoner wants bail, sir,' answered the policeman.

'Name?'

'George Anthony Richardson.'

'Yes, yes—but I mean the prisoner's name.'

'That's what I'm telling you. "George Anthony Richardson, four-nought-two, Cromwell Road"—that's the name on the sheet, and I heard him give it myself.'

'And I thought, of course, it must be you,' put in Clara; 'and I wondered what dreadful thing could have happened —until Horrex appeared and told me you were safe, and Herbert too——'

'I think,' said I, going to the door again and taking the tray from Horrex, 'that you were not to talk. Drink this, please.'

She took the glass, but with a rebellious face. 'Oh, if you take that tone with me——'

'I do. And now,' I turned to the constable, 'what name did he give for his surety?'

'Herbert Jarmayne, same address.'

'Herbert Jarmayne?' I glanced at Clara, who nodded back, pausing as she lifted her glass. 'Ah! yes—yes, of course. How much?'

'Two tenners.'

'Deep answering deep. Drunk and disorderly, I suppose?'

'Blind. He was breaking glasses at Toscano's and swearing he was Sir Charles Wyndham in *David Garrick*: but he settled down quiet at the station, and when I left he was talking religious and saying he pitied nine-tenths of the world, for they were going to get it hot.'

'Trewlove!' I almost shouted, wheeling round upon Clara.

'I beg your pardon?'

'No, of course—you wouldn't understand. But all the same it's Trewlove!' I cried, radiant. 'Eh?'—this to Horrex, mumbling in the doorway—'the cab outside? Step along, constable: I'll follow in a moment—to identify your prisoner, not to bail him out.' Then as he touched his helmet and marched out after Horrex: 'By George, though! Trewlove!' I muttered, meeting Clara's eye and laughing.

'So you've said,' she agreed doubtfully; 'but it seems a funny sort of explanation.'

'It's as simple as A B C,' I assured her. 'The man at Marlborough Street is the man who let you this house.'

'I took it through an agent.'

'I'm delighted to hear it. Then the man at Marlborough Street is the man for whom the agent let the house.'

'Then you are not Mr. Richardson—not "George Anthony" —and you didn't write *Larks in Aspic*?' said she, with a flattering shade of disappointment in her tone.

'Oh! yes, I did.'

'Then I don't understand in the least—unless—unless——' She put out two deprecating hands. 'You don't mean to tell me that this is your house, and we 've been living in it without your knowledge! Oh! why didn't you tell me?'

'Come, I like that!' said I. 'You 'll admit, on reflection, that you haven't given me much time.'

But she stamped her foot. 'I 'll go upstairs and pack at once,' she declared.

'That will hardly meet the case, I 'm afraid. You forget that your brother is downstairs: and by his look, when I left him, he 'll take a deal of packing.'

'Herbert?' She put a hand to her brow. 'I was forgetting. Then you are not Herbert's friend after all?'

'I have made a beginning. But in fact, I made his acquaintance at Vine Street just now. Trewlove—that 's my scoundrel of a butler—has been making up to him under my name. They met at the house-agent's, probably. The rogue models himself upon me: but when it comes to letting my house—— By the way, have you paid him by cheque?'

'I paid the agent. I knew nothing of you until Herbert announced that he 'd made your acquaintance——'

'Pray go on,' said I, watching her troubled eyes. 'It would be interesting to hear how he described me.'

'He used a very funny word. He said you were the rummiest thing in platers he 'd struck for a long while. But, of course, he was talking of the other man.'

'Of course,' said I gravely: whereupon our eyes met, and we both laughed.

'Ah, but you are kind!' she cried. 'And when I think how we have treated you—if only I *could* think——' Her hand went up again to her forehead.

'It will need some reparation,' said I. 'But we 'll discuss that when I come back.'

'Was—was Herbert very bad?' She attempted to laugh, but tears suddenly brimmed her eyes.

'I scarcely noticed,' said I; and, picking up my hat, went out hurriedly.

* F

V

Trewlove in his Marlborough Street cell was a disgusting object—offensive to the eye and to one's sense of the dignity of man. At sight of me he sprawled, and when the shock of it was over he continued to grovel until the sight bred a shame in me for being the cause of it. What made it ten times worse was his curious insensibility—even while he grovelled—to the moral aspect of his behaviour.

'You will lie here,' said I, 'until to-morrow morning, when you will probably be fined fifty shillings and costs, plus the cost of the broken glass at Toscano's. I take it for granted that the money will be paid?'

'I will send, sir, to my lodgings for my cheque-book.'

'It's a trifling matter, no doubt; but since you will be charged under the name of William John Trewlove, it will be a mistake to put "G. A. Richardson" on the cheque.'

'It was an error of judgment, sir, my giving your name here.'

'It was a worse one,' I assured him, 'to append it to the receipt for Miss Jarmayne's rent.'

'You don't intend to prosecute, Mr. George?'

'Why not?'

'But you don't, sir; something tells me that you don't.'

Well, in fact (as you may have guessed), I did not. I had no desire to drag Miss Jarmayne into further trouble; but I resented that the dog should count on my clemency without knowing the reason of it.

'In justice to myself, sir, I 'ave to tell you that I shouldn't 'ave let the 'ouse to *hanybody*. It was only that, she being connected with the stage, I saw a hopening. Mr. 'Erbert was, as you might say, a hafterthought: which, finding him so affable, I thought I might go one better. He cost me a pretty penny first and last. But when he offered to introjuice me—and me, at his invite, going back to be put up at No. 402 like any other gentleman—why, 'ow could I resist it?'

'If I forbear to have you arrested, Trewlove, it will be on condition that you efface yourself. May I suggest some foreign country, where, in a colony of the Peculiar People —unacquainted with your past——'

'I 'm tired of them, sir. Their style of life don't suit me— nor yours—I 've tried 'em both, and I give it up—I 'm too late to learn; but I 'll say this for it, it cures you of wantin' to go back and be a Peculiar. Now, if you 've no objection, sir, I thought of takin' a little public down Putney way.'

. . . . . .

'You mean it?' asked Clara, a couple of hours later.

'I mean it,' said I.

'And I am to live on here alone as your tenant?'

'As my tenant, and so long as it pleases you.' I struck a match to light her bedroom candle, and with that we both laughed, for the June dawn was pouring down on us through the stairway skylight.

'Shall I see you to-morrow, to say good-bye?'

'I expect not. We shall catch the first boat.'

'The question is, will you get Herbert awake in time to explain matters?'

'I 'll undertake that. Horrex has already packed for him. Oh, you needn't fear: he 'll be right enough at Ambleteuse, under my eye.'

'It 's good of you,' she said slowly; 'but why are you doing it?'

'Can't say,' I answered lightly.

'Well, good-bye, and God bless you!' She put out her hand. 'There 's nothing I can say or do to——'

'Oh, yes, by the way, there is,' I interrupted, tugging a key off my chain. 'You see this? It unlocks the drawers of a writing-table in your room. In the top left-hand drawer you will find a bundle of papers.'

She passed up the stair before me and into the room. 'Is

this what you want?' she asked, reappearing after a minute with my manuscript in her hand. 'What is it? A new comedy?'

'The makings of one,' said I. 'It was to fetch it that I came across from Ambleteuse.'

'And dropped into another.'

'Upon my word,' said I, 'you are right, and to-night's is a better one—up to a point.'

'What are you going to call it?'

'*My Tenant.*'

For a moment she seemed to be puzzled. 'But I mean the other,' said she, nodding towards the manuscript in my hand.

'Indeed, that is its name,' said I, and showed her the title on the first page. 'And I've a really splendid idea for the third act,' I added as we shook hands.

I mounted the stairs to my room, tossed the manuscript into a chair, and began to wind up my watch.

'But this other wants a third act too!' I told myself suddenly.

.   .   .   .   .   .

You will observe that once or twice in the course of this narrative my pen has slipped and inadvertently called Miss Jarmayne 'Clara.'

MATTHEW ARNOLD

I do not hold up Joubert as a very astonishing and powerful genius, but rather as a delightful and edifying genius. . . . He is the most prepossessing and convincing of witnesses to the good of loving light. Because he sincerely loved light, and did not prefer to it any little private darkness of his own, he found light. . . . And because he was full of light he was also full of happiness. . . . His life was as charming as his thoughts.   For certainly it is natural that the love of light, which is already in some measure the possession of light, should irradiate and beatify the whole life of him who has it.

MANY a reader of *Essays in Criticism* must have paused and in thought transferred to Matthew Arnold these words of his in praise of Joubert, as well as the fine passage in which he goes on to ask What, in literature, we mean by fame?   Only two kinds of authors (he tells us) are secure of fame: the first being the Homers, Dantes, Shakespeares, 'the great abiding fountains of truth,' whose praise is for ever and ever.   But beside these sacred personages stand certain elect ones, less majestic, yet to be recognized as of the same family and character with the greatest, 'exercising like them an immortal function, and like them inspiring a permanent interest.'   The fame of these also is assured.   'They will never, like the Shakespeares, command the homage of the multitude; but they are safe; the multitude will not trample them down.'

To this company Matthew Arnold belongs.   We all feel it, and some of us can give reasons for our confidence; but perhaps, if all our reasons were collected, the feeling would be found to reach deeper into certainty than any of them.   He was never popular, and never will be.   Yet no one can say that, although at one time he seemed to vie with the public in distrusting it, his poetry missed its mark.   On the other hand, while his critical writings had swift and almost instantaneous effect for good, the repute they brought him was moderate and largely made up of misconception.   For the mass of his country-men he came somehow to personify a number of things which their minds vaguely associated with kid gloves, and by his ironical way of playing with the misconception he did more than a little to confirm it.   But in truth Arnold was a serious man who saw life as a serious business and chiefly relied, for making the best of it, upon a serene common sense.   He had elegance, to be sure, and was inclined—at any rate, in contro-versy—to be conscious of it; but it was elegance of that plain Attic order to which common sense gives the law and almost the inspiration.   The man and the style were one.   Alike in his life and his writings he observed and preached the golden mean, with a mind which was none the less English and practical if, in expressing it, he deliberately and almost defiantly avoided that emphasis which Englishmen love to a fault.

Matthew Arnold, eldest son of Dr. Thomas Arnold, the famous Head Master of Rugby, was born on Christmas Eve, 1822, at Laleham on the Thames, where his father at that time taught private pupils.   The child was barely six years old when the family removed to Rugby, and at seven he returned to Lale-ham to be taught by his uncle, the Rev. John Buckland.   In August, 1836, he proceeded to Winchester, but was removed at the end of a year and entered Rugby, where he remained until he went up to Balliol College, Oxford, in 1841, with an open scholarship.   He had written a prize poem at Rugby—the subject, *Alaric at Rome*; and on this performance he improved by taking the Newdigate in 1843—the subject, *Cromwell*.   But we need waste no time on these exercises, which are of interest only to people interested in such things.   It is better worth noting that the boy had been used to spending his holidays, and now spent a great part of his vacations, at Fox How, near Grasmere, a house which Dr. Arnold had taken to refresh his eyes and his spirits after the monotonous ridge and furrow, field and hedgerow, around Rugby; and that, as Mr. Herbert Paul puts it, young Matthew 'thus grew up under the shadow of Wordsworth, whose brilliant and penetrating interpreter he was destined to become.' Genius collects early, and afterwards distils from recollection; and if its spirit, like that of the licentiate Pedro Garcias, is to be disinterred, he who would find Matthew Arnold's must dig in and around Fox How and Oxford.

At Oxford, which he loved passionately, he 'missed his first,' but atoned for this, three months later, by winning a fellowship at Oriel. (This was in 1844–5. His father had died in 1842.) He stayed up, however, but a short while after taking his degree: went back to Rugby as an assistant master; relinquished this in 1847 to become private secretary to Lord Lansdowne, then President of the Council; and was by him appointed in 1851 to an Inspectorship of Schools, which he retained for five-and-thirty years. In 1851, too, he married Frances Lucy Wightman, daughter of a Judge of the Queen's Bench; and so settled down at the same time to domestic happiness and to daily work which, if dull sometimes, was not altogether ungrateful as it was never less than conscientiously performed.

Meanwhile, in 1849, he had put forth a thin volume, *The Strayed Reveller, and other Poems, by A*; which was followed in 1852 by *Empedocles on Etna, and other Poems, by A*. In 1853 he dropped anonymity and under the title *Poems, by Matthew Arnold* republished the contents of these two volumes, omitting *Empedocles*, with a few minor pieces, and adding some priceless things, such as *Sohrab and Rustum*, *The Church of Brou*, *Requiescat*, and *The Scholar-Gipsy*.

'It was received, we believe, with general indifference,' wrote Mr. Froude of the first volume, in *The Westminster Review*, 1854. We need not trouble to explain the fact, beyond saying that English criticism was just then at about the lowest ebb it reached in the last century, and that the few capable ears were occupied by the far more confident voice of Tennyson and the far more disconcerting one of Browning: but the fact—surprising when all allowance has been made—must be noted, for it is important to remember that the most and best of Arnold's poetry was written before he gained the world's ear, and that he gained it not as a poet but as a critic. In 1855 appeared *Poems by Matthew Arnold, Second Series,* of which only *Balder Dead* and *Separation* were new; and in 1858 *Merope* with its Preface: but in the interval between them he had been elected Professor of Poetry at Oxford (May 1857).

The steps by which a reputation grows, the precise moment at which it becomes established, are often difficult to trace and fix. The poems, negligently though they had been received at first, must have helped: and, since men who improve an office are themselves usually improved by it, assuredly the professorship helped too. The lectures on Homer which adorned Arnold's first tenure of the Chair strike a new note of criticism, speak with a growing undertone of authority beneath their modest professions, and would suffice to explain—if mere custom did not even more easily explain—why in 1862 he was re-elected for another five years. But before 1865, no doubt, the judicious who knew him had tested him by more than his lectures, and were prepared for *Essays in Criticism.*

Although we are mainly concerned here with the poems, a word must be said on *Essays in Criticism,* which Mr. Paul pronounces to be 'Mr. Arnold's most important work in prose, the central book, so to speak, of his life.' Mr. Saintsbury calls it 'the first full and varied, and perhaps always the best, expression and illustration of the author's critical attitude, the detailed manifesto and exemplar of the new critical method, and so one of the epoch-making books of the later nineteenth century in English'—and on this subject Mr. Saintsbury has a peculiar right to be heard.

Now for a book to be 'epoch-making' it must bring to its age something which its age conspicuously lacks: and *Essays in Criticism* did this. No one remembering what Dryden did, and Johnson, and Coleridge, and Lamb, and Hazlitt, will pretend that Arnold invented English criticism, or that he did well what these men had done ill. What he did, and they missed doing, was to treat criticism as a deliberate disinterested art, with laws and methods of its own, a proper temper, and certain standards or touchstones of right taste by which the quality of any writing, as literature, could be tested. In other words he introduced authority and, with authority, responsibility, into a business which had hitherto been practised at the best by brilliant nonconformists and at the worst by Quarterly Reviewers, who, taking for their motto *Judex damnatur cum nocens absolvitur*, either forgot or never surmised that to punish the guilty can be but a corollary of a higher obligation—to discover the truth. Nor can any one now read the literature of that period without a sense that Arnold's teaching was indispensably needed just then. A page of Macaulay or of Carlyle dazzles us with its rhetoric; strikes, arrests, excites us with a number of things tellingly put and in ways we had scarcely guessed to be possible; but it no longer convinces. It does not even dispose us to be convinced, since (to put it vulgarly) we feel that the author 'is not out after' truth; that Macaulay's William III is a figure dressed up and adjusted to prove Macaulay's thesis, and that the France of Carlyle's *French Revolution* not only never existed but, had it ever existed, would not be France. Arnold helping us, we see these failures—for surely that history is a failure which, like Cremorne, will not bear the daylight—to be inevitable in a republic of letters where laws are not and wherein each author writes at the top of his own bent, indulging and exploiting his personal eccentricity to the fullest. It has probably been the salvation of our literature that in the fourteenth century the Latin prevailed over the Anglo-Saxon line of its descent, and that in the forming of our verse as well as of our prose we had, at the critical moments, the literatures of Latin races, Italian or French, for models and correctives; as it was the misfortune of the Victorian period before 1865 that its men of genius wrote with eyes turned inward upon themselves or, if outward, upon that German literature which, for all its great qualities, must ever be dangerous to Englishmen because it flatters and encourages their special faults.[1]

Of Arnold from 1865 onward—of the books in which he enforced rather than developed his critical method (for all the gist of it may be found in *Essays in Criticism*)—of his incursions into the fields of politics and theology—much might be written, but it would not be germane to our purpose. *New Poems*, including *Bacchanalia, or the New Age, Dover Beach*, and the beautiful *Thyrsis*, appeared in 1867; and thereafter for the last twenty years of his life he wrote very little in verse, though the fine *Westminster Abbey* proved that the Muse had not died in him. He used his hold upon the public ear to preach some sermons which, as a good citizen, he thought the nation needed. In his hard-working official life he rendered services which those of us who engage in the work of English education are constantly and gratefully recognizing in their effects; and we still toil in the wake of his ideals. He retired in November, 1886. He died on April 15th, 1888, of heart failure: he had gone to Liverpool to meet his eldest daughter on her return from the United States, and there, in running to catch a tram-car, he fell and died in a moment. He was sixty-five, but in appearance carried his years lightly. He looked, and was, a distinguished and agreeable man. Of good presence and fine manners; perfect in his domestic relations, genial in company and radiating cheerfulness; setting a high aim to his official work yet ever conscientious in details; he stands (apart from his literary achievement) as an example of the Englishman at his best. He cultivated this best deliberately. His daily note-books were filled with quotations, high thoughts characteristically chosen and jotted down to be borne in mind; and some of these—such

[1] That Matthew Arnold himself over-valued contemporary German literature does not really affect our argument.

as *Semper aliquid certi proponendum est* and *Ecce labora et noli contristari!*—recur again and again. But the result owed its amiability also to that 'timely relaxation' counselled by Milton:

> To measure life, learn thou betimes, and know
>   Toward solid good what leads the nearest way;
>   For other things mild Heav'n a time ordains,
> And disapproves that care, though wise in show,
>   That with superfluous burden loads the day,
>   And when God sends a cheerful hour, refrains.

To those, then, who tell us that Arnold's poetic period was brief, and imply that it was therefore disappointing, we might answer that this is but testimony to the perfect development of a life which in due season used poetry and at the due hour cast it away, to proceed to things more practical. But this would be to err almost as deeply as those who tell us that Arnold, as he himself said of Gray, 'never spoke out'—whereas Arnold habitually spoke out, and now and then even too insistently. Again it would be a mistake for us to apply to him *au pied de la lettre* the over-sad verses:

> Youth rambles on life's arid mount,
>   And strikes the rock, and finds the vein,
> And brings the water from the fount,
>   The fount which shall not flow again.

> The man mature with labour chops
>   For the bright stream a channel grand,
> And sees not that the sacred drops
>   Ran off and vanish'd out of hand.

> And then the old man totters nigh,
>   And feebly rakes among the stones.
> The mount is mute, the channel dry;
>   And down he lays his weary bones.

Yet it were stupid not to recognize that here is contained a certain amount of general truth and of truth particularly applicable to Arnold. 'The poet,' Mr. Saintsbury writes of him (and it sums up the matter), 'has in him a vein, or, if the metaphor be preferred, a spring, of the most real and rarest poetry. But the vein is constantly broken by faults, and never very thick; the spring is intermittent, and runs at times by drops only.' Elsewhere Mr. Saintsbury speaks of his 'elaborate assumption of the singing-robe,' a phrase very happily critical. Arnold felt —no man more deeply—the majesty of the poet's function: he solemnly attired himself to perform it: but the singing-robe was not his daily wear. The ample pall in which Tennyson swept, his life through, as to the manner born; the stiffer skirts in which Wordsworth walked so complacently; these would have intolerably cumbered the man who protested that even the title of Professor made him uneasy. Wordsworth and Tennyson were bards, authentic and unashamed; whereas in Arnold, as Sir William Watson has noted,

> Something of worldling mingled still
> With bard and sage.

There was never a finer worldling than Matthew Arnold: but the criticism is just.

The critics, while noting this, have missed something which to us seems to explain much in Arnold's verse. We said just now that English literature has been fortunate in what it owes to the Latin races; we may add that it has been most fortunate in going to Italy for instruction in its verse, to France for instruction in its prose. This will be denied by no one who has studied Elizabethan poetry or the prose of the 'Augustan' age: and as little will any one who has studied the structure of poetry deny that Italy is the natural, France the unnatural, school for an English poet. The reason is not that we understand Italian better than French history and with more sympathy—though this, too, scarcely admits of dispute; nor again that the past of Italy appeals to emotions of which poetry is the consecrated language. It lies in the very structure and play of the language; so that an Englishman who has but learnt how to pronounce the Italian vowels can read Italian poetry passably. The accent comes to him at once; the lack of accent in French remains foreign after many months of study. Now although Arnold was no great admirer of French poetry (and indeed had a particular dislike for the Alexandrine), France was, to him, among modern nations, the heir of those classical qualities which differentiate the Greek from the barbarian, and his poetry seems ever to be striving to reproduce the Greek note through verse subdued to a French flatness of tone, as though (to borrow a metaphor from another art) its secret lay in low relief. But an English poet fighting against emphasis is as a man fighting water with a broom: and an English poet, striving to be unemphatic, must yet contrive to be various, or he is naught. Successfully as he managed his prose, when he desired it to be emphatic Arnold had, in default of our native methods of emphasis, to fall back upon that simple repetition which irritates so many readers. In his poetry the devices are yet more clumsy. We suppose that no English poet before or since has so cruelly overworked the interjection 'Ah!' But far worse than any number of 'ah!'s' is Arnold's trick of italic type:

How *I* bewail you! . . .

We mortal millions live *alone* . .

In the rustling night-air comes the answer:
'Wouldst thou *be* as these are? *Live* as they!' . . .

a device almost unpardonable in poetry. So when he would give us variety, as in *Tristram and Iseult*, Arnold has no better resource than frequent change of metre: and although

every reader must have felt the effect of that sudden fine
outburst

> What voices are these on the clear night-air?
> What lights in the court—what steps on the stair? . . .

yet some must also have reflected that the great masters, having
to tell a story, choose their one metre and, having chosen, so
adapt and handle it that it tells all. *Sohrab and Rustum* indeed
tells itself perfectly, from its first line to its noble close. But
Sohrab and Rustum is, and professes to be, an episode. *Balder*
is little more, and most readers find *Balder,* in spite of its fine
passages and general dignity, long enough. Arnold—let it be
repeated—was not a bard: not a Muse-intoxicated man. He
had not the bardic, the architectonic, gift. 'Something of the
worldling' in him forbade any such fervour as, sustained day
after day for years, gave the world *Paradise Lost,* and inci-
dentally, no doubt, made Milton's daughters regret at times
that their father was not as ordinary men.

Nor had Arnold an impeccable ear for rhyme (in *The New
Sirens,* for instance, he rhymes 'dawning' with 'morning'): and
if we hesitate to follow the many who have doubted his ear for
rhythm, it is not for lack of apparently good evidence, but
because some of his rhythms which used to give us pause have
come, upon longer acquaintance, to fascinate us: and the explanation may be, as we have hinted, that they follow the
French rather than the Italian use of accent, and are strange to
us rather than in themselves unmusical. Certainly the critics
who would have us believe that *The Strayed Reveller* is an
unmusical poem will not at this time of day persuade us by
the process of taking a stanza or two and writing them down
in the form of prose. We could do the same with a dozen
lines of *The Tempest* or *Antony and Cleopatra,* were it worth
doing; and prove just as much, or as little.

Something of Arnold's own theory of poetry may be extracted
from the prefaces of 1853 and 1854. They contain, like the

prefaces of Dryden and of Wordsworth, much wisdom; but the world, perhaps even more wisely, refuses to judge a poet by his theory, which (however admirable) seldom yields up his secret. Yet Arnold had a considered view of what the poet should attempt and what avoid; and that he followed it would remain certain although much evidence were accumulated to prove that he who denounced 'poetry's eternal enemy, Caprice,' could himself be, on occasion, capricious. He leaves the impression that he wrote with difficulty; his raptures, though he knew rapture, are infrequent. But through all his work there runs a strain of serious elevated thought, and on it all there rests an air of composure equally serious and elevated—a trifle statuesque, perhaps, but by no means deficient in feeling. No one can read, say, the closing lines of *Mycerinus* and fail to perceive these qualities. No one can read any considerable portion of his work and deny that they are characteristic. Nor, we think, can any one study the poetry of 1850 and thereabouts without being forced to admit that it needed these qualities of thoughtfulness and composure which Arnold brought to it. He has been criticized for discovering in Tennyson a certain 'deficiency in intellectual power.' But is he by this time alone in that discovery? And if no lack of thoughtfulness can be charged against Browning—as it cannot—is not Browning violent, unchastened, far too often energetic for energy's sake? Be it granted that Arnold in poetical strength was no match for these champions: yet he brought to literature, and in a happy hour, that which they lacked, insisting by the example of his verse, as well as by the precepts of his criticism, that before anything becomes literature it must observe two conditions—it must be worth saying, and it must be worthily written.

Also he continued, if with a difference, that noble Wordsworthian tradition which stood in some danger of perishing—chiefly, we think, beneath the accumulation of rubbish piled upon it by its own author during his later years. That which Matthew Arnold disinterred and repolished may have been but

a fragment. His page has not, says Mr. Watson, 'the deep,
authentic mountain-thrill.' We grant that Arnold's feeling for
Nature has not the Wordsworthian depth: but so far as it
penetrates it is genuine. Lines such as

> While the deep-burnish'd foliage overhead
> Splintered the silver arrows of the moon . . .

may owe their felicity to phrase rather than to feeling. The
Mediterranean landscape in *A Southern Night* may seem almost
too exquisitely elaborated. Yet who can think of Arnold's
poetry as a whole without feeling that Nature is always behind
it as a living background?—whether it be the storm of wind
and rain shaking Tintagel—

> I forgot, thou comest from thy voyage—
> Yes, the spray is on thy cloak and hair . . .

or the scent-laden water-meadows along Thames, or the pine
forests on the flank of Etna, or an English garden in June, or
Oxus, its mists and fens and 'the hush'd Chorasmian waste.'
If Arnold's love of natural beauty have not those moments of
piercing *apprehension* which in his master's poetry seem to break
through dullness into the very heaven: if he have not that secret
which Wordsworth must have learnt upon the Cumbrian
mountains, from moments when the clouds drift apart and the
surprised climber sees all Windermere, all Derwentwater,
shining at his feet; if on the other hand his philosophy of life,
rounded and complete, seem none too hopeful, but call man back
from eager speculations which man will never resign: if it repress,
where Browning encouraged, our quest after

> Thoughts hardly to be pack'd
> Within the narrow act,
> Fancies that broke through language and escaped . . .

yet his sense of atmosphere, of background, of the great stage
on which man plays his part, gives Arnold's teaching a wonderful *comprehension*, within its range. 'This,' we say, 'is poetry

we can trust, not to flatter us, but to sustain, console.' If the
reader mistake it for the last word on life his trust in it will be
illusory. It brings rather that

> lull in the hot race
> Wherein he doth for ever chase
> That flying and elusive shadow, rest.
> An air of coolness plays upon his face,
> And an unwonted calm pervades his breast;
> And then . . .

(if after protesting against italics in poetry we may italicize
where, for once, Arnold missed the opportunity)

> he *thinks* he knows
> The hills where his life rose,
> And the sea where it goes.

CARMEN HELLESTONIENSE

Ann. MCMVII in Floralia Compositum [1]

CONFITEMINI, O molles
agni humilesque colles,
   hodie cur exultetis:
tu praesertim, magnum Mare,
fac me certiorem quare
haud dedignas crura dare
   hiphoorariis in fretis?

Venit annus, venit mensis,
cum Praefectus Londinensis
   redit in paterna rura:
quem advenientem gratu-
latur urbs in commeatu
tympanis et aeris flatu:
   Ergo (aiunt) damus crura.

Venit mensis, venit dies,
Hellestoniensis quies
   ruit in immensum sonum:
foris, foras, tum in forum
per praesepia caballorum [2]
ducimus antiquum chorum
   O qua musica trombonum!

---

[1] Welcoming Sir William Purdie Treloar, Bart., Lord Mayor of London, to his ancestral town of Helston in Cornwall, 8th May 1907, when he took part in the 'Furry' or Feast of Flora annually held on that day. The inhabitants go out early to the fields to gather flowers and green branches, and returning dance through the streets and houses, in and out of the open doors.—Q.

[2] The festivities include a horse show.—Q.

Venit dies, venit hora,
venit et solennis Flora
   mane quae postridie nonas
Maias lucens exoptata
nos e portis, nos in prata
margaritis constellata
   vocat nectere coronas.

Ambarvales prorsus retro
(Locuples in curru petro-
   lensĭ, Lazarus in pannis)
Maiae praedum reportantes
irruamus corybantes
te nostratem salutantes
   'Macte tu redi quotannis!'

Eja collis cum agnello
Cantat 'He's a jolly good fellow!'
   id quod nemo denegare
audet: 'mos est hic, ut malis,
Militaris vel Navalis,
hunc et Studii Generalis,
   proles solet celebrare!'

Tuque nostras, Anglicanae
Urbis Metropolitanae
   et tutamen et decor,
terram repetitam unde
partus es ter pede tunde,
Vir honorificabunde
   Gulielme P. Treloar!

COLERIDGE

THE story of Coleridge's life is hard to write and, in a sense, even harder to read: hard to write because the innumerable lapses, infirmities, defections of the will, all claiming—as facts —to be chronicled, cannot but obscure that lovable living presence to which all his contemporaries bore witness and to which the biographer must hold fast or his portrait misses most that is true and essential; and hard to read because the reader, at the hundredth instance of Coleridge's taking the wrong coach, or forgetting to write to his wife and family, or accepting money and neglecting the conditions on which it was bestowed, is apt to let Christian charity go to the winds, and so on his part, too, to miss, nor care that he misses, the better Coleridge which is the real Coleridge, the affectionate forgiving Coleridge, so anxious to cure his faults, so eager to make people *see*, so childlike and yet condemned to sit

> obscure
> In the exceeding lustre and the pure
> Intense irradiation of a mind.

The story not only exasperates the temper; it dodges the understanding, and leaves even the patient reader in such bewilderment as, no doubt, afflicted the much-enduring Odysseus after a third attempt to embrace his mother in the Shades. For Providence (as De Quincey put it) set 'perpetual relays' along Coleridge's path through life. We pursue the man and come up with group after group of his friends: and each, as we demand, 'What have you done with Coleridge?' answers, 'Coleridge? That wonderful fellow? . . . He was here just now, and we helped him forward a little way.'

The late James Dykes Campbell (to whose *Life of Coleridge*

the reader is referred) took up his task with enthusiasm and performed it with astonishing success. He honoured the poet's memory a little 'on this side idolatry.' Yet as we follow his condensed narrative we feel the growth of misgivings in the writer's mind, and at the close he has to make a clean breast of them. 'If,' says he, 'my presentment of what I believe to be the truth be not found to tend, on the whole, to raise Coleridge in the eyes of men, I shall, I confess, feel both surprised and disappointed.'

I am sure that the temple, with all the rubble which blended with its marble, must have been a grander whole than any we are able to reconstruct for ourselves from the stones which lie about the field. The living Coleridge was ever his own apology—men and women who neither shared nor ignored his shortcomings, not only loved him but honoured and followed him. This power of attraction, which might almost be called universal, so diverse were the minds and natures attracted, is itself conclusive proof of very rare qualities. We may read and re-read his life, but we cannot know him as the Lambs, or the Wordsworths, or Poole, or Hookham Frere, or the Gillmans, or Green knew him. Hatred as well as love may be blind, but friendship has eyes, and their testimony may wisely be used in correcting our own impressions.

Samuel Taylor Coleridge was born on October 21, 1772, at the vicarage of Ottery St. Mary in Devonshire, the youngest of nine sons by a second marriage. His father, the Reverend John Coleridge, was an amiable, absent-minded scholar, and apparently somewhat unpractical. We are told that he printed several books by subscription, and he tried to improve the Latin grammars in use by calling the ablative case the 'quale-quare-quidditive.' He died in 1781, and a few months later young Samuel obtained a presentation to Christ's Hospital.

The school and the Coleridge of those days were afterwards depicted in imperishable colours by Charles Lamb, who, though Coleridge's junior by two years, had become a Blue-coat boy some months earlier. In *Christ's Hospital Five-and-Thirty*

Years Ago, by one of those tricks which were dear to him and endear him to us, Lamb professedly supplements his own *Recollections of Christ's Hospital* with the recollections of a lad not fortunate like him in having a home and parents near.

I was a poor friendless boy. My parents, and those who should care for me, were far away. Those few acquaintances of theirs, which they could reckon upon being kind to me in the great city, after a little forced notice, which they had the grace to take of me on my first arrival in town, soon grew tired of my holiday visits. They seemed to them to recur too often, though I found them few enough; and, one after another, they all failed me, and I felt myself alone among six hundred playmates.

O the cruelty of separating a poor lad from his early homestead! The yearnings which I used to have towards it in those unfledged years! How, in my dreams, would my native town (far in the west) come back, with its church, and trees, and faces! How I would wake weeping, and in the anguish of my heart exclaim upon sweet Calne in Wiltshire!

The child is Coleridge, of course, and sweet Calne in Wiltshire is sweet Ottery in Devon, disguised. Of course Coleridge felt this loneliness: a nature so sensitive could not help feeling it; and sixteen years later in *Frost at Midnight* he feelingly recalled it, and promised his own child a happier fate. But, equally of course, he did not feel it all the time. His earliest letters contain allusions to half-crowns and 'a plumb cake,' and in due course, as he grows up, the theme changes naturally to raiment. 'You will excuse me for reminding you that, as our holidays commence next week, and I shall go out a good deal, a good pair of breeches will be no inconsiderable accession to my appearance,' the pair in use being 'not altogether well adapted for a female eye.'

In due course, too, he became a Grecian, fell in love and wrote boyish poetry: and both the love-making and the versifying, though no great matters at the time, were destined to have more formidable consequences than usually attach themselves to youthful experiments. The young lady who inspired them was a Miss Mary Evans, a widow's daughter, and sister of a small Blue-coat boy whom Coleridge had protected.

And oh! from sixteen to nineteen what hours of paradise had Allen [a schoolfellow] and I in escorting the Miss Evanses home on a Saturday, who were then at a milliner's . . . and we used to carry thither, of a summer morning, the pillage of the flower-gardens within six miles of town, with sonnet or love-rhyme wrapped round the nosegay.

But not all the inspiration came from Miss Evans. That of the love-making she shared, if a Christ's Hospital tradition be true, with the daughter of the school 'nurse'; to whom the poem *Genevieve* was addressed. ('For the head boys to be in love with these young persons was an institution of long standing,' says Mr. Dykes Campbell.) That of Coleridge's poetic awakening she undoubtedly shared with the Rev. William Lisle Bowles, as we learn from Chapter I of *Biographia Literaria*. Critic after critic has found occasion for wonder in this; though in truth there is none at all. To begin with, Bowles's sonnets are by no means bad; and, moreover, even to-day they are perceptibly, if palely, tinged with the dawn that was breaking over English poetry. Doubtless, had the book which fell into his hands as he was entering his seventeenth year been a volume of Blake, or of Cowper, or of Burns, his young conversion would have been more striking; would, at any rate, have made a better story. But by 1790 or thereabouts the new poetic movement was 'in the air,' as we say: a youth might take infection from any one, nor did it greatly matter from whom. Had Coleridge derived it from a stronger source the results might have been more precipitate, more violent. As it was, the blameless *Sonnets*—these and the equally blameless society of the Evans girls—weaned him from metaphysics and theology, on which he was immaturely feeding, and weaned him gently. He swore assent to Bowles: Bowles 'did his heart more good' than all other books 'excepting the Bible': but in his own attempts at versifying he still observed, even timidly, the conventions.

In January, 1791, the Committee of Almoners of Christ's Hospital emancipated him, with an Exhibition, to Jesus College, Cambridge. He started well. In 1792 he gained the Browne Gold Medal for a Sapphic Ode on the Slave Trade, and barely missed (on Porson's selection) the Craven Scholarship. In November, 1793, he bolted from Cambridge, in a fright of his college debts, or in a wild fit following on Mary Evans's rejection of his addresses. Both causes are suspected, and the two may have acted in combination. At all events he found his way to London, and on the second of December enlisted in the 15th or King's Light Dragoons, sinking all but his initials and his unlikeness to other men in the alias of Silas Tomkyn Comberbacke. Probably a worse light dragoon—he was short of stature, fat, and unwieldy—never occupied, or failed to occupy, a saddle. In April, 1794, his relatives procured his discharge, and Jesus College readmitted him. In June he visited his old schoolfellow Allen at Oxford, and there became acquainted with Robert Southey of Balliol. Mr. Robert Southey was then a youth of 'violent principles,' out of which—his friends and Coleridge aiding—the famous scheme of Pantisocracy was hastily incubated. Mr. Campbell summarizes it thus:

'Twelve gentlemen of good education and liberal principles are to embark with twelve ladies in April next,' fixing themselves in some 'delightful part of the new back settlements of America.' The labour of each man for two or three hours a day, it was imagined, would suffice to support the colony. The produce was to be common property, there was to be a good library, and ample leisure was to be devoted to study, discussion, and the education of the children on a settled system. The women were to be employed in taking care of the infant children and in other suitable occupations, not neglecting the cultivation of their minds. Among other matters not yet determined was 'whether the marriage contract shall be dissolved, if agreeable to one or both parties.' Every one was 'to enjoy his own religious and political opinions, provided they do not encroach on the rules previously made.' 'They calculate that every gentleman providing £125 will be sufficient to carry the scheme into execution.'

While Pantisocracy was hatching, Coleridge had departed on a walking-tour in Wales. On the thirteenth of July he reached Wrexham, and there, standing at the inn window, he spied Mary Evans coming down the street with her sister. 'I sickened,' he writes, 'and wellnigh fainted, but instantly retired.' The two sisters, it appears, had caught sight of him. They 'walked by the window four or five times, as if anxiously.' But the meeting, the possible reconcilement, were not to be. Coleridge fled to Bristol, joined his friend Southey there, with other Pantisocrats, including a family of young ladies named Fricker. Southey married Edith Fricker. Coleridge—such things happen in the revulsion of disappointed passion—married Sara Fricker. The marriage, says Mr. Campbell, was not made in Heaven. It was in great measure brought about by Southey.

Heaven alone knows—but no one who loves Coleridge can help wistfully guessing—what Dorothy Wordsworth might have made of him, as his wife. We have, perhaps, no right to guess at these things, but we cannot help it. He met her too late, by a little while, as it was all but too late that he met William Wordsworth. The Coleridges, after a brief experience of housekeeping at Clevedon and Bristol—interrupted by a tour to collect subscriptions for a projected newspaper, *The Watchman*—hied them down with their first-born to Nether Stowey in Somerset, to be neighbours of Thomas Poole, an admiring friend and a good fellow. To Nether Stowey, in July, 1797, came Wordsworth with his 'exquisite sister,' and were joined by Charles Lamb—all three as the Coleridges' guests. (The visit is commemorated in *This Lime-Tree Bower my Prison.*) At the end of his week's holiday Lamb returned to London; the Wordsworths, charmed by Coleridge's society,

removed themselves but three miles away, to Alfoxden, and set
up house.

Then the miracle happened.   Coleridge had already published
a volume of verse and brought it to a second edition: but it
contained no promise of what was to come.   Wordsworth was
meditating the Muse, if the word 'meditating' can be used of
a composition so frantic as *The Borderers*; but that he (the
slower to take fire) would within a year be writing *Tintern
Abbey* was a thing impossible, which nevertheless befell.   Brother,
sister, and friend—these three, as Coleridge has testified—became one soul.   'They saw as much of one another as if the
width of a street, and not a pair of coombes, had separated their
several abodes'; and in the soul of that intimacy, under the
influence of Dorothy—herself the silent one, content to en-
courage, criticize, admire—wrapped around by the lovely soli-
tudes of the Quantocks—Coleridge and Wordsworth found
themselves poets, speaking with new voices in a new dawn.
On the thirteenth of November, at half-past four in the afternoon, the three friends set off to walk to Watchet, on their way
to the Exmoor country, intending to defray their expenses by
the sale of a poem which the two men were to compose by the
way.   Before the first eight miles had been covered, the plan
of joint authorship had broken down, and Coleridge took the
poem into his sole hands.   He wrought at it until the following
March.   On the twenty-third of that month, writes Dorothy,
'Coleridge dined with us.   He brought his ballad [*The Ancient
Mariner*] finished.   We walked with him to the Miner's house.
A beautiful evening, very starry, the horned moon.'   We
feel that the stars were out with excuse, to celebrate the birth
of a star.

The Ancient Mariner sets one reflecting that, after all, the men
of the Middle Ages had much to say for themselves, who connected poetry with magic, and thought of Virgil as a wizard.
As we said just now, by taking small pains we can understand
that the sonnets of Bowles—pale, faded essays as they appear

to us—wore a different complexion in the sunrise of 1790.   But
we can ignore the time and circumstance of its birth, ignore the
theorizings out of which it sprang, ignore Wordsworth and his
prefaces and the taste on which they made war; and still, after
more than a hundred years, *The Ancient Mariner* is the wild
thing of wonder, the captured star, which Coleridge brought in
his hands to Alfoxden and showed to Dorothy and William
Wordsworth.   Not in the whole range of English poetry—not
in Shakespeare himself—has the lyrical genius of our language
spoken with such a note.

> A voice so thrilling ne'er was heard . . .
> Breaking the silence of the seas
> Among the farthest Hebrides.

Its music is as effortless as its imagery.   Its words do not
cumber it: exquisite words come to it, but it uses and straightway forgets them.   Not Shakespeare himself, unless by snatches,
so sublimated the lyrical tongue, or obtained effects so magical
by the bearest necessary means.   Take

> The many men, so beautiful!
> And they all dead did lie.

Or

> The moving Moon went up the sky,
> And nowhere did abide;
> Softly she was going up,
> And a star or two beside.

Or

> The body of my brother's son
> Stood by me, knee to knee:
> The body and I pull'd at one rope,
> But he said nought to me.

Here, and throughout, from the picture of the bride entering the
hall to that of the home-coming in the moon-lit harbour, every
scene in the procession belongs to high romance, yet each is
conjured up with that economy of touch we are wont to call

classical. We forget almost, listening to the voice, that there are such things as words.

> And now 'twas like all instruments,
> Now like a lonely flute;
> And now it is an angel's song,
> That makes the Heavens be mute.

If, in criticism, such an epithet be pardonable, we would call that voice seraphic; if such a simile, we would liken it to a seraph's, musing, talking before the gate of Paradise in the dawn.

Critics, allowing the magic of the poem, proceed to stultify the admission by inquiring why Coleridge did not follow it up and write others like it. The question, when foolishness has put it, can in terms of foolishness be readily answered. Coleridge yielded his will to opium. He had already begun to contract the habit, and he soon became a man capable (in Hazlitt's phrase) of doing anything which did not present itself as a duty. Once or twice, in *Christabel* and in *Kubla Khan*, he found new and divine openings, but his will could not sustain the flight, and the rest of the story of him as a poet resolves itself into repeated futile efforts to carry *Christabel* to a conclusion.

All this is true enough, or at least can be made convincing by any one who sets forth the story of Coleridge's subsequent aberrations. But before we blame his weakness let us ask ourselves if it be conceivably within one man's measure to produce a succession of poems on the plane of *The Ancient Mariner*; and, next, if—the magic granted, as it must be granted—it would not almost necessarily exhaust a man. In other words, let us inquire if, in a man who performed that miracle, his failure to perform others may not be more charitably set down to a divine exhaustion than charged upon his frailties. Surely by *Christabel* itself that question is answered; and almost as indisputably by *Kubla Khan*. Coleridge himself tells us that he began *Christabel* in 1797; that is, either before or during the composition of *The Ancient Mariner*. Between the conception of the two poems there was no interval of opium-taking. Yet who, studying *Christabel*, can, after the first two or three pages have been turned, believe that the poem could ever and by any possibility have been finished? Coleridge, no doubt, believed that it could: but in his struggles to finish it he was fighting against stronger adversaries than opium; against fate and a providence under which, things being what they are, their consequences will be what they will be.

The metre of *Christabel*, perfectly handled by its inventor, probably suffers in our ears by association with the jingle of Scott, and the vastly worse jingle of Byron, who borrowed it in turn. It has since been utterly vulgarized, and the very lilt of it nowadays suggests *The Mistletoe Bough*, melodrama, and the balladry of *Bow Bells*. Yet, and although the suspicion may be unworthy, one cannot help tracing something of *Bow Bells* back to an origin in such lines as

> Why waxed Sir Leoline so pale,
> Murmuring o'er the name again,
> 'Lord Roland de Vaux of Tryermaine'?

In short, there are some to which *Christabel* rings false, painfully false, here and there, in spite of its witchery. Yet, where it rings true, we ask, Was there ever such pure romantic music?

> Is the night chilly and dark?
> The night is chilly, but not dark.
> The thin gray cloud is spread on high,
> It covers but not hides the sky.
> The moon is behind, and at the full:
> And yet she looks both small and dull.
> The night is chill, the cloud is gray:
> 'Tis a month before the month of May,
> And the Spring comes slowly up this way.

Of *Kubla Khan*, even if 'a person . . . from Porlock' had not interrupted it, who will contend that it could ever have been finished, or even continued to any length? It abides the most entrancing magical fragment in English poetry; more than this it never could have been or have hoped to be.

Some three weeks after that starry evening on which Coleridge, his immortal ballad finished, walked with his friends, reciting it, we find Wordsworth writing to a friend that he, too, has been 'very rapidly adding to his stock of poetry,' and that the season is advancing with strides, 'and the country becomes almost every day more lovely.' The splendour of that summer in the Quantocks has passed into the history of our literature. Coleridge's best harvest was done; Wordsworth's—longer of continuance, yet brief in comparison with its almost insufferably long aftermath—on the point of ripening. The brother and sister quitted Alfoxden at midsummer. In September Coleridge met them in London and voyaged with them on a happy, almost rollicking, jaunt to Hamburg. The *Lyrical Ballads* had been published a few days before, Coleridge contributing *The Ancient Mariner* (or, to spell it accurately, *The Rime of the Ancyent Marinere*), *The Nightingale*, *The Foster-Mother's Tale*, and *The Dungeon*. The two friends had launched their thunderbolt, and went off gaily. It was a real thunderbolt, too; a book to which the over-worked epithet 'epoch-making' may for once in a way be applied without strain on the truth; but for the moment England took it with her habitual phlegm. Mrs. Coleridge sent news that 'the *Lyrical Ballads* are not liked at all by any.'

At Hamburg, after a few crowded days, the travellers separated —Coleridge for Ratzeburg, intent on acquiring a thorough knowledge of German. He returned to Nether Stowey in July, 1799, and towards the close of the year met the Wordsworths again and toured with them through the Lake Country. Thither in June, 1800, he wandered back to them from London and Stowey. They had installed themselves at Dove Cottage, Grasmere, and in July the Coleridges settled at Greta Hall, Keswick, twelve miles away. Wordsworth was now working at the height of his powers: but to Coleridge the renewed intimacy brought no secondary spring. For him there was never to be another Stowey. And here, both fortunately and unfortunately, the story may break off: unfortunately, because his poetic period had come to an end (he had, he writes to Thelwall, 'for ever renounced poetry for metaphysics,' and moreover was beginning his long slavery to opium); fortunately, because its end releases us from following him to Malta and Bristol, through quarrels and patchings-up of friendship, through wanderings, returns, vows and defections, partial recoveries, relapses and despairs, to the long-drawn sunset of his life in the home of the Gillmans at Highgate.

Let two things be noted, however, before we give assent to those who write contemptuously of Coleridge and his infirmity. The first is, that even in the lowest depths he still fought, and in the end he *did* emerge with the victory. He had won it at a terrible cost; the fight had killed a hundred splendid potentialities; but though scarred, battered, enfeebled, the man emerged, and with his manhood still in his hands, though they trembled on the prize. Next let us, reading of quarrels and misunderstandings between him and his friends, note how, as time effaces the petty circumstance of each, so the essential goodness of the man shines through, more and more clearly; how, in almost any given quarrel, as the years go on, we see that after all Coleridge was in the right. He knew his weakness: but at least it taught him to be tender towards the weaknesses of his fellows, and no man had a better reason to ask of his sufferings

> But wherefore, wherefore fall on me?
> To be beloved is all I need,
> And whom I love, I love indeed.

As this affectionate disposition made him all but unintelligible to the Southeys and Hazlitts of his time, and lay somewhat outside the range of self-centred Wordsworth, whose fault in friendship was that of the Dutch in matters of commerce,[1] so

[1] 'But this, my dear sir, is a mistake to which affectionate natures are too liable, though I do not remember to have ever seen it noticed—the mistaking *those who are desirous and well pleased to be loved by you, for those who love you.*'—Coleridge to Allsop, 2nd December 1818. (The reference is to Wordsworth.)

the very brilliance of his intellect too often isolated him within
the circle of its own light.   But on this Shelley has said the
last word:

> You will see Coleridge—he who sits obscure
> In the exceeding lustre and the pure
> Intense irradiation of a mind
> Which, with its own internal lightning blind,
> Flags wearily through darkness and despair—
> A cloud-encircled meteor of the air,
> A hooded eagle among blinking owls.

In justice and in decency we should strive to imagine Coleridge
as he impressed those who loved him and listened to him in his
great days of promise; not the Coleridge of later Highgate days,
the spent giant with whose portrait Carlyle made brutal play to
his own ineffaceable discredit; nor even the Coleridge of 1816,
the 'archangel a little damaged'—as Lamb, using a friend's
privilege, might be allowed to describe him in a letter to Wordsworth, a friend of almost equal standing; not these, but the
Coleridge of whom the remembrance was the abiding thought
in Lamb's mind and on his lips during the brief while he survived him—'Coleridge is dead.'   'His great and dear spirit
haunts me. . . . Never saw I his likeness, nor probably the
world can see again.   I seem to love the house he died at more
passionately than when he lived. . . . What was his mansion
is consecrated to me a chapel.'   If we must dwell at all on the
later Coleridge, let it be in the spirit of his own most beautiful
epitaph:

> Stop, Christian passer-by!—Stop, child of God,
> And read with gentle breast.   Beneath this sod
> A poet lies, or that which once seem'd he.
> O, lift one thought in prayer for S. T. C.;
> That he who many a year with toil of breath
> Found death in life, may here find life in death!
> Mercy for praise—to be forgiven for fame
> He ask'd, and hoped, through Christ.   Do thou the same!

None the less, in a world ever loath to admit that omelets involve the breaking of eggs, men will go on surmising what might have been, what full treasures of poetry Coleridge might have left, had he never drunk opium, had he eschewed metaphysics, had he married Dorothy Wordsworth, had he taken a deal of advice his friends gave him in good intent to rescue the Coleridge which God made (with their approval) and the creature marred. 'He lived until 1834,' wrote the late Dr. Garnett. 'If every year of his life had yielded such a harvest as 1797, he would have produced a greater amount of high poetry than all his contemporaries put together.' Yes, indeed! and *Kubla Khan* has this in common with a cow's tail—that it only lacks length to reach the moon. And yet, vain though these speculations are, we do wrong to laugh at them, for their protest goes deeper than their reasoning; and while fate tramples on things of beauty the indignant human heart will utter it. *Quis desiderio sit pudor aut modus*, when a poet—and such a poet—is broken in his prime?

On the other hand, the question sometimes raised—whether, in the Quantock time, when the pair learnt to be poets, Coleridge owed more to Wordsworth, or Wordsworth to Coleridge—is, as Sir Thomas Browne would say, puzzling, but not beyond all conjecture: and we raise it again because we think it usually receives the wrong answer. It is usually argued that Coleridge received more than he gave, because he was the more impressionable. We might oppose this with the argument that Coleridge probably gave more than he received, as his presence and talk were the more inspiring. But let us look at a date or two. In June, 1797, Coleridge wrote *This Lime-Tree Bower my Prison*, and it contains such lines as these:

> Yet still the solitary humble-bee
> Sings in the bean-flower! Henceforth I shall know
> That Nature ne'er deserts the wise and pure . . .

and

> No sound is dissonant which tells of Life.

* G

Frost at Midnight is dated February, 1798, and it contains the passage beginning

> Therefore all seasons shall be sweet to thee. . . .

The exquisite *Nightingale* belongs to the summer of 1798, and contains the images of the 'night-wandering man,' of the nightingale

> That crowds, and hurries, and precipitates
> With fast thick warble his delicious notes . . .

of the other birds awake in the bushes with

> Their bright, bright eyes, their eyes both bright and full . . .

and that most lovely picture of the infant hushing his woe as he gazes up at the moon through the orchard boughs:

> While his fair eyes, that swam with undropped tears,
> Did glitter in the yellow moonbeam!   Well!—
> It is a father's tale.   But if that Heaven
> Should give me life, his childhood shall grow up
> Familiar with these songs, that with the night
> He may associate joy.

Now the first thing to be noted of these lines, these images, is that they are what we now call Wordsworthian; some, the very best Wordsworthian; but all Wordsworthian with an intensity to which (if we study his verse chronologically) we find that in 1798 Wordsworth had never once attained—or once only, in a couple of lines of *The Thorn*.   When Coleridge wrote these things, Wordsworth was writing *We are Seven*, *Goody Blake*, *Simon Lee*, and the rest.   It was only after, though soon after, Coleridge had written them that Wordsworth is seen capable of such lines as

> The still sad music of humanity . . .

or of

> The stars of midnight shall be dear
> To her; and she shall lean her ear
>   In many a secret place.

This note Coleridge might teach to Wordsworth, as Wordsworth might improve on it and make it his own. But that other note—the lyrical note of *The Ancient Mariner*—was incommunicable. He bequeathed it to none, and before him no poet had approached it; hardly even Shakespeare, on the harp of Ariel.

'EOTHEN'

ALEXANDER WILLIAM KINGLAKE was born in 1809, the son of a country gentleman—Mr. W. Kinglake of Wilton House, Taunton. He was educated at Eton and Trinity College, Cambridge, and from Cambridge proceeded to Lincoln's Inn. For some years he practised with moderate success at the Chancery Bar; but his circumstances were easy, and permitted him to spend a long holiday as so many Englishmen would choose to spend it, in the hard delights of travel. The result for us is *Eothen*. It took the town in 1844, as it deserved. It remains one of the little classics of the midnineteenth century; nor could one readily name a book more genuinely English and of its class. Written with a fastidious polish worthy of Congreve, it keeps the reader constantly in mind of Congreve's famous request to Voltaire, that he wished to be visited not as an author but as a plain gentleman. 'Here is my story,' the writer seems to say, 'and you may take it or leave it. The trouble I may have chosen to spend on it is my own affair.' And the manner of the book was repeated in Kinglake's manner of treating his success. He turned his back on it and resumed his legal work.

Ten years later the Nearer East (as we call it nowadays) claimed him again, and on more serious business. On the outbreak of war with Russia he accompanied his friend Lord Raglan to the Crimea. For insight into the national feeling of those days, when Great Britain awoke to war after forty years of peace, we may turn to Tennyson's *Maud* and read its call for 'the glory of manhood' to stand once more 'on its ancient height,' its protest against 'the cobweb woven across the cannon's throat,' its scornful trust

That the smooth-faced snub-nosed rogue would leap from his counter
    and till,
And strike, if he could, were it but with his cheating yard-wand, home.

(For we had just then to learn over again, and not for the last time, the recurring lesson that war is the swindler's fattest opportunity.) Napier, in his *History of the War in the Peninsula*, lets fall a remark that the British are a bellicose rather than a military people. He might have added that they are incurably given to mistaking war for a form of sport, and might find their tribal emblem of Victory in a statue of Picton fighting the Battle of Quatre Bras (as he did) in a tall hat. Kinglake, who consented after Lord Raglan's death to write a history of the war, could never get over his habit of regarding a battle as a sort of glorified steeplechase or fox-hunt, and in the crisis of a fight has usually to fall back on these noble sports for a criticism or a simile.

Meanwhile he had retired from the Bar, and entered Parliament in 1857 as member for Bridgwater. He held the seat until 1869, when he lost it on petition, and thenceforward gave himself up to his History. The first volume appeared in 1863, the final one in 1887. He died Jan. 2, 1891, of a slow and painful malady, which had driven him to retire from London, where society had known him for many years as one of its most graceful talkers. His conversation was temperate and restrained, nor would he ever (writes one who knew him) enter into that competition for celebrity in which men of less delicacy found pleasure.

He was content to wait his turn; he would not claim it, but when it came he took it, and he was sure of attention as soon as his low firm voice was heard. He liked a few friends rather than many; and even when he talked and the whole table listened, there was something confidential in his method. He wore a Damascus blade, but kept it for the most part sheathed. It was only when challenged, or when an injustice was offered to somebody else than himself, that you saw the flash of this polished and glittering steel; and whoever felt its point or edge did not care for another experience. The first volume of his History, and the chapter on the Emperor of the French, show what he could do when provoked, and how he hated an impostor. His spoken style was, of course, less elaborate, but hardly less finished, and such was his reserve of character that you had to know him well before you discovered how many were his resources and gifts.[1]

The Invasion of the Crimea is a monumental work, exquisitely written throughout, and containing many splendid pages that will rank with the best prose of its century. That it lives as a whole is less certain. Kinglake started with the two indispensable qualifications prescribed by Lucian for his perfect historian: he had political insight and the faculty of expression, and he had both in a high degree. He could 'superinduce upon events the charm of order,' and set forth an intricate tale with perfect lucidity. But his fastidiousness allowed his theme to overweight him. As time removes the events of 1854–5, men read of them more carelessly; interested, indeed, but no longer overshadowed by them; disposed, rightly or wrongly, to regard them as no such tremendous matters after all. But with the historian this very natural process was reversed. Time—and he spent thirty years over the task—but emphasized for him the perspective it was diminishing for his readers. If they are critics they recognize the mere writing, so carefully vivid, for a kind which is not produced without strain; but they need not be critics to feel the burden of the subject and, oppressed by it, to transfer their sympathy from the story to the author.

In *Eothen* the author is young; young and full of that ὕβρις which he would have been apt to translate, in metaphor, as 'beans.' His theme is what he chooses to make it, and the laboured brilliance of the composition is, so to speak, a part of the fun—an overflow of the indefatigable high spirits that have already carried him across the desert and through plague-stricken Cairo. Artifice, though apparent enough, detracts nothing from the freshness or genuineness of *Eothen*, as it detracts nothing from the freshness and genuineness (say) of *Venus and Adonis*; for artifice is natural to youth. We allow for it before

[1] From *London Letters*, by the late George W. Smalley.

passing his claim, in the preface, that his narrative conveys 'not those impressions which *ought to have been* produced upon any "well-constituted mind," but those which were really and truly received at the time of his rambles by a headstrong and not very amiable traveller, whose prejudices in favour of other people's notions were then exceedingly slight.' As a fact, the unconventionality he achieves is often but conventionality inverted; and once, at least, he comes near to confessing this when a comment of his brings him up short, face to face with—

the humbling proof that I am subject to that nearly immutable law which compels a man with a pen in his hand to be uttering now and then some sentiment not his own. It seems as though the power of expressing regrets and desires by written symbols were coupled with a condition that the writer should from time to time express the regrets and desires of other people—as though, like a French peasant under the old *régime*, he was bound to perform a certain amount of work *upon the public highways*.

'I rebel,' he says, 'as stoutly as I can against this horrible *corvée*.' Yes, but the purely original man would pass the temptation—nay, if he yielded, would even yield—without being aware of it. It is not by dint of being unamiable—at times even truculently unamiable—that Kinglake can escape the tradition of *The Sentimental Journey*. At times, when the right opportunity presents itself, this defiantly unsentimental traveller has to halt and render due literary toll to sentiment. He does it with a good set face and pays down royally. But the coin, when you test it, rings on a half-hearted note. It is worth remarking that his prose, at these checks, has a trick of loosening its knees into the iambics of blank verse. 'But soon the genial morn burst down from heaven, And stirred the blood so gladly through our veins. . . . The baggage-horses served us for a drag, And kept us to the rate of little more Than five miles in the hour; but now and then . . .' Damascus, when our traveller reaches it, calls for a strong effort of sentiment, and he responds with his very best. Because it is his best it has nothing to do with Damascus, but everything with England. The waters and gardens of his green spot of exile call up memories, real or fictitious, of an English country house deserted, with grass in the stable-yard and the shrubberies relapsing into wilderness. 'Just there, in October mornings, the keeper would wait with the dogs and the guns: no keeper now.' And the locked wicket leads to regret for days when the path was clear, and you 'chase that phantom of a muslin sleeve that once weighed warm upon your arm.' It is all extremely well done; but it ends in a tangle of iambic decasyllables:

Wild as that, the nighest woodland of a deserted home in England, but without its sweet sadness [perhaps, for an Englishman], is the sumptuous garden of Damascus. Forest trees, tall and stately enough, if you could see their lofty crests, yet lead a tussling life of it below, with their branches struggling against strong numbers of bushes and wilful shrubs. The shade upon the earth is black as night. High, high above your head, and on every side all down to the ground, the thicket is hemmed in, and choked up by the interlacing boughs that droop with the weight of roses, and load the slow air with their damask breath.

Two or three rhapsodical passages, such as this inspired by Damascus, shine with great effect against the *morgue britannique* which is the author's general manner. But obviously too many of them would have spoilt the book; and therefore it was extremely fortunate that, under pledge to write as he felt, he suffered no strong emotions as he walked about Jerusalem, but on the contrary 'was rudely chilled at the foot of Zion by disenchanting scenes.' To have felt 'as he ought' would have involved a dangerous flight of fine writing, whereas the worldly tone he actually adopts in describing the Holy Sepulchre is safer and very artistically wayward.

Nevertheless, and although more derivative than Kinglake suspected and would have us believe, *Eothen* is a genuine book, and carries the general impress of truth. The writer confesses himself 'a headstrong and not very amiable traveller.' That he was headstrong, his defying the plague at Cairo, his lonely ride across the desert to Suez, his serio-comic invasion of Satalieh—these and half a dozen other adventures—more than sufficiently prove. That he was unamiable, at times even unfeeling, we gather from at least a score of small hints. Possibly he exhibits this failing with design, and lays on the colours too strongly. In any case, he was young and in the saddle—his 'loved saddle'—with Homer in his soul and the East before him; and strong youth is intolerant of weakness or disease. The later King-lake, wise, tempered by years, and dying of a slow inward agony, must have looked back on some passages in this book with a very wistful forgiveness. In any case, if *Eothen* throws some light on the reasons why our English are not precisely loved when they travel, it also helps us to understand why they travel, and (convincingly) why they are feared. This particular traveller may sometimes do violence to our feelings; but he seldom fails to thrill them, and it is with a touch of racial pride that we follow and watch how sometimes by cool audacity, alone against numbers, sometimes by sheer bullying, he opposes himself to the depressed and succumbing mind of the Mussul-man, sweeps away all resistance, and not only comes triumphing out of difficulty, but with the population of a province at his feet suing his illusory power for protection.

This dominance of the Western will over the East may be a passing one—may in great measure have passed already. It is almost certainly transitory in comparison with the spell of the East upon Western imagination. Of the two in interplay, at a happy moment, Kinglake gives us a sketch only, but a finished sketch, vivid and fascinating.

THREE OPEN LETTERS

TO THE RIGHT REVEREND ARCHIBALD ROBERTSON, D.D..
LORD BISHOP OF EXETER

I

MY LORD,

It is now many years since we last met, and you may well be surprised at my addressing you in this public manner. Yet, and however unconsciously, you provoked it some months ago when I received the prospectus of a certain 'Association for the Permanent Care of the Feeble-Minded,' and this was recommended to me by your lordship's name and that of the Bishop of Truro on the list of its Executive Committee. Shocked as I was by the objects of that Association, as declared in the circular (which I will presently quote), I could not carry my trouble to my own diocesan and friend, the Bishop of Truro; for he was a dying man, already far within the shadow across the edge of which the voices of men, if they reach at all, carry but empty vexings. He is dead since then, and at the moment I write they have not yet installed his successor—whose hands for some time will be full of other business. Yet this business, too, is important as I shall try to show. I remember that during my childhood—as long before—the diocese of Exeter covered all Cornwall, even to the Scillies; and I can appeal on more personal grounds. For you were Dean of our old college at Oxford; the first don from whom, as a raw freshman, I took kindly advice. You, of course, have clean forgotten it all: but such an interview is to the boy one of the scenes of his life, and I recall the room now, its background of bookshelves, our positions at the table, and you, as you leant, uttering wise counsel. . . .

Well now, my lord, after these many years you come—or a circular comes with the authority of your name (now advanced in public honour, but always a name of command to me)— asking your old pupil to join a Society, the objects of which are thus defined:

(1) To awaken the public to the danger to the community of allowing the multiplication of the Feeble-Minded to continue unchecked.

(2) To obtain reliable statistics with regard to the number of Feeble-Minded in the South-Western Counties, and to press for such legislation as may be needed.

(3) To establish one or more institutions for the care and improvement of the Feeble-Minded, *and to promote their happiness while providing for their permanent detention.*

I italicize these last words, my lord; and in the course of my argument shall tell you why. But, for a start, I will ask if (1) and (2) find themselves in the order you would have placed them when you lived in Oxford and taught Aristotle to young men? Would you not then have instructed us that the obligation to obtain 'reliable statistics' came before that of 'awakening the public' to a danger which the statistics might, or might not, prove to be real? And would you, in those days, have mixed up in one sentence the demand for clear information with the answer, begging one for legislation? I submit that you would have done nothing of the sort. It would have offended your self-respect.

In those days, too, you taught us that things have their right names, and that men are to be distrusted who start by mixing up the meaning of words. You must of your own past forgive me if, when a man talks of a 'home' and I discover him to mean a house of detention, I judge that he is trying to deceive me, and if I go on to judge that his mind is not honest. The word 'home' has many connotations, beautiful and sacred; but permanent detention is not one of them. 'Permanent detention' means imprisonment for life. You cannot deny that. Well, now, see how it runs—'*and to promote their happiness while providing for their imprisonment for life.*' Say now, my lord, how do you like the look of it?

Again, when your Association talks of 'the permanent *care* of the Feeble-Minded' what does it mean precisely? It uses language conveying that its primary tender care is for these unhappy people. But does it mean this? I think not: for I observe that the first of its three main objects is 'to awaken the public to the danger *to the community* of allowing the multiplication of the Feeble-Minded,' etc.: and again I think not because, as your lordship very well knows, the methods proposed include (1) permanent deprivation of liberty, (2) segregation of the sexes, and even (3) 'sterilization,' which means castration or something of the sort. *Salus civitatis suprema lex*; it may be necessary—I will take this point by and by—to deprive a man of his manhood in order to save the State. But for God's sake, and if we would not incur Christ's rebuke upon the Pharisees, let us not pretend that we are doing it in love for our victim. I have before me a newspaper which, in an account of the International Eugenics Congress held last week in London, reports Dr. Saleeby to have urged 'that when segregation was asked for they must not tell the State that it was in the interests of the race but (that it was) in the interests of the individual affected'! I can hardly believe that Dr. Saleeby—a highly distinguished man—uttered this horrible cant; but, if he did, I would tell Dr. Saleeby that a community which accepts the moral standard of his argument has reached a point of degradation at which ten thousand male imbeciles and as many females may mate without making things worse. If we are all to be committed to this revolting campaign upon the helpless, at least let us go into it as men, neither deceiving ourselves with false words, nor insulting our victims with hypocritical professions: and before Dr. Saleeby troubles the world with his bowels he should teach them to yearn honestly.

Well, now, you will admit, my lord, that if this campaign

upon the Feeble-Minded be a necessity, it is a very sad one; so sad that the necessity should be made plain to us by irrefragable proof. But is that happening? The Eugenists tell us that they are men of science, and that what they say is for us unscientific men to accept. But, be it said with all respect to these experts, that is not quite final. *We*, and not the experts only, are to be made responsible. If there be a Day of Judgment, *we* shall have to stand at the bar facing these poor wastrels and answer if we wronged their helplessness. That is a very terrible thought to me, my lord. In my own small way as a magistrate I may be called on to sentence such a fellow-creature to lifelong loss of liberty, even to mutilation. I see myself interrogating the unhappy bewildered eye, the inarticulate tongue, seeking to pierce to what of intellect gropes behind them—myself, too, groping after the mystery which sets me in judgment over this hunted thing. No, by Heaven! Such wits as Heaven has lent me I will use first on the experts before I do their dirty work. I have known experts—literary experts, at any rate. One of them sent me, the other day, a poem he had discovered in the library of Trinity College, Dublin, and made bold to attribute it (I believe) to Hagthorpe. 'Was it not a gem?' It was: it was also familiar to me as a lyric of Ben Jonson's, printed in every edition of his works: and the man who sent it to me bore a European reputation as a specialist in the Elizabethan drama!

Scientific experts may be less fallible. But using such wits as Heaven has lent me, I put this to you, my lord: we know (in Hamlet's phrase) what a piece of work is man! how noble in reason! how infinite in faculty! in form and moving how express and admirable! in action how like an angel! in apprehension how like a god! Yet we know also, how by the most trivial of accidents, the mechanical pressure of less than an inch of bone upon the grey matter of the brain, this godlike creature is changed to a maniac, at war with the stuffing of his mattress. Then who shall say (I ask) but that some small mechanical touch may be equally potent to recall numbers of our Feeble-Minded back to grace of mind and body?

> Some vital spring adjusted,
> Some faculty that rusted
> Cleansed to legitimate use—
> Some undeveloped action stirred, some juice
> Of God; distilling dropt into the core—

That is what my reason suggests to me.   Now what do these specialists bring to overawe it?

Nothing; or next to nothing.

They have not even produced real statistics to prove that the mating of the Feeble-Minded results in such a wholesale generation of Feeble-Mindedness as they pretend to be an instant danger to the community.   Where are the figures that alone could justify our beginning to lend an ear to these frantic cures?   I cannot find them anywhere.   Will you supply me with them, my lord?

But—supposing the figures supplied, and that they are convincing—how, with our present knowledge of *causes* (the experts' knowledge, if you will), can we be certain of a cure? Why, if you have read the reports of the recent Eugenics Congress, you must have perceived that the quacks are all at sea and bumping their heads one against another in the silly gale they only have raised.   Of the incestuous union of brother and sister was born—a Cleopatra.   And Edward II, an imbecile, begat Edward III with descendants who numbered amongst them the Black Prince, Henry V, Edward IV, Henry VIII, Queen Elizabeth, and Queen Victoria!

The kindest word to be said for these ignoramuses is a prayer that they may be forgiven because they know not what they do. But in their ignorant cocksureness they have managed to thrust a Bill upon Parliament: and this Bill has reached a second reading almost without opposition.   I propose to examine it in a second letter, and am meanwhile, my lord,

Your obedient servant,

ARTHUR QUILLER-COUCH.

II

My Lord,

There lies before me the copy of a Bill called the 'Mental Deficiency Bill,' which has already passed a second reading in the House of Commons and will shortly be sent to Committee. It is fathered by the Right Hon. Reginald McKenna, His Majesty's Principal Secretary of State for Home Affairs, and I think you already know something of Mr. McKenna; but I do not think you can have gauged him unless you have carefully studied the provisions of this Bill.

By this Bill—which, unless Englishmen bestir themselves and take it by the throat, will speedily become an Act—any person, 'capable of earning his living under favourable circumstances,' but adjudged incapable (I will presently tell you how) of competing on equal terms with his normal fellows, or of managing himself or his affairs with ordinary prudence, shall be deemed to be a 'defective' (Par. 17, 2), and may be assigned to one or other of several classes which include (17, 1):

(1) Those in whose case it is desirable in the interests of the community that they should be deprived of the opportunity of procreating children, and

(2) Those in whose case such other circumstances exist *as may be specified in any order made by the Secretary of State* as being circumstances which make it desirable that they should be dealt with under this Act.

Now let us take these two provisions in reverse order:

No. 2, gloss it as you will, is simply *lettre de cachet* back again among civilized men.   The Home Secretary may, if he find any person inconvenient to him, simultaneously find him 'incapable of managing his affairs with ordinary prudence,' and by an 'order' commit the poor wretch to lifelong detention without a trial.   Hideous as this sounds, *it is in the Bill.*

'Oh,' you will say, 'but good Mr. McKenna and his successors will never in this Christian England of ours, dream of committing such an infamy!'   Are you so sure?   It was the good Mr. McKenna who, the other day, invoked a statute, which for a hundred years had been a dead letter, to imprison a political opponent whose activity just then would have been inconvenient to the Government.   You, my lord, may be enjoying a sudden recovery of faith in Mr. McKenna: but there are some of us who, after the imprisonment of Mr. Tom Mann, do not propose to trust this politician—as the vulgar saying goes—one inch further than we can fling him.   Possibly in time you, too, may revert to your distrust.   But, and anyhow, why give to him, or to any man, this power of secretly consigning any one to a living death?

But it needs not be Mr. McKenna.   By Paragraph 20 of this precious Bill *any* relative or friend (sweet word) who wants to get somebody out of the way may make *private* application to a magistrate.   It needs—so far as I can see—only one magistrate, and at the best a couple of medical certificates, and if the magistrate and the 'friend' happen to be in collusion, the poor devil may be put away without further parley.   Nay, if he has the pluck to kick an intrusive doctor to the door, *no medical certificate is needed.*   He will be sentenced as recalcitrant and carted off to a house of detention for a year.   If, at the end of a year, the Commissioners (to be appointed under the Act) refuse to set him free, he is closed up for five years, and then again for another five years, and so on until death releases him.   That until each dark quinquennium has expired he may lift any voice from the tomb does not appear.

My lord, I have been a writer now these twenty-five years, and I cannot remember to have written in that time sentences so vile as those which I am now copying from an Act of Parliament proposed by a Liberal Government—a Government into the cause of which some of us, through three campaigns, flung such energies as men give for the sake of high hopes.   Let the hopes be: but our trust, at least, was that liberty to a Liberal

Government was as chastity to a woman. Of each it is true that, once broken, it descends by easier and yet easier lapses to the standard of a strumpet, or of Mr. McKenna.

I am sorry to drag your lordship further, but it is necessary. Paragraph 27, Section (2), would enact that:

When any person tried before any court of assize or quarter sessions *is acquitted*, the court may, if it appears that there is reasonable ground for believing that he is defective, *notwithstanding any enactment or rule of law to the contrary*, order him to be examined as to his mental condition, and for that purpose, if necessary, to be detained in an institution for defectives pending the examination, and for such time as may be required for the presentation of a petition for an order under the Act.

Where *it appears to the police authority* that any person charged with an offence is a defective they shall communicate with the local authority and it shall be *the duty of the police authority to bring before the court such evidence as to his mental condition as may be available*.

In other words, a jury of his peers finds a man innocent of a charge brought against him. Then the police, who have brought this wrongful charge, choose a second and more deadly shot out of their locker. As the innocent man steps free, he is re-arrested and charged again. 'No, to be sure,' says 'the Court,' 'you are guiltless of the deed of which you were just now accused. But all the same the public think you unable to manage your affairs with ordinary prudence, and that you should be deprived of the opportunity of procreating children. Therefore, innocent man, you will go to prison for life.'

Shall we call a brief halt, my lord, and before we deal with yet worse abominations—yes, there are worse to come—will you let me fumigate the air with a pipe of tobacco while you turn over in mind two questions I would here put to you?

In the first place, I think you must know well enough that in practice these precious enactments will be put in force only upon the poor, or upon the children of the poor. Yet stay! I must make one small reservation—they may here and there be used by some rich and unscrupulous man to get an inheritance made void and to be rid of an unhappy none-too-strong-minded child who stands in the succession to wealth. (You might study the history of the Annesley suit in this connection.) With this reservation I put it to you that the victims of this Act will be moneyless persons. Yet you know well that dukes and millionaires have begotten monstrous children, and that at least one marquis has been declared incapable of managing his affairs. Do you believe for one moment that the net of the 'Mental Deficiency' Bill will be drawn around *these?*

Secondly, I put it to you, who studied such questions in the old days, that *this law falls into no proper category of law. It is not law at all: it is Experiment by Legal Process.* Certain scientific or quasi-scientific men have started a theory or two. For these theories they can produce nothing that begins to amount to proof: and since they cannot, even in modern England, run about emasculating children by private licence, they get a Bill introduced whereby the State shall do their dirty work of experimenting—of course, upon the weak and helpless. I wonder if you at all realize the strength of the mania that has taken hold of these Eugenists or to what fantastic cruelties it can persuade them. No? . . . Then courage, my lord! Pick up your pastoral staff, and we will wade through a yet deeper and filthier stream.

Some little while ago the Chief Magistrate of the most populous town in your diocese seriously proposed that children of weak intellect should be put to a painless death. (It was kind of him to make it painless!) Will you harden your face while I hold for a moment that suggestion steadily up to your nostrils? . . . Yes, my lord, it will do you good in the end. . . . Bethink you (it is painfully known to us, who have to deal with these 'cases' on a County Education Committee) that a mother clings passionately to her child who is born 'afflicted,' and more passionately as a rule to the idiot child than to the deaf or the dumb. Next bethink that the 'deficiency' of few children, or none, can be determined—even for purposes of a certificate—until the mother has suckled it, weaned it and (God knows, with what alternations of hope and woe) learnt, as love only can teach, to shield its helplessness by a thousand sweet devices. Lastly, bethink you of a policeman or an 'inspector' of some sort calling on that mother and demanding, 'Your child is weak-minded. Hand it to me, please, that I may lead it away and kill it (as proposed by a late Chief Magistrate of Plymouth), or that I may imprison it for life (as, your consent not asked, I am authorized to do by Act of Parliament which may be cited as the Mental Deficiency Act, 1912).'

My lord, I know you to be a good man. Pardon me, but do you still press me to join your damned Association?

> Your lordship's obedient servant,
> (but not in this),
> ARTHUR QUILLER-COUCH.

III

MY LORD,

Let me, at the outset of this third and last letter state quite unequivocally what I mean by saying that the Eugenists behind Mr. McKenna's Bill adduce for their theories 'nothing that begins to amount to proof.' I mean something fatal to all their statistics, which, though they were piled to the moon would yet rest on a base incurably rotten, *since in classifying A or B as 'normal' or 'defective' these people have no standard at all.* They are using loose indefinite terms which not only can be made to vary at will but cannot even be hindered from conveying a dozen different denotations (let alone connotations) to as many different minds. What, for example, does your Eugenist understand by 'normal'? Is he himself, by any chance, normal? We know that he cannot reason scientifically; but can he, as a set-off, throw a discus or a cricket-ball, or sail a boat, or ride to hounds, or shoot straight, or walk forward steadily under an enemy's fire?—in fine can he do any of the score of things that would come within the ambit of any Hellenic conception of the normal man? Before discussing your Eugenist's capacity to breed 'fitness' I want to know what, to his mind, 'fitness' is. (What *is* Mrs. Todgers' Notion of a Wooden Leg?) Before he pokes his quasi-scientific thumb into God's machinery, he might at least tell us *that*. What sort of man does he *want* to breed? Is it a Philip Sidney or a Roosevelt? a Leonardo da Vinci or a Bismarck? a Francis of Assisi or a John D. Rockefeller—or perchance some nice mean between these last two? At present his modest demand would seem to be that we should turn him loose with a gelding-knife in one hand and in the other a legal permit to find out what in the devil's name he really does want! For my part, my lord (to follow an idle speculation for a moment), if asked what kind of man we should aim at breeding as likely to be most salutary to the State, I should answer, 'One who held by clear thinking, while sensitively aware that we walk encompassed by mysteries.' Such a man, combining Hebrew reverence with the straight outlook of an old Greek, would needs be gracious in himself and serviceable to his fellows:

> Sweetly to ease, loose, and bind,
> As need requires, this frail fall'n human kind.

But such a man would be the polar opposite of your modern Eugenist, who rushes in where angels fear to tread, flourishes words which have no defined relation to things, talks of 'homes' where he intends prisons or barracks, or of 'permanent care' when he means to mutilate or to immure a fellow-creature for life, and (worst of all) wraps his cruel accost in professions of tender solicitude for the victim.

What again does he understand by 'abnormal,' seeing that he has no 'norm'? Or by 'defective'? Deficiency—a falling short (of what?)—is in the nature of things a word of degree: and amid the many thousand shades of human imperfection where is that degree to be fixed? Someone at one of these Congresses—I think it was Dr. Saleeby again—defied the whole world to show him a 'normal' child born of defective parents: and I don't know what he means by 'normal,' as neither does he. But if he care to risk a black eye, I will engage to introduce him to two lusty brothers who daily pass my door—each an intelligent servant valued by his employer, each the father of a healthy family, and each (I dare swear) quick to resent a word against either of their parents, although both father and mother might easily have been 'sequestrated' under the provisions of Mr. McKenna's Bill.[1] From men who argue before taking the trouble to define their terms even to themselves, I believe you, my lord—as a scholar trained in dialectic—would in the old days have turned aside with a politely dissembled weariness. '*Quis est iste?*—Who is this that darkeneth counsel by words without knowledge?' But when, of their half-baked sciences, these muddy reasoners offer to improve on the works of Almighty God—to bind the sweet influences of Pleiades, and bring forth Mazzaroth in (or out of) his season—why then indeed my eyebrows go up to find you in their company.

I suspect, though, that by this time you are heartily tired of them, as am I. Shall we drop them here and, going on together, conclude our walk by following reverently along the edge of a speculation at which they would doubtless smile?

Your predecessor in the cathedral throne of Exeter provoked even such a smile when he went down and confirmed a number of inmates of the Starcross Asylum. The smile widened when, being a very simple sincere man, he explained (I forget the exact words) that in his experience persons of weak intellect were peculiarly amenable to the Christian Faith. The laugh was cheap and came easy. Yet I rather choose to remember with

[1] The Eugenist, by the way, on his own showing would prove too much for his brief. If, as he asserts, the defective 'breed like rabbits' and have been doing so unrestrained for centuries, our villages long before this would have been swamped out with 'village idiots,' whereas, and as every one knows, nothing of the sort has happened.

how sweet a charity for centuries the poor folk of Europe have suffered and fed their half-wits, naming them 'God's fools.' Ponder that name, my lord . . . I remember also a thing that happened in the small town where I was born. Listen: for this is a true story:

A native of that town, who had emigrated to South Africa and prospered, returned to it after many years for a brief visit. *Nescio qua natale solum dulcedine.* . . . This man came back somewhat haughtily curious to discover if any one would recognize him. Well, no one did; not even the farmer, his old employer, who came down the aisle on Sunday and held out the alms-bag. But, as the exile walked out of the church porch, a man caught at his hand, mumbling his name, laughing in his eyes with glad welcome. It was the town idiot, Dicky Winny, at whom as a boy he had been used to fling stones. While the exile wondered, the idiot first spread a palm some four feet from the ground—'Pete—little boy—*so* high!' Then he stooped and made pretence to pick up a flint and fling it. 'Pete—he fling *so.* . . . These boys' (spitting, shaking his head with infinite contempt) 'nowadays—no good at all!'

Upon this story the Eugenist would probably make some such comment as that 'if the poor fool had only been shut up, he had never been pelted.' To which I should retort, 'Sir, the story is not for you: but if you must still be teaching, go home and teach your children not to follow your example of stoning the weak.' I hope, however, that you, my lord, may read it as a deeper parable. I think you must sometimes have preached of the inscrutable purposes of God, and warned men against leaving hidden things out of account or interpreting them too rashly. Now when you see a mother poring over an imbecile child, searching for some answer of love in the vacant eyes, or when I tell you of this grown idiot laughing and forgiving his fellows under an affliction that would tempt *us* to curse God and die, does it not occur to you that after all these poor 'fools of God' may be serving some divine purpose in the world and serving it more happily than we deem? to cleanse and soften with tears some mother's eyes, which else had grown hard with petty cares; to remind grumbling men how easily their lot had deserved lamentation; to unlock in small dispersed societies the waters of universal charity and to keep them evidently running? Who are we, my lord, to deny that these witless ones—yes, or even these Eugenists—may have their place in the great pattern?

> God sits upon His hill,
> And sees the shadows fly;
> And if He laugh at fools, why should He not?

It may even be that He has provided himself with these Eugenists, as ancient kings kept Fools, for ironical delectation in hours of leisure.

I wonder, my lord, if you can recall a vacation ramble we once took together, and a most beautiful, pitiful sight we beheld in the course of it. We halted beside a river, across which—in greed or in ignorance—men had built a dam just too high for the salmon to leap; nor had they supplied any 'ladder' for the fish to ascend by successive easy assaults. Do you remember how we sat and watched the lovely things hurling themselves up against that brutal dam; leaping some twenty feet in air, some forty leaps to minute—bruising their bright sides upon the masonry and tumbling back into the lower pool, that was all aseethe with creatures mad to reach the head-waters and deposit their spawn?

What impulse urged them, baffled again and again, to persist at that tremendous leap? My grandfather (who was a patient man of science and spent his life in observing and recording the habits of fish, without attempting to teach the Almighty how to improve them) permitted himself in his chapter on the Salmon (*A History of the Fishes of the British Islands*, vol. iv, p. 173) an indignant paragraph upon men who intrude such barriers upon Nature. He lived before men had invented such sciences—arts, rather— as Eugenics or, 'How to be Dirty in the Drawing-Room'; and his answer to the question 'Why should these salmon pant for the upper streams?' would have been, 'They do it as I track them, following after but not disputing the divine wisdom'; even as to the claims of the Eugenists I am sure he will have quoted the great smashing answer in Esdras:

Before the waters of the world stood, or ever the winds blew; before it thundered or lightened, or ever the foundations of paradise were laid; before the fair flowers were seen, or ever the moveable powers were established; before the measures of the firmament were named, or ever the chimneys in Sion were hot; and ere the present years were sought out, or ever the inventions of them that now sin were turned; then did I consider these things, and they were all made through me alone, and through none other. By me also they shall be ended, and by none other.

My lord, I put it to you plainly that it were a sin and wickedness for us, knowing so little as we know, to promote the Bill now before Parliament.   Forgive me that I have used some coarse words upon it: they were the fittest for a very dirty subject which has begun to recommend itself as a parlour science. But—for I am very earnest in this matter—I ask something more than your forgiveness.   Will you—if these three letters of mine have at all opened your eyes to the infamy of the Bill and its proposals—make a noble return upon yourself and say, 'I find this thing to be evil, and it no longer has my consent'? That would be such an utterance as great men—and only they —dare to make; and for a smaller matter, my lord, it would vindicate at a stroke the trust and admiration, founded these years ago, of

Your old pupil and still obedient servant,

ARTHUR QUILLER-COUCH.

JENIFER'S LOVE

SMALL is my secret—let it pass—
Small in your life the share I had,
Who sat beside you in the class,
    Awed by the bright superior lad:
        Whom yet with hot and eager face
        I prompted when he missed his place.

For you the call came swift and soon:—
    But sometimes in your holidays
You met me trudging home at noon
    To dinner through the dusty ways,
        And recognized, and with a nod
        Passed on, but never guessed—thank God!

Truly our ways were separate.
    I bent myself to hoe and drill,
Yea, with an honest man to mate,
    Fulfilling God Almighty's will;
        And bore him children.   But my prayers
        Were yours—and, only after, theirs.

While you—still loftier, more remote,
    You sprang from stair to stair of fame,
And you 've a riband on your coat,
    And you 've a title to your name.
        But have you yet a star to shine
        Above your bed, as I o'er mine?

THE ART OF PARODY

An Introduction to *Parodies and Imitations Old and New,* edited by J. A. S. Adam and B. C. White. 1912.

SAYS Ruskin, in his lecture on *The Mystery of Life and its Arts*—'The moment a man can really do his work he becomes speechless about it. All words become idle to him— all theories.' With a rhetorical flourish he goes on to ask: 'Does a bird need to theorize about building its nest, or boast of it when built?'

Well, as to the bird, I don't know, and (with all respect) I very much doubt if Ruskin knew; though by the noise the sparrows were making, a few weeks ago, in the ivies outside this window of mine, I should judge that—as they say in Parliament—'the answer to the second part of the question is in the affirmative.' But if Ruskin be right in his general proposition, that a man straightway falls silent about any work he can really do, it would seem that the editors of this anthology in asking me to write a Preface have paid a left-handed compliment, the blow of which is sharpened rather than softened by their gracefully including two or three parodies of my own.

Well, well—*en los nidos de antaño no hai pájaros hogaño!* I may theorize a little, perhaps, about last year's nests.

Now, the first thing to be said about Parody is that it plays with the gods: its fun is taken with Poetry, which all good men admit to be a beautiful and adorable thing, and some would have to be a holy thing.[1] It follows then that Parody must be

[1] There are, of course, false gods in Poetry. But parodies of these directly expose their falsity, while parodies of true poetry subtly pay homage to its truth. Moreover, we may say generally that in parody, as elsewhere, exposure of the false (though useful and necessary) ranks below illustration of the true.

delicate ground, off which the profane and vulgar should be carefully warned.   A deeply religious man may indulge a smile at this or that in his religion; as a truly devout lover may rally his mistress on her foibles, since for him they make her the more enchanting.   Without being conscious of it, he knows unerringly 'how far to go,' as they say; he cannot offend, because his true reverence does not so much control as permeate him:

> Thou art my life, my love, my heart,
>   The very eyes of me:

and the tone of the laugh tells of that sweet understanding.   So, or almost so, it should be with the parodist.   He must be friends with the gods, and worthy of their company, before taking these pleasant liberties with them.   Nor, if we keep a mind at once fearless and modest in approaching them, shall we fail of that friendship, thanks to their magnificent condescension.   As Emerson has noted:

It is remarkable that involuntarily we always read as superior beings.   Universal history, the poets, the romancers, do not in their stateliest picture—in the sacerdotal, the imperial palaces, in the triumphs of will or of genius—anywhere lose our ear, anywhere make us feel that we intrude, that this is for our betters; but rather it is true that, in their grandest strokes, there we feel most at home.   All that Shakespeare says of the King, yonder slip of a boy that reads in the corner feels to be true of himself. . . .

If this be true—and I think no one will dispute it—then the more shame must we feel when an outsider comes along and takes advantage of their noble condescension to call hail-fellow with Milton, for example, or to slap Wordsworth on the back. A David may dance before the ark, to which an Uzzah may not put forth a hand: and even David must lay his account with Michal's shocked protestantism.

The material, then, on which Parody works is Poetry, and preferably great Poetry.   Its method consists in a nice apposition of the incongruous, catching as nearly as possible the authentic speech of the bard and applying it unexpectedly, even absurdly, to things beneath his notice; thereby reminding him that he is mortal without denying—rather, insisting—that he is divine.   In its easiest form Parody will take his actual words, and turn them to some new and ridiculous connotation.   It is a trick not far removed from punning; yet, when well executed, it gives pleasure, I think, to any one not born a prig.   For an instance, I choose a few lines of Mr. Hartley Carrick's, one of our younger parodists.   He takes Wordsworth's *She was a Phantom of Delight*, and applies the actual words, or some of them, which in our minds carry their own associations, to— a motor-omnibus.

> *It was a phantom of delight*
> *When first it gleam'd upon my sight,*
> And seem'd to hint a time of bliss
> In store for the metropolis . . .
> A *perfect* motor, *nobly plann'd*
> To traverse Holborn and the Strand. . . .
>
> But now from early morn till e'en
> I hear *the pulse of the machine*
> That clatters past my humble door
> In one unending shriek and roar;
> With aching head and deafen'd ear
> I note with apprehensive fear
> *The traveller 'twixt life and death*
> Endeavour to regain his breath,
> As once again it skids away
> To haunt, to startle, and waylay.

At the risk of being numbered among the friends of Mr. Peter Magnus, I confess that these absurdities amuse me.   But now let us compare the above with a specimen of parody carried almost, if not quite, to its fullest powers, and for this purpose

let us choose another 'imitation' of Wordsworth, this time by
J. K. Stephen (genius untimely lost):

Poetic Lamentation on the Insufficiency of Steam Locomotion in the Lake District

Bright Summer spreads his various hue
 O'er nestling vales and mountains steep,
Glad birds are singing in the blue,
 In joyous chorus bleat the sheep.
But men are walking to and fro,
 Are riding, driving, far and near,
And nobody as yet can go
 By train to Buttermere.

Wake, England, wake! 'tis now the hour
 To sweep away this black disgrace—
The want of locomotion proves
 In so enjoyable a place.
Nature has done her part, and why
 Is mightier Man in his to fail?
I want to hear the porters cry,
 'Change here for Ennerdale!'

 . . . .

Presumptuous Nature! do not rate
 Unduly high thy humble lot,
Nor vainly strive to emulate
 The fame of Stephenson and Watt.
The beauties which thy lavish pride
 Has scatter'd through the smiling land
Are little worth till sanctified
 By Man's completing hand.

The form is here true Wordsworth, from the verbose title to
the last exquisite quatrain, with scarcely a lapse.   'Enjoyable'
in stanza 2 is not quite Wordsworth, but a little more than
Wordsworth, and 'the fame of Stevenson and Watt' occupies

Stephen for a moment with his own cleverness. On the other hand, what, for example, could be more exquisitely Wordsworthian in operation of mind and in actual cadence of speech than—

> But men are walking to and fro,
> Are riding, driving, far and near . . .?

There is more than this: with almost diabolical cunning Stephen has seized on the subject that of all others would have engaged Wordsworth; has turned it upside down; and has presented the poet uttering to us in his own authentic words precisely the last sentiments his admirers would expect him to utter. And yet again (so clever it is), we are left with a frolic doubt (remembering Wordsworth's ineradicable streak of the prosaic and his actual return upon himself in his later years) that somehow, had it been possible to fill the great man up with laughing gas, in the moments preceding unconsciousness he might not improbably have uttered these very sentiments as he would assuredly have cast them in similar words. I call this the perfection of Parody.

But if the parodist can do so much as this, it follows further that Parody must be a form of Criticism, and may be enlightening as it is vivacious. Again I turn for the simplest illustration to the work of a young practitioner. Some years ago, in his last Oxford lectures, Mr. Froude lamented that no poet in this country had arisen to undertake a national epic of the great Elizabethan seamen; a hint which has since been acted on by Mr. Alfred Noyes in his fine *Drake*, an epic poem in twelve books. Now in any long poem of the sea there inheres the difficulty that while the action of Epic has to be rapid and the verse correspondingly rapid (as Matthew Arnold noted in his Lectures *On Translating Homer*), actually the business of seafaring is full of patience and *longueurs*. You cannot upon the wide Atlantic hustle action and reaction to and fro as upon the fields of windy Troy. Homer, when he came to the *Odyssey*, dodged a part of this difficulty by casting a whole mass of his hero's adventures into the form of reported speech—a traveller's yarn at the court of Alcinous; and another part he could dodge because he was dealing with the purely fictitious, and could introduce a shipwreck or a miracle whenever things were getting slow. But in these days you cannot play tricks like this with Drake, whose voyages are matters of history. This difficulty, then, was inherent in Mr. Noyes's subject, and it seems to me very shrewdly detected and hit off in Mr. Wilfrid Blair's parody:

THE NOYES OF BATTLE [1]

Meanwhile the wind had changed, and Francis Drake
Put down the helm, and drove against the seas.
Once more the wind changed, and the simple seaman,
Full-fraught with weather-wisdom, once again
Put down the helm, and so drove on, until
The everlasting and omnipotent
Dawn, through the splendid gloom and golden clouds
Broke: and a great, golden, gilded galleon
In raggy piles of gloom and shaggy splendour
Rose up against them, clouded with the dawn.

Plushed, plumed, and purpled on the imperious poop,
Crusty with cramoisie the Spaniards stood.
They quite refused surrender, till Drake cried
'I am El Draque!'—At once they recognized
The name, tho' spoken with a Devon burr.
Down came their flag at once upon the deck,
As when a fragment of the ceiling falls.

Brief and delicious simile!

So with instructions to the wheel
Drake went below, and had a glass of grog.

For a second and more accomplished illustration, let us take James Smith's famous parody of Crabbe in *Rejected Addresses*.

[1] *Poets on the Isis.* Oxford: B. H. Blackwell, 1910.

Crabbe is a very considerable poet: for a certain power of
poignancy, hard yet human, and (its best quality) stark clear of
sentiment, you will hardly find his match.   But he exhibited
this power in versified stories, and in the art of introducing and
laying out a story he was incurably clumsy and could be bald,
unpoetical to the last degree.   Those of us who love him best
must have smiled oftenest over such passages as:

> Peter had heard there were in London then—
> Still have they being!—workhouse-clearing men,
> Who, undisturbed by feelings just or kind,
> Would parish-boys to needy tradesmen bind . . .

The difficulty here is somewhat cognate with that of logging
Drake's voyages: and perhaps among narrative poets Homer
stands alone in his handling of flat intervals, his skill in poetizing
such operations as cooking a dinner or hauling up a boat so that
while never aspiring above their due level in the narrative they
never fall below the grand manner.   Crabbe ('a Pope in worsted
stockings') avoided, to be sure, the Charybdis of Pope and his
compeers.   He seldom or never clothed triviality in fine and
banal writing such as:

> The Heavens illumed by Sol's bright ray

or

> Inoculation! heavenly maid, descend,

which was the approved way to talk of the weather or of
Dr. Jenner's vaccine.   On the other hand, at the beginning of
a tale he would bump for twenty or thirty lines together upon
a Scylla commonplace so bald and awkward that James Smith's
famous lines contain more of criticism than of exaggeration:

> John Richard William Alexander Dwyer
> Was footman to Justinian Stubbs, Esquire;
> But when John Dwyer 'listed in the Blues,
> Emanuel Jennings polish'd Stubbs's shoes.
> Emanuel Jennings brought his youngest boy
> Up as a corn-cutter—a safe employ.

This is fun and criticism together; and as criticism it indicates at once Crabbe's 'worsted stockings' and his frequent, almost habitual clumsiness in starting them out for a walk.

Again, could the fatuity of the ordinary Prize Poem be better rationalized in twenty pages of prose than it was by the parodist who summarized all the Oxford Newdigates in one line?—

> What though no cenotaph enshrine thy bones!

Or, again, has the banality of poetic diction ever received a shrewder knock than it did from the parodies of the *Anti-Jacobin*?

> The feather'd tribes on pinions cleave the air;
> Not so the mackerel, and, still less, the bear.

Or yet, again, could the musical flagrancies of our latest and greatest Strauss, and the affabilities of all the eighteenth-century Odes to Saint Cecilia, be more neatly touched than they are by Mr. Charles L. Graves simply opposing them in an

ODE TO DISCORD

> Hence, loathéd Melody, whose name recalls
> The mellow fluting of the nightingale
>   In some sequester'd vale,
>   The Murmur of the stream
>   Heard in a dream,
> Or drowsy plash of distant waterfalls.
> But thou, divine Cacophony, assume
> The rightful overlordship in her room,
> And with Percussion's stimulating aid
> Expel the heavenly but no longer youthful maid.

The mischief with Parody is that while no neater or swifter vehicle of criticism has ever been invented, the most of men practise it in youth, as a way of breaking their teeth upon literature, and abandon it as middle age brings the critical judgment which it would seem designed to convey. There

*H

once was an Aristophanes to whom years but brought fresh gusto in the gentle art: and our own times have in England, in Mr. Owen Seaman, a parodist as near perfection as our language is likely to achieve—for his first living rival, Mr. A. G. Godley, is an Horatian rather than a parodist, and indeed his line has lain in that direction from the first.   Calverley, Hilton of *The Light Green*, J. K. Stephen, all died young.   Perhaps the gods loved them.   For, as I said at the start, Parody plays with the gods; and, as George Meredith says in his *Essay on Comedy*— and we may reverently apply it to the gods: 'You may estimate your capacity for Comic perception by being able to detect the ridicule of them you love, without loving them less: and more by being able to see yourself somewhat ridiculous in dear eyes, and accepting the correction their image of you proposes.'

INAUGURAL LECTURE
CAMBRIDGE, WEDNESDAY, JANUARY 29, 1913

IN all the long quarrel set between philosophy and poetry I know of nothing finer, as of nothing more pathetically hopeless, than Plato's return upon himself in his last dialogue 'The Laws.' There are who find that dialogue (left unrevised) insufferably dull, as no doubt it is without form and garrulous. But I think they will read it with a new tolerance, maybe even with a touch of feeling, if upon second thoughts they recognize in its twistings and turnings, its prolixities and repetitions, the scruples of an old man who, knowing that his time in this world is short, would not go out of it pretending to know more than he does, and even in matters concerning which he was once very sure has come to divine that, after all, as Renan says, 'La verité consiste dans les nuances.' Certainly 'the soul's dark cottage battered and decayed' does in that last dialogue admit some wonderful flashes,

> From Heaven descended to the low-roofed house
> Of Socrates,

or rather to that noble 'banquet-hall deserted' which aforetime had entertained Socrates.

Suffer me, Mr. Vice-Chancellor and Gentlemen, before reaching my text, to remind ourselves of the characteristically beautiful setting. The place is Crete, and the three interlocutors—Cleinias a Cretan, Megillus a Lacedaemonian, and an Athenian stranger—have joined company on a pilgrimage to the cave and shrine of Zeus, from whom Minos, first lawgiver of the island, had reputedly derived not only his parentage but much parental instruction. Now the day being hot, even scorching, and the road from Cnossus to the Sacred Cave a

long one, our three pilgrims, who have foregathered as elderly
men, take it at their leisure, and propose to beguile it with talk
upon Minos and his laws. 'Yes, and on the way,' promises
the Cretan, 'we shall come to cypress-groves exceedingly tall
and fair, and to green meadows, where we may repose ourselves
and converse.' 'Good,' assents the Athenian. 'Ay, very
good indeed, and better still when we arrive at them. Let us
push on.'

So they proceed. I have said that all three are elderly men;
that is, men who have had their opportunities, earned their wages,
and so nearly earned their discharge that now, looking back on
life, they can afford to see Man for what he really is—at his best
a noble plaything for the gods. Yet they look forward, too, a
little wistfully. They are of the world, after all, and nowise so
tired of it, albeit disillusioned, as to have lost interest in the
game or in the young who will carry it on. So Minos and his
laws soon get left behind, and the talk (as so often befalls with
Plato) is of the perfect citizen and how to train him—of education, in short; and so, as ever with Plato, we are back at length
upon the old question which he could never get out of his
way—What to do with the poets?

It scarcely needs to be said that the Athenian has taken hold
of the conversation, and that the others are as wax in his hands.
'O Athenian stranger,' Cleinias addresses him—'inhabitant of
Attica I will not call you, for you seem to deserve rather the
name of Athene herself, because you go back to first principles.'
Thus complimented, the stranger lets himself go. Yet somehow
he would seem to have lost speculative nerve.

It was all very well in the 'Republic,' the ideal State, to be
bold and declare for banishing poetry altogether. But elderly
men have given up pursuing ideals; they have 'seen too many
leaders of revolts.' Our Athenian is driving now at practice
(as we say), at a well-governed State realizable on earth; and
after all it is hard to chase out the poets, especially if you yourself happen to be something of a poet at heart. Hear, then,

the terms on which, after allowing that comedies may be performed, but only by slaves and hirelings, he proceeds to allow serious poetry.

And if any of the serious poets, as they are termed, who write tragedy, come to us and say: 'O strangers, may we go to your city and country, or may we not, and shall we bring with us our poetry? What is your will about these matters?'—how shall we answer the divine men? I think that our answer should be as follows:

'Best of strangers,' we will say to them, 'we also, according to our ability, are tragic poets, and our tragedy is the best and noblest: for our whole state is an imitation of the best and noblest life. . . . You are poets and we are poets, both makers of the same strains, rivals and antagonists in the noblest of dramas, which true law alone can perfect, as our hope is. Do not then suppose that we shall all in a moment allow you to erect your stage in the Agora, and introduce the fair voices of your actors, speaking above our own, and permit you to harangue our women and children and the common people in language other than our own, and very often the opposite of our own. For a State would be mad which gave you this licence, until the magistrates had determined whether your poetry might be recited and was fit for publication or not. Wherefore, O ye sons and scions of the softer Muses! first of all show your songs to the Magistrates and let them compare them with our own, and if they are the same or better, we will give you a chorus; but if not, then, my friends, we cannot.'

Lame conclusion! Impotent compromise! How little applicable, at all events, to *our* Commonwealth! though, to be sure (you may say) we possess a relic of it in His Majesty's Licenser of Plays. As you know, there has been so much heated talk of late over the composition of the County Magistracy; yet I give you a countryman's word, Sir, that I have heard many names proposed for the Commission of the Peace, and on many grounds, but never one on the ground that its owner had a conservative taste in verse!

Nevertheless, as Plato saw, we must deal with these poets somehow. It is possible (though not, I think, likely) that in

the ideal State there would be no Literature, as it is certain
there would be no Professors of it; but since its invention men
have never been able to rid themselves of it for any length of
time. *Tamen usque recurret.* They may forbid Apollo, but
still he comes leading his choir, the Nine:

> Ἄκλητος μὲν ἔγωγε μένοιμί κεν· ἐς δὲ καλεύντων
> Θαρσήσας Μοίσαισι σὺν ἀμετέραισιν ἱκοίμαν.

And he may challenge us English boldly! For since Chaucer,
at any rate, he and his train have never been ἄκλητοι to us—
least of all here in Cambridge.

Nay, we know that he should be welcome. Cardinal Newman, proposing the idea of a University to the Roman Catholics
of Dublin, lamented that the English language had not, like the
Greek, 'some definite words to express, simply and generally,
intellectual proficiency or perfection, such as "health," as used
with reference to the animal frame, and "virtue," with reference
to our moral nature.' Well, it is a reproach to us that we do
possess the term: and perhaps again a reproach to us that our
attempts at it—the word 'culture' for instance—have been apt
to take on some soil of controversy, some connotative damage,
from over-preaching on the one hand and impatience on the
other. But we do earnestly desire the *thing*. We do prize
that grace of intellect which sets So-and-so in our view as
'a scholar and a gentleman.' We do wish as many sons of this
University as may be to carry forth that lifelong stamp from her
precincts; and—this is my point—from our notion of such a
man the touch of literary grace cannot be excluded. I put to
you for a test Lucian's description of his friend Demonax:

His way was like other people's; he mounted no high horse; he
was just a man and a citizen. He indulged in no Socratic irony.
But his discourse was full of Attic grace; those who heard it went
away neither disgusted by servility nor repelled by ill-tempered
censure, but on the contrary lifted out of themselves by charity, and
encouraged to more orderly, contented, hopeful lives.

I put it to you, that Lucian needs not to say another word, but we know that Demonax had loved letters, and partly by aid of them had arrived at being such a man.   No; by consent of all, Literature is a nurse of noble natures, and right reading makes a full man in a sense even better than Bacon's; not replete, but complete rather, to the pattern for which Heaven designed him.   In this conviction, in this hope, public-spirited men endow Chairs in our Universities, sure that Literature is a good thing if only we can bring it to operate on young minds.

That he has in him some power to guide such operation a man must believe before accepting such a Chair as this.   And now, Sir, the terrible moment is come when your ξένος must render some account—I will not say of himself, for that cannot be attempted—but of his business here.   Well, first let me plead that while you have been infinitely kind to the stranger, feasting him and casting a gown over him, one thing not all your kindness has been able to do.   With precedents, with traditions such as other Professors enjoy, you could not furnish him.   The Chair is a new one, or almost new, and for the present would seem to float in the void, like Mahomet's coffin. Wherefore, being one who (in my Lord Chief Justice Crewe's phrase) would 'take hold of a twig or a twine-thread to uphold it'; being also prone (with Bacon) to believe that 'the counsels to which Time hath not been called, Time will not ratify'; I do assure you that, had any legacy of guidance been discovered among the papers left by my predecessor, it would have been eagerly welcomed and as piously honoured.   O, trust me, Sir! —if any design for this Chair of English Literature had been left by Dr. Verrall, it is not I who would be setting up any new stage in your agora!   But in his papers—most kindly searched for me by Mrs. Verrall—no such design can be found.   He was, in truth, a stricken man when he came to the Chair, and of what he would have built we can only be sure that, had it been this or had it been that, it would infallibly have borne the impress of one of the most beautiful minds of our generation.   The gods saw otherwise; and for me, following him, I came to a trench and stretched my hands to a shade.

For me, then, if you put questions concerning the work of this Chair, I must take example from the artist in *Don Quixote*, who being asked what he was painting answered modestly, 'That is as it may turn out.' The course is uncharted, and for sailing directions I have but these words of your Ordinance:

It shall be the duty of the Professor to deliver courses of lectures on English Literature from the age of Chaucer onwards, and otherwise to promote, so far as may be in his power, the study in the University of the subject of English Literature.

And I never even knew that English Literature had a 'subject'; or, rather, supposed it to have several! To resume:

The Professor shall treat this subject on literary and critical rather than on philological and linguistic lines:

—a proviso which at any rate cuts off a cantle, large in itself, if not comparatively, of the new Professor's ignorance. But I ask you to note the phrase 'to promote, so far as may be in his power, the study'—not, you will observe, 'to teach'; for this absolves me from raising at the start a question of some delicacy for me, as Green launched his *Prolegomena to Ethics* upon the remark that 'an author who seeks to gain general confidence scarcely goes the right way to work when he begins with asking whether there really is such a subject as that of which he proposes to treat.' In spite of—mark, pray, that I say *in spite of*—the activity of many learned Professors, some doubt does lurk in the public mind if, after all, English Literature can, in any ordinary sense, be taught, and if the attempts to teach it do not, after all, justify (as Wisdom is so often justified of her grandparents) the silent sapience of those old benefactors who abstained from endowing any such Chairs.

But that the study of English Literature can be promoted in young minds by an elder one, that their zeal may be encouraged, their tastes directed, their vision cleared, quickened, enlarged—

this, I take it, no man of experience will deny. Nay, since our two oldest Universities have a habit of marking one another with interest—an interest, indeed, sometimes heightened by nervousness—I may point out that all this has been done of late years, and eminently done, by a Cambridge man you gave to Oxford. This, then, Mr. Vice-Chancellor—this or something like this, Gentlemen—is to be my task if I have the good fortune to win your confidence.

Let me, then, lay down two or three principles by which I propose to be guided. (1) For the first principle of all I put to you that in studying any work of genius we should begin by taking it *absolutely*; that is to say, with minds intent on discovering just what the author's mind intended; this being at once the obvious approach to its meaning (its τὸ τί ἦν εἶναι, the 'thing it was to be'), and the merest duty of politeness we owe to the great man addressing us. We should lay our minds open to what he wishes to tell, and if what he has to tell be noble and high and beautiful, we should surrender and let soak our minds in it.

Let me premise that in claiming, even insisting upon, the first place for this *absolute* study of a great work I use no disrespect towards those learned scholars whose labours will help you, Gentlemen, to enjoy it afterwards in other ways and from other aspects; since I hold there is no surer sign of intellectual ill-breeding than to speak, even to feel, slightingly of any knowledge oneself does not happen to possess. Still less do I aim to persuade you that any one should be able to earn a Cambridge degree by the process (to borrow Macaulay's phrase) of reading our great authors 'with his feet on the hob,' a posture I have not even tried, to recommend it for a contemplative man's recreation. These editors not only set us the priceless example of learning for learning's sake: but even in practice they clear our texts for us, and afterwards—when we go more minutely into our author's acquaintance, wishing to learn all we can about him—by increasing our knowledge of detail they enhance our delight. Nay, with certain early writers—say Chaucer or Dunbar, as with certain highly allusive ones—Bacon, or Milton, or Sir Thomas Browne—some apparatus must be supplied from the start. But on the whole I think it a fair contention that such helps to studying an author are secondary and subsidiary; that, for example, with any author who by consent is less of his age than for all time, to study the relation he bore to his age may be important indeed, and even highly important, yet must in the nature of things be of secondary importance, not of the first.

But let us examine this principle a little more attentively— for it is the palmary one. As I conceive it, that understanding of literature which we desire in our Euphues, our gracefully minded youth, will include knowledge in varying degree, yet is itself something distinct from knowledge. Let us illustrate this upon Poetry, which the most of us will allow to be the highest form of literary expression, if not of all artistic expression. Of all the testimony paid to Poetry, none commands better witness than this—that, as Johnson said of Gray's *Elegy*, it 'abounds with images which find a mirror in every mind, and with sentiments to which every bosom returns an echo.' When George Eliot said, 'I never before met with so many of my own feelings expressed just as I should like them,' she but repeated of Wordsworth (in homelier, more familiar fashion) what Johnson said of Gray; and the same testimony lies implicit in Emerson's fine remark that 'universal history, the poets, the romancers'—all good writers, in short—'do not anywhere make us feel that we intrude, that this is for our betters. Rather it is true that, in their greatest strokes, there we feel most at home.' The mass of evidence, of which these are samples, may be summarized thus: As we dwell here between two mysteries, of a soul within and an ordered Universe without, so among us are granted to dwell certain men of more delicate intellectual fibre than their fellows—men whose minds have, as it were, filaments to intercept, apprehend, conduct, translate home to us stray messages between these two mysteries, as modern telegraphy has learnt to search out, snatch, gather home human messages astray over waste waters of the Ocean.

If, then, the ordinary man be done this service by the poet, that (as Dr. Johnson defines it) 'he feels what he remembers to have felt before, but he feels it *with a great increase of sensibility*'; or even if, though the message be unfamiliar, it suggest to us, in Wordsworth's phrase, to 'feel that we are greater than we know,' I submit that we respond to it less by anything that usually passes for knowledge, than by an improvement of sensibility, a tuning up of the mind to the poet's pitch; so that the man we are proud to send forth from our Schools will be remarkable less for something he can take out of his wallet and exhibit for knowledge, than for *being* something, and that 'something' a man of unmistakable intellectual breeding, whose trained judgment we can trust to choose the better and reject the worse.

But since this refining of the critical judgment happens to be less easy of practice than the memorizing of much that passes for knowledge—of what happened to Harriet or what Blake said to the soldier—and far less easy to examine on, the pedagogic mind (which I implore you not to suppose me confusing with the scholarly) for avoidance of trouble tends all the while to dodge or obfuscate what is essential, piling up accidents and irrelevancies before it until its very face is hidden. And we should be the more watchful not to confuse the pedagogic mind with the scholarly since it is from the scholar that the pedagogue pretends to derive his sanction; ransacking the great genuine commentators—be it a Skeat or a Masson or (may I add for old reverence' sake?) an Aldis Wright—fetching home bits of erudition, *non sua poma*, and announcing 'This *must* be the true Sion, for we found it in a wood.'

Hence a swarm of little school-books pullulates annually, all upside down and wrong from beginning to end; and hence a worse evil afflicts us, that the English schoolboy starts with a false perspective of any given masterpiece, his pedagogue urging, obtruding, the poem or the play itself, is seen in distorted glimpses, if not quite blocked out of view.

This same temptation—to remove a work of art from the category for which the author designed it into another where it can be more conveniently studied—reaches even above the schoolmaster to assail some very eminent critics. I cite an example from a book of which I shall hereafter have to speak with gratitude as I shall always name it with respect—*The History of English Poetry*, by Dr. Courthope, some time Professor of Poetry at Oxford. In his fourth volume, and in his estimate of Fletcher as a dramatist, I find this passage:

But the critical test of a play's quality is only applied when it is read. So long as the illusion of the stage gives credit to the action, and the words and gestures of the actor impose themselves on the imagination of the spectator, the latter will pass over a thousand imperfections which reveal themselves to the reader, who, as he has to satisfy himself with the drama of silent images, will not be content if this in any way falls short of his conception of truth and nature,

—which seems equivalent to saying that the crucial test of the frieze of the Parthenon is its adaptability to an apartment in Bloomsbury. So long as the illusion of the Acropolis gave credit to Pheidias's design, and the sunlight of Attica imposed its delicate intended shadows edging the reliefs, the countrymen of Pericles might be tricked; but the visitor to the British Museum, as he has to satisfy himself with what happens indoors in the atmosphere of the West Central Postal Division of London, will not be content if Pheidias in any way fall short of *his* conception of truth and nature. Yet Fletcher (I take it) constructed his plays as plays; the illusion of the stage, the persuasiveness of the actor's voice, were conditions for which he wrought, and on which he had a right to rely; and, in short, any critic behaves uncritically who, distrusting his imagination to recreate the play as a play, elects to consider it in the category of something else.

In sum, if the great authors never oppress us with airs of condescension, but, like the great lords they are, put the meanest of us at our ease in their presence, I see no reason why we should pay to any commentator a servility not demanded by his master.

My next two principles may be more briefly stated.

(2) I propose next, then, that since our investigations will deal largely with style, that curiously personal thing; and since (as I have said) they cannot in their nature be readily brought to rule-of-thumb tests, and may therefore so easily be suspected of evading all tests, of being mere dilettantism; I propose (I say) that my pupils and I rebuke this suspicion by constantly aiming at the concrete, at the study of such definite beauties as we can see presented in print under our eyes; always seeking the author's intention, but eschewing, for the present at any rate, all general definitions and theories, through the sieve of which the particular achievement of genius is so apt to slip. And having excluded them at first in prudence, I make little doubt we shall go on to exclude them in pride. Definitions, formulae (some would add, creeds) have their use in any society in that they restrain the ordinary unintellectual man from making himself a public nuisance with his private opinions. But they go a very little way in helping the man who has a real sense of prose or verse. In other words, they are good discipline for some thyrsus-bearers, but the initiated have little use for them. As Thomas à Kempis 'would rather feel compunction than understand the definition thereof,' so the initiated man will say of the 'Grand Style,' for example—'Why define it for me?' When Viola says simply:

> I am all the daughters of my father's house,
> And all the brothers too,

or Macbeth demands of the Doctor:

> Canst thou not minister to a mind diseased,
> Pluck from the memory a rooted sorrow . . .?

or Hamlet greets Ophelia, reading her Book of Hours, with

> Nymph, in thy orisons
> Be all my sins remembered!

or when Milton tells of his dead friend how

> Together both, ere the high lawns appear'd
> Under the opening eyelids of the morn,
> We drove afield,

or describes the battalions of Heaven:

> On they move
> Indissolubly firm; nor obvious hill,
> Nor strait'ning vale, nor wood, nor stream divides
> Their perfect ranks,

or when Gray exalts the great commonplace:

> The boast of heraldry, the pomp of power,
> And all that beauty, all that wealth e'er gave,
> Awaits alike th' inevitable hour.
> The paths of glory lead but to the grave,

or when Keats casually drops us such a line as

> The journey homeward to habitual self,

or, to come down to our own times and to a living poet, when I open on a page of William Watson and read:

> O ancient streams, O far descended woods,
> Full of the fluttering of melodious souls! . . .

'why then (will say the initiated one), why worry me with any definition of the Grand Style in English, when here, and here, and again here—in all these lines, simple or intense or exquisite or solemn—I recognize and feel the *thing*?'

Indeed, Sir, the long and the short of the argument lie just here. Literature is not an abstract Science, to which exact definitions can be applied. It is an Art rather, the success of which depends on personal persuasiveness, on the author's skill to give as on ours to receive.

(3) For our third principle I will ask you to go back with

me to Plato's wayfarers, whom we have left so long under the cypresses; and loth as we must be to lay hands on our father Parmenides, I feel we must treat the gifted Athenian stranger to a little manhandling. For did you not observe—though Greek was a living language and to his metropolitan mind the only language—how envious he showed himself to seal up the well, or allow it to trickle only under permit of a public analyst: to treat all innovation as suspect, even as, a hundred odd years ago, the Lyrical Ballads were suspect?

But the very hope of this Chair, Sir (as I conceive it), relies on the courage of the young. As Literature is an Art and therefore not to be pondered only, but practised, so ours is a living language and therefore to be kept alive, supple, active in all honourable use. The orator can yet sway men, the poet ravish them, the dramatist fill their lungs with salutary laughter or purge their emotions by pity or terror. The historian 'superinduces upon events the charm of order.' The novelist —well, even the novelist has his uses; and I would warn you against despising any form of art which is alive and pliant in the hands of men. For my part, I believe, bearing in mind Mr. Barrie's *Peter Pan* and the old bottles he renovated to hold that joyous wine, that even Musical Comedy, in the hands of a master, might become a thing of beauty. Of the Novel, at any rate—whether we like it or not—we have to admit that it does hold a commanding position in the literature of our times, and to consider how far Mr. Lascelles Abercrombie was right the other day when he claimed, on the first page of his brilliant study of Thomas Hardy, that 'the right to such a position is not to be disputed; for here, as elsewhere, the right to a position is no more than the power to maintain it.' You may agree with that or you may not; you may or may not deplore the forms that literature is choosing nowadays; but there is no gainsaying that it is still very much alive. And I would say to you, Gentlemen, 'Believe, and be glad that Literature and the English tongue are both alive.' Carlyle, in his explosive way, once demanded of his countrymen, 'Shakespeare or India? If you had to surrender one to retain the other, which would you choose?' Well, our Indian Empire is yet in the making, while the works of Shakespeare are complete and purchasable in whole calf; so the alternatives are scarcely *in pari materia*; and moreover let us not be in a hurry to meet trouble half-way. But in English Literature, which, like India, is still in the making, you have at once an Empire and an emprise. In that alone you have inherited something greater than Sparta. Let us strive, each in his little way, to adorn it.

But here at the close of my hour, the double argument, that Literature is an Art and English a living tongue, has led me right up to a fourth principle, the plunge into which (though I foresaw it from the first) all the coward in me rejoices at having to defer to another lecture. I conclude then, Gentlemen, by answering two suspicions, which very likely have been shaping themselves in your minds. In the first place, you will say, 'It is all very well for this man to talk about "cultivating an increased sensibility," and the like; but we know what *that* leads to—to quackery, to aesthetic chatter: "Isn't this pretty? Don't you admire that?"' Well, I am not greatly frightened. To begin with, when we come to particular criticism I shall endeavour to exchange it with you in plain terms; a manner which (to quote Mr. Robert Bridges' *Essay on Keats*) 'I prefer, because by obliging the lecturer to say definitely what he means, it makes his mistakes easy to point out, and in this way the true business of criticism is advanced.' But I have a second safeguard, more to be trusted: that here in Cambridge, with all her traditions of austere scholarship, any one who indulges in loose discinct talk will be quickly recalled to his tether. Though at the time Athene be not kind enough to descend from heaven and pluck him backward by the hair, yet the very *genius loci* will walk home with him from the lecture room, whispering monitions, cruel to be kind.

'But,' you will say alternatively, 'if we avoid loose talk on

these matters we are embarking on a mighty difficult business.'
Why, to be sure we are; and that, I hope, will be half the enjoyment. After all, we have a number of critics among whose
methods we may search for help—from the Persian monarch
who, having to adjudicate upon two poems, caused the one
to be read to him, and at once, without ado, awarded the prize
to the other, up to the great Frenchman whom I shall finally
invoke to sustain my hope of building something; that is if
you, Gentlemen, will be content to accept me less as a Professor
than as an Elder Brother.

The Frenchman is Sainte-Beuve, and I pay a debt, perhaps
appropriately here, by quoting him as translated by the friend
of mine, now dead, who first invited me to Cambridge and
taught me to admire her—one Arthur John Butler, some time
a Fellow of Trinity, and later a great pioneer among Englishmen in the study of Dante.   Thus while you listen to the appeal
of Sainte-Beuve, I can hear beneath it a more intimate voice,
not for the first time encouraging me.

Sainte-Beuve then—*si magna licet componere parvis*—is delivering an Inaugural Lecture in the École Normale, the date
being April 12th, 1858.   'Gentlemen,' he begins, 'I have written
a good deal in the last thirty years; that is, I have scattered
myself about a good deal; so that I need to gather myself
together, in order that my words may come before you with
all the more freedom and confidence.'   That is his opening;
and he ends:

As time goes on, you will make me believe that I can for my part
be of some good to you: and with the generosity of your age you
will repay me, in this feeling alone, far more than I shall be able to
give you in intellectual direction, or in literary insight.   If in one
sense I bestow on you some of my experience, you will requite me,
and in a more profitable manner, by the sight of your ardour for
what is noble: you will accustom me to turn oftener and more
willingly towards the future in your company.   You will teach me
again to hope.

PIPES IN ARCADY

I HARDLY can bring myself to part with this story, it has been such a private joy to me. Moreover, that I have lain awake in the night to laugh over it is no guarantee of your being passably amused. Yourselves, I dare say, have known what it is to awake in irrepressible mirth from a dream which next morning proved to be flat and unconvincing. Well, this my pet story has some of the qualities of a dream; being absurd, for instance, and almost incredible, and even a trifle inhuman. After all, I had better change my mind, and tell you another——

But no; I will risk it, and you shall have it, just as it befel.

    •   •   •   •   •

I had taken an afternoon's holiday to make a pilgrimage: my goal being a small parish church that lies remote from the railway, five good miles from the tiniest of country stations; my purpose to inspect—or say, rather, to contemplate—a Norman porch, for which it ought to be widely famous. (Here let me say that I have an unlearned passion for Norman architecture—to enjoy it merely, not to write about it.)

To carry me on my first stage I had taken a crawling local train that dodged its way somehow between the regular expresses and the 'excursions' that invade our Delectable Duchy from June to October. The season was high midsummer, the afternoon hot and drowsy with scents of mown hay; and between the rattle of the fast trains it seemed that we, native denizens of the Duchy, careless of observation or applause, were executing a *tour de force* in that fine indolence which has been charged as a fault against us. That we halted at every station goes without saying. Few sidings—however inconsiderable or, as it might seem, fortuitous—escaped the flattery of our prolonged sojourn.

218

We ambled, we paused, almost we dallied with the butterflies lazily afloat over the meadow-sweet and cow-parsley beside the line; we exchanged gossip with station-masters, and received the congratulations of signalmen on the extraordinary spell of fine weather. It did not matter. Three market-women, a pedlar, and a local policeman made up with me the train's complement of passengers. I gathered that their business could wait; and as for mine—well, a Norman porch is by this time accustomed to waiting.

I will not deny that in the end I dozed at intervals in my empty smoking compartment; but wish to make it clear that I came on the Vision (as I will call it) with eyes open, and that it left me staring, wide awake as Macbeth.

Let me describe the scene. To the left of the line as you travel westward there lies a long grassy meadow on a gentle acclivity, set with three or four umbrageous oaks and backed by a steep plantation of oak saplings. At the foot of the meadow, close alongside the line, runs a brook, which is met at the meadow's end by a second brook which crosses under the permanent way through a culvert. The united waters continue the course of the first brook, beside the line, and maybe for half a mile farther; but, a few yards below their junction, are partly dammed by the masonry of a bridge over which a country lane crosses the railway; and this obstacle spreads them into a pool some fifteen or twenty feet wide, overgrown with the leaves of the arrow-head, and fringed with water-flags and the flowering rush.

Now I seldom pass this spot without sparing a glance for it; first because of the pool's still beauty, and secondly because many rabbits infest the meadow below the coppice, and among them for two or three years was a black fellow whom I took an idle delight in recognizing. (He is gone now, and his place knows him no more; yet I continue to hope for sight of a black rabbit just there.) But this afternoon I looked out with special interest because, happening to pass down the line two days before, I had noted a gang of navvies at work on the culvert; and among them, as they stood aside to let the train pass, I had recognized my friend Joby Tucker, their ganger, and an excellent fellow to boot.

Therefore my eyes were alert as we approached the curve that opens the meadow into view, and—as I am a Christian man, living in the twentieth century—I saw this Vision: I beheld beneath the shade of the midmost oak eight men sitting stark naked, whereof one blew on a flute, one played a concertina, and the rest beat their palms together, marking the time; while before them, in couples on the sward, my gang of navvies rotated in a clumsy waltz watched by a ring of solemn ruminant kine.

I saw it. The whole scene, barring the concertina and the navvies' clothes, might have been transformed straight from a Greek vase of the best period. Here, in this green corner of rural England on a workaday afternoon (a Wednesday, to be precise), in full sunlight, I saw this company of the early gods sitting, naked and unabashed, and piping, while twelve British navvies danced to their music. . . . I saw it; and a derisive whistle from the engine told me that driver and stoker saw it too. I was not dreaming, then. But what on earth could it mean? For fifteen seconds or so I stared at the Vision . . . and so the train joggled past it and rapt it from my eyes.

I can understand now the ancient stories of men who, having by hap surprised the goddesses bathing, never recovered from the shock but thereafter ran wild in the woods with their memories.

At the next station I alighted. It chanced to be the station for which I had taken my ticket; but anyhow I should have alighted there. The spell of the vision was upon me. The Norman porch might wait. It is (as I have said) used to waiting, and in fact it has waited. I have not yet made another holiday to visit it. Whether or no the market-women and the local policeman had beheld, I know not. I hope not, but now shall never know. . . . The engine-driver, leaning in converse with the station-master, and jerking a thumb backward, had certainly beheld. But I passed him with averted eyes, gave up my ticket, and struck straight across country for the spot.

I came to it, as my watch told me, at twenty minutes after five. The afternoon sunlight still lay broad on the meadow. The place was unchanged save for a lengthening of its oak-tree shadows. But the persons of my Vision—naked gods and navvies—had vanished. Only the cattle stood, knee-deep in the pool, lazily swishing their tails in protest against the flies; and the cattle could tell me nothing.

. . . . . .

Just a fortnight later, as I spent at St. Blazey junction the forty odd minutes of repentance ever thoughtfully provided by our railway company for those who, living in Troy, are foolish enough to travel, I spied at some distance below the station a gang of men engaged in unloading rubble to construct a new siding for the clay-traffic, and at their head my friend Mr. Joby Tucker. The railway company was consuming so much of my time that I felt no qualms in returning some part of the compliment, and strolled down the line to wish Mr. Tucker good day. 'And, by the by,' I added, 'you owe me an explanation. What on earth were you doing in Treba meadow two Wednesdays ago—you and your naked friends?'

Joby leaned on his measuring rod and grinned from ear to ear.

'You see'd us?' he asked, and, letting his eyes travel along the line, he chuckled to himself softly and at length. 'Well, now, I 'm glad o' that. 'Fact is, I 've been savin' up to tell 'ee about it, but (thinks I) when I tells Mr. Q. he won't never believe.'

'I certainly saw you,' I answered; 'but as for believing——'

'Iss, iss,' he interrupted, with fresh chucklings; 'a fair knock-out, wasn' it? . . . You see, they was blind—poor fellas!'

'Drunk?'

'No, sir—blind—"pity the pore blind"; three-parts blind, anyways, an' undergoin' treatment for it.'

'Nice sort of treatment!'

'Eh? You don't understand. See'd us from the train, did 'ee? Which train?'

'The 1.35 ex Millbay.'

'Wish I 'd a-knowed you was watchin' us. I 'd ha' waved my hat as you went by, or maybe blawed 'ee a kiss—that bein' properer to the occasion, come to think.'

Joby paused, drew the back of a hand across his laughter-moistened eyes, and pulled himself together, steadying his voice for the story.

· · · · · ·

'I 'll tell 'ee what happened, from the beginnin'. A gang of us had been sent down, two days before, to Treba meadow, to repair the culvert there. Soon as we started work we found the whole masonry fairly rotten, and spent the first afternoon (that was Monday) underpinnin', while I traced out the extent o' the damage. The farther I went, the worse I found it; the main mischief bein' a leak about midway in the culvert, on the down side; whereby the water, perc'latin' through, was un-packin' the soil, not only behind the masonry of the culvert, but right away down for twenty yards and more behind the stone-facing where the line runs alongside the pool. All this we were forced to take down, shorein' as we went, till we cut back pretty close to the rails. The job, you see, had turned out more serious than reported; and havin' no one to consult, I kept the men at it.

'By Wednesday noon we had cut back so far as we needed, shorein' very careful as we went, and the men workin' away cheerful, with the footboards of the expresses whizzin' by close over their heads, so 's it felt like havin' your hair brushed by machinery. By the time we knocked off for dinner I felt pretty easy in mind, knowin' we 'd broke the back o' the job.

'Well, we touched pipe and started again. Bein' so close to the line I 'd posted a fella with a flag—Bill Martin it was—to keep a look out for the down-trains; an' about three o'clock or a little after he whistled one comin'. I happened to be in the culvert at the time, but stepped out an' back across the brook, just to fling an eye along the embankment to see that all was clear. Clear it was, an' therefore it surprised me a bit, as the train hove in sight around the curve, to see that she had her brakes on, hard, and was slowin' down to stop. My first thought was that Bill Martin must have taken some scare an' showed her the red flag. But that was a mistake; besides she must have started the brakes before openin' sight on Bill.'

'Then why on earth was she pulling up?' I asked. 'It couldn't be signals.'

'There ain't no signal within a mile of Treba meadow, up or down. She was stoppin' because—but just you let me tell it in my own way. Along she came, draggin' hard on her brakes an' whistlin'. I knew her for an excursion, and as she passed I sized it up for a big school-treat. There was five coaches, mostly packed with children, an' on one o' the coaches was a board—"Exeter to Penzance." The four front coaches had corridors, the tail one just ord'nary compartments.

'Well, she dragged past us to dead-slow, an' came to a standstill with her tail coach about thirty yards beyond where I stood, and, as you might say, with its footboard right over-hangin' the pool. You mayn't remember it, but the line just there curves pretty sharp to the right, and when she pulled up, the tail coach pretty well hid the rest o' the train from us. Five or six men, hearin' the brakes, had followed me out of the culvert and stood by me, wonderin' why the stoppage was. The rest were dotted about along the slope of th' embankment. And then the curiousest thing happened—about the curiousest thing I seen in all my years on the line. A door of the tail coach opened and a man stepped out. He didn't jump out, you understand, nor fling hisself out; he just stepped out into

air, and with that his arms and legs cast themselves anyways
an' he went down sprawlin' into the pool. It 's easy to say
we ought t' have run then an' there an' rescued him; but for
the moment it stuck us up starin' an',—Wait a bit! You han't
heard the end.

'I hadn't fairly caught my breath, before another man stepped
out! He put his foot down upon nothing, same as the first,
overbalanced just the same, and shot after him base-over-top
into the water.

'Close 'pon the second man's heels appeared a third. . . .
Yes, sir, I know now what a woman feels like when she 's
goin' to have the scritches.[1] I 'd have asked someone to pinch
me in the fleshy part o' the leg, to make sure I was alive an'
awake, but the power o' speech was taken from us. We just
stuck an' stared.

'What beat everything was the behaviour of the train, so to
say. There it stood, like as if it 'd pulled up alongside the pool
for the very purpose to unload these unfort'nit' men; an' yet
takin' no notice whatever. Not a sign o' the guard—not a
head poked out anywheres in the line o' windows—only the
sun shinin', an' the steam escapin', an' out o' the rear compartment this procession droppin' out an' high-divin' one after
another.

'Eight of 'em! Eight, as I am a truth-speakin' man—but
there! you saw 'em with your own eyes. Eight! and the last
of the eight scarce in the water afore the engine toots her
whistle an' the train starts on again, round the curve an'
out o' sight.

'She didn' leave us no time to doubt, neither, for there the
poor fellas were, splashin' an' blowin', some of 'em bleatin' for
help, an' gurglin', an' for aught we know drownin' in three-
to-four feet o' water. So we pulled ourselves together an' ran
to give 'em first aid.

'It didn' take us long to haul the whole lot out and ashore;

[1] Hysterics.

and, as Providence would have it, not a bone broken in the party. One or two were sufferin' from sprains, and all of 'em from shock (but so were we, for that matter), and between 'em they must ha' swallowed a bra' few pints o' water, an' muddy water at that. I can't tell ezackly when or how we discovered they was all blind, or near-upon blind. It may ha' been from the unhandiness of their movements an' the way they clutched at us an' at one another as we pulled 'em ashore. Hows'ever, blind they were; an' I don't remember that it struck us as anyways singular, after what we'd been through a'ready. We fished out a concertina, too, an' a silver-mounted flute that was bobbin' among the weeds.

'The man the concertina belonged to—a tall fresh-complexioned young fella he was, an' very mild of manner—turned out to be a sort o' leader o' the party; an' he was the first to talk any sense. "Th-thank you,' he said. "They told us Penzance was the next stop."

'"Hey?" says I.

'"They told us," he says again, plaintive-like, feelin' for his spectacles an' not finding 'em, "that Penzance was the next stop."

'"Bound for Penzance, was you?" I asks.

'"For the Land's End," says he, his teeth chatterin'. I set it down the man had a stammer, but 'twas only the shock an' the chill of his duckin'.

'"Well," says I, "this ain't the Land's End, though I dessay it feels a bit like it. Then you wasn' *thrown* out?" I says.

'"Th-thrown out?" says he. "N-no. They told us Penzance was the next stop."

'"Then," says I, "if you got out accidental you've had a most providential escape, an' me an' my mates don't deserve less than to hear about it. There's bound to be inquiries after you when the guard finds your compartment empty an' the door open. Maybe the train'll put back; more likely they'll send a search-party; but anyways you're all wet through, an'

I

the best thing for health is to off wi' your clothes an' dry 'em, this warm afternoon."

"'I dessay,' says he, "you'll have noticed that our eyesight is affected."

"'All the better if you're anyways modest,' says I. 'You couldn' find a retirededer place than this—not if you searched: an' *we* don't mind."

'Well, sir, the end was we stripped 'em naked as Adam, an' spread their clothes to dry 'pon the grass. While we tended on 'em the mild young man told us how it had happened. It seems they'd come by excursion from Exeter. There's a blind home at Exeter, an' likewise a cathedral choir, an' Sunday school, an' a boys' brigade, with other sundries; an' this year the good people financin' half a dozen o' these shows had discovered that by clubbin' two sixpences together a shillin' could be made to go as far as eighteenpence; and how, doin' it on the co-op, instead of an afternoon treat for each, they could manage a two days' outin' for all—Exeter to Penzance an' the Land's End, sleepin' one night at Penzance, an' back to Exeter at some ungodly hour the next. It's no use your askin' me why a man three-parts blind should want to visit the Land's End. There's an attraction about that place, an' that's all you can say. Everybody knows as 'tisn' worth seein', an' yet everybody wants to see it. So why not a blind man?

'Well, this Happy Holiday Committee (as they called themselves) got the Company to fix them up with a special excursion; an' our blind friends—bein' sensitive, or maybe a touch above mixin' wi' the school-children an' infants—had packed themselves into this rear compartment separate from the others. One of 'em had brought his concertina, an' another his flute, and what with these an' other ways of passin' the time they got along pretty comfortable till they came to Gwinear Road: an' there for some reason they were held up an' had to show their tickets. Anyways, the staff at Gwinear Road went along the train collectin' the halves o' their return tickets. "What's the name o' this station?" asks my blind friend, very mild an' polite. "Gwinear Road," answers the porter; "Penzance next stop." Somehow this gave him the notion that they were nearly arrived, an' so, you see, when the train slowed down a few minutes later an' came to a stop, he took the porter at his word, an' stepped out. Simple, wasn't it? But in my experience the curiousest things in life are the simplest of all, once you come to inquire into 'em.'

'What I don't understand,' said I, 'is how the train came to stop just there.'

Mr. Tucker gazed at me rather in sorrow than in anger. 'I thought,' said he, "twas agreed I should tell the story in my own way. Well, as I was saying, we got those poor fellas there, all as naked as Adam, an' we was helpin' them all we could—some of us wringin' out their underlinen an' spreading it to dry, others collectin' their hats, an' tryin' which fitted which, an' others even dredgin' the pool for their handbags an' spectacles an' other small articles, an' in the middle of it some-one started to laugh. You'll scarce believe it, but up to that moment there hadn't been so much as a smile to hand round; an' to this day I don't know the man's name that started it— for all I can tell you, I did it myself. But this I do know, that it set off the whole gang like a motor-engine. There was a sort of "click," an' the next moment——

'Laugh? I never heard men laugh like it in my born days. Sort of recoil, I s'pose it must ha' been, after the shock. Laugh? There was men staggerin' drunk with it and there was men rollin' on the turf with it; an' there was men cryin' with it, holdin' on to a stitch in their sides an' beseechin' every one also to hold hard. The blind men took a bit longer to get going; but by gosh, sir! once started they laughed to do your heart good. O Lord, O Lord! I wish you could ha' see that mild-mannered spokesman. Somebody had fished out his spectacles for 'en, and that was all the clothing he stood in—that, an' a grin. He fairly beamed; an' the more he beamed the more we rocked, callin' on 'en to take pity an' stop it.

'Soon as I could catch a bit o' breath, "Land's End next stop!" gasped I. "O, but this *is* the Land's End! This is what the Land's End oughter been all the time, an' never was yet. O, for the Lord's sake," says I, "stop beamin', and pick up your concertina an' pitch us a tune!"

'Well, he did too. He played us "Home, sweet home" first of all—'mid pleasures an' palaces—an' the rest o' the young men sat around 'en an' started clappin' their hands to the tune; an' then some fool slipped an arm round my waist. I'm only thankful he didn't kiss me. Didn't think of it, perhaps; couldn't ha' been that he wasn't capable. It must ha' been just then your train came along. An' about twenty minutes later, when we was gettin' our friends back into their outfits, we heard the search-engine about half a mile below, whistlin' an' feelin' its way up very cautious towards us.

'They was sun-dried an' jolly as sandhoppers—all the eight of 'em—as we helped 'em on board an' wished 'em ta-ta! The search-party couldn' understand at all what had happened—in so short a time, too—to make us so cordial; an' somehow we didn' explain—neither we nor the blind men. I reckon the whole business had been so loonatic we felt it kind of holy. But the pore fellas kept wavin' back to us as they went out o' sight around the curve, an' maybe for a mile beyond. I never heard,' Mr. Tucker wound up meditatively, 'if they ever reached the Land's End. I wonder?'

'But, excuse me once more,' said I. 'How came the train to stop as it did?'

'To be sure. I said just now that the curiousest things in life were, gen'rally speakin', the simplest. One o' the school-children in the fore part of the train—a small nipper of nine—had put his head out o' the carriage window and got his cap blown away. That's all. Bein' a nipper of some resource, he wasted no time, but touched off the communicatin' button an' fetched the whole train to a standstill. George Simmons, the guard, told me all about it last week, when I happened across him an' asked the same question you 've been askin'. George was huntin' through the corridors to find out what had gone wrong; that 's how the blind men stepped out without his noticin'. He pretended to be pretty angry wi' the young tacker. "Do 'ee know," says George, "it 's a five-pound fine if you stop a train without good reason?" "But I *had* a good reason," says the child. "My mother gave 'levenpence for that cap, an' 'tis a bran' new one.'"

LECTURE ON JARGON

CAMBRIDGE, 1 MAY 1913

I ASK leave this morning to interpose some words upon a kind of writing which, from a superficial likeness, commonly passes for prose in these days, and by lazy folk is commonly written for prose, yet actually is not prose at all; my excuse being the simple practical one that, by first clearing this sham prose out of the way, we shall the better deal with honest prose when we come to it. The proper difficulties of prose will remain: but we shall be agreed in understanding what it is, or at any rate what it is not, that we talk about. I remember to have heard somewhere of a religious body in the United States of America which had reason to suspect one of its churches of accepting spiritual consolation from a coloured preacher—an offence against the laws of the Synod—and dispatched a Disciplinary Committee with power to act; and of the Committee's returning to report itself unable to take any action under its terms of reference, for that while a person undoubtedly coloured had undoubtedly occupied the pulpit and had audibly spoken from it in the Committee's presence, the performance could be brought within no definition of preaching known or discoverable. So it is with that infirmity of speech—that flux, that determination of words to the mouth, or to the pen—which, though it be familiar to you in parliamentary debates, in newspapers, and as the staple language of Blue Books, Committees, Official Reports, I take leave to introduce to you as prose which is not prose and under its real name of Jargon.

You must not confuse this Jargon with what is called Journalese. The two overlap, indeed, and have a knack of assimilating each other's vices. But Jargon finds, maybe, the most of its votaries among good douce people who have never written to or for a newspaper in their life, who would never talk of 'adverse climatic conditions' when they mean 'bad weather'; who have never trifled with verbs such as 'obsess,' 'recrudesce,' 'envisage,' 'adumbrate,' or with phrases such as 'the psychological moment,' 'the true inwardness,' 'it gives furiously to think.' Jargon dallies with Latinity—'sub silentio,' 'de die in diem,' 'cui bono?' (always in the sense, unsuspected by Cicero, of 'What is the profit?')—but not for the sake of style. Your journalist at the worst is an artist in his way: he daubs paint of this kind upon the lily with a professional zeal; the more flagrant (or, to use his own word, arresting) the pigment, the happier is his soul. Like the Babu he is trying all the while to embellish our poor language, to make it more floriferous, more poetical—like the Babu for example who, reporting his mother's death, wrote, 'Regret to inform you, the hand that rocked the cradle has kicked the bucket.'

There is metaphor: *there* is ornament: *there* is a sense of poetry, though as yet groping in a world unrealized. No such gusto marks—no such zeal, artistic or professional, animates—the practitioners of Jargon, who are, most of them (I repeat), douce respectable persons. Caution is its father: the instinct to save everything and especially trouble: its mother, Indolence. It looks precise, but is not. It is, in these times, *safe*: a thousand men have said it before and not one to your knowledge had been prosecuted for it. And so, like respectability in Chicago, Jargon stalks unchecked in our midst. It is becoming the language of Parliament: it has become the medium through which Boards of Government, County Councils, Syndicates, Committees, Commercial Firms, express the processes as well as the conclusions of their thought and so voice the reason of their being.

Has a Minister to say 'No' in the House of Commons? Some men are constitutionally incapable of saying 'no': but the Minister conveys it thus—'The answer to the question is in the negative.' That means 'no.' Can you discover it to mean anything else, or anything more except that the speaker is a pompous person?—which was no part of the information demanded.

That is Jargon, and it happens to be accurate.   But as a rule Jargon is by no means accurate, its method being to walk circumspectly around its target; and its faith, that having done so it has either hit the bull's-eye or at least achieved something equivalent, and safer.

Thus the Clerk of a Board of Guardians will minute that

In the case of John Jenkins deceased, the coffin provided was of the usual character.

Now this is not accurate.   'In the case of John Jenkins deceased,' for whom a coffin was supplied, it was wholly superfluous to tell us that he is deceased.   But actually John Jenkins never had more than one case, and that was the coffin.   The Clerk says he had two—a coffin in a case: but I suspect the Clerk to be mistaken, and I am sure he errs in telling us that the coffin was of the usual character: for coffins have no character, usual or unusual.

For another example (I shall not tell you whence derived):

In the case of every candidate who is placed in the first class [So you see the lucky fellow gets a case as well as a first class.   He might be a stuffed animal: perhaps he is] the class-list will show by some convenient mark (1) the Section or Sections for proficiency in which he is placed in the first class and (2) the Section or Sections (if any) in which he has passed with special distinction.

'The Section or Sections (if any)'—But, how, if they are not any, could they be indicated by a mark however convenient?

The Examiners will have regard to the style and method of the candidate's answers, and will give credit for excellence *in these respects*.

Have you begun to detect the two main vices of Jargon?   The first is that it uses circumlocution rather than short straight speech.   It says 'In the case of John Jenkins deceased, the coffin' when it means 'John Jenkins's coffin': and its yea is not yea, neither is its nay nay: but its answer is in the affirmative or in the negative, as the foolish and superfluous 'case' may be. The second vice is that it habitually chooses vague woolly abstract nouns rather than concrete ones. I shall have something to say by and by about the concrete noun, and how you should ever be struggling for it whether in prose or in verse. For the moment I content myself with advising you, if you would write masculine English, never to forget the old tag of your Latin Grammar:

> Masculine will only be
> Things that you can touch and see.

But since these lectures are meant to be a course in First Aid to writing, I will content myself with one or two extremely rough rules: yet I shall be disappointed if you do not find them serviceable.

The first is: Whenever in your reading you come across one of these words, *case, instance, character, nature, condition, persuasion, degree*—whenever in writing your pen betrays you to one or another of them—pull yourself up and take thought. If it be 'case' (I choose it as Jargon's dearest child—'in Heaven yclept Metonymy') turn to the dictionary, if you will, and seek out what meaning can be derived from *casus*, its Latin ancestor: then try how, with a little trouble, you can extricate yourself from that case.

Here are some specimens to try your hand on:

(1) All those tears which inundated Lord Hugh Cecil's head were dry in the case of Mr. Harold Cox.

Poor Mr. Cox! left gasping in his aquarium!

(2) [From a cigar-merchant] In any case, let us send you a case on approval.

(3) It is contended that Consols have fallen in consequence: but such is by no means the case.

'*Such*,' by the way, is another spoilt child of Jargon, especially in Committee's Rules—'Co-opted members may be eligible

*I

as such; such members to continue to serve for such time as'
—and so on.

(4) Even in the purely Celtic areas, only in two or three cases do
the Bishops bear Celtic names.

For 'cases' read 'dioceses.'

Instance. In most instances the players were below their form.

But what were they playing at? Instances?'

Character—Nature. There can be no doubt that the accident was
caused through the dangerous nature of the spot, the hidden character
of the by-road, and the utter absence of any warning or danger
signal.

Mark the foggy wording of it all! And yet the man hit
something and broke his neck! Contrast that explanation
with the verdict of a coroner's jury in the west of England
on a drowned postman—'We find that deceased met his death
by an act of God, caused by sudden overflowing of the river
Walkham and helped out by the scandalous neglect of the
way-wardens.'

The Aintree course is notoriously of a trying nature.
On account of its light character, purity and age, Usher's whisky
is a whisky that will agree with you.
Order. The mésalliance was of a pronounced order.
Condition. He was conveyed to his place of residence in an
intoxicated condition.

'He was carried home drunk.'

Quality and *Section.* Mr. ——, exhibiting no less than five works,
all of a superior quality, figures prominently in the oil section.

This was written of an exhibition of pictures.

Degree. A singular degree of rarity prevails in the earlier editions
of this romance.

That is Jargon. In prose it runs simply 'The earlier editions
of this romance are rare'—or 'are very rare'—or even (if you

believe what I take to doubt) 'are singularly rare'; which should mean that they are rarer than the editions of any other work in the world.

Now what I ask you to consider about these quotations is that in each the writer was using Jargon to shirk prose, palming off periphrases upon us when with a little trouble he could have gone straight to the point. 'A singular degree of rarity prevails,' 'the accident was caused through the dangerous nature of the spot,' 'but such is by no means the case.' We may not be capable of much; but we can all write better than that, if we take a little trouble. In place of, 'the Aintree course is of a trying nature' we can surely say 'Aintree is a trying course' or 'the Aintree course is a trying one'—just that and nothing more.

Next, having trained yourself to keep a look out for these worst offenders (and you will be surprised to find how quickly you get into the way of it), proceed to push your suspicions out among the whole cloudy host of abstract terms. 'How excellent a thing is sleep,' sighed Sancho Panza; 'it wraps a man round like a cloak'—an excellent example, by the way, of how to say a thing concretely: a Jargoneer would have said that 'among the beneficent qualities of sleep its capacity for withdrawing the human consciousness from the contemplation of immediate circumstances may perhaps be accounted not the least remarkable.' How vile a thing—shall we say?—is the abstract noun! It wraps a man's thoughts round like cotton wool.

Here is a pretty little nest of specimens, found in *The Times* newspaper by Messrs. H. W. and E. G. Fowler, authors of that capital little book *The King's English*:

One of the most important reforms mentioned in the rescript is the unification of the organization of judicial institutions and the guarantee for all the tribunals of the independence necessary for securing to all classes of the community equality before the law.

I do not dwell on the cacophony; but, to convey a straightforward piece of news, might not the Editor of *The Times* as well employ a man to write:

One of the most important reforms is that of the Courts, which need a uniform system and to be made independent. In this way only can men be assured that all are equal before the law.

I think he might.

A day or two ago the musical critic of the *Standard* wrote this:

MR. LAMOND IN BEETHOVEN

Mr. Frederick Lamond, the Scottish pianist, as an interpreter of Beethoven has few rivals. At his second recital of the composer's works at Bechstein Hall on Saturday afternoon he again displayed a complete sympathy and understanding of his material that extracted the very essence of aesthetic and musical value from each selection he undertook. The delightful intimacy of his playing and his unusual force of individual expression are invaluable assets, which, allied to his technical brilliancy, enable him to achieve an artistic triumph. The two lengthy Variations in E flat major (Op. 35) and in D major, the latter on the Turkish March from 'The Ruins of Athens,' when included in the same programme, require a master hand to provide continuity of interest. *To say that Mr. Lamond successfully avoided moments that might at times, in these works, have inclined to comparative disinterestedness, would be but a moderate way of expressing the remarkable fascination with which his versatile playing endowed them,* but *at the same time* two of the sonatas given included a similar form of composition, and no matter how intellectually brilliant may be the interpretation, the extravagant use of a certain mode is bound in time to become somewhat ineffective. In the Three Sonatas, the E major (Op. 109), the A major (Op. 2, No. 2), and the C major (Op. 111), Mr. Lamond signalized his perfect insight into the composer's varying moods.

Will you not agree with me that here is no writing, here is no prose, here is not even English, but merely a flux of words to the pen?

Here again is a string, a concatenation—say, rather, a tiara

—of gems of purest ray serene from the dark unfathomed caves of a Scottish newspaper:

The Chinese viewpoint, as indicated in this letter, may not be without interest to your readers, because it evidently is suggestive of more than an academic attempt to explain an unpleasant aspect of things which, if allowed to materialize, might suddenly culminate in disaster resembling the Chang-Sha riots. It also ventures to illustrate incidents having their inception in recent premature endeavours to accelerate the development of Protestant missions in China; but we would hope for the sake of the interests involved that what my correspondent describes as 'the irresponsible ruffian element' may be known by their various religious designations only within very restricted areas.

Well, the Chinese have given it up, poor fellows! and are asking the Christians—as to-day's newspapers inform us—to pray for them. Do you wonder? But that is, or was, the Chinese 'viewpoint'—and what a willow-pattern viewpoint! Observe its delicacy. It does not venture to interest or be interesting; merely to be 'not without interest.' But it does 'venture to illustrate incidents'—which, for a viewpoint, is brave enough: and this illustration 'is suggestive of more than an academic attempt to explain an unpleasant aspect of things which, if allowed to materialize, might suddenly culminate.' *What* materializes? The unpleasant aspect? or the things? Grammar says the 'things,' 'things which if allowed to materialize.' But things are materialized already, and as a condition of their being things. It must be the aspect then, that materializes. But, if so, it is also the aspect that culminates, and an aspect, however unpleasant, can hardly do that, or at worst cannot culminate in anything resembling the Chang-Sha riots. . . . I give it up.

Let us turn to another trick of Jargon: the trick of Elegant Variation, so rampant in the Sporting Press that there, without needing to attend these lectures, the undergraduate detects it for laughter:

Hayward and C. B. Fry now faced the bowling, which apparently had no terrors for the Surrey crack. The old Oxonian, however, took some time in settling to work. . . .

Yes, you all recognize it and laugh at it. But why do you practise it in your essays? An undergraduate brings me an essay on Byron. In an essay on Byron I expect, nay exact, that Byron shall be mentioned again and again. But my undergraduate has a blushing sense that to call Byron Byron twice on one page is indelicate. So Byron, after starting bravely as Byron, in the second sentence turns into 'that great but unequal poet' and thenceforward I have as much trouble with Byron as ever Telemachus with Proteus to hold and pin him back to his proper self. Half-way down the page he becomes 'the gloomy master of Newstead': overleaf he is reincarnated into 'the meteoric darling of society': and so proceeds through successive avatars—'this arch-rebel,' 'the author of *Childe Harold*,' 'the apostle of scorn,' 'the ex-Harrovian, proud, but abnormally sensitive of his club-foot,' 'the martyr of Missolonghi,' 'the pageant-monger of a bleeding heart.' Now this again is Jargon. It does not, as most Jargon does, come of laziness; but it comes of timidity, which is worse. In literature as in life he makes himself felt who not only calls a spade a spade but has the pluck to double spades and re-double.

For another rule—just as rough and ready, but just as useful: Train your suspicions to bristle up whenever you come upon 'as regards,' 'with regard to,' 'in respect of,' 'in connection with,' 'according as to whether,' and the like. They are all dodges of Jargon, circumlocutions for evading this or that simple statement: and I say that it is not enough to avoid them nine times out of ten, or nine-and-ninety times out of a hundred. You should *never* use them. Though I cannot admire his style, I admire the man who wrote to me, 'Re Tennyson—your remarks anent his *In Memoriam* make me sick': for though *re* is not a preposition of the first water, and 'anent' has enjoyed its day, the finish crowned the work. But here are a few specimens far, very far, worse:

The special difficulty in Professor Minocelsi's case [our old friend 'case' again] arose in *connection with* the view he holds *relative to* the historical value of the opening pages of Genesis.

That is Jargon. In prose, even taking the miserable sentence as it stands constructed, we should write 'the difficulty arose over the view he holds about the historical value,' etc.

From a popular novelist:

I was entirely indifferent *as to* the results of the game, caring nothing at all *as to* whether *I had losses or gains*—

Cut out the first 'as' in 'as to,' and the second 'as to' altogether, and the sentence begins to be prose—'I was entirely indifferent to the results of the game, caring nothing at all whether I had losses or gains.'

But why, like Dogberry, have 'had losses'? Why not simply 'lose.' Let us try again. 'I was entirely indifferent to the results of the game, caring nothing at all whether I won or lost.'

Still the sentence remains absurd: for the second clause but repeats the first without adding one jot. For if you care not at all whether you win or lose, you must be entirely indifferent to the results of the game. So why not say 'I was careless if I won or lost,' and have done with it?

A man of simple and charming character, he was fitly *associated with* the distinction of the Order of Merit.

I take this gem with some others from a collection made three years ago, by the *Oxford Magazine*; and I hope you admire it as one beyond price. 'He was associated with the distinction of the Order of Merit' means 'he was given the Order of Merit.' If the members of that Order make a society then he was associated with them; but you cannot associate a man with a distinction. The inventor of such fine writing would doubtless have answered Canning's Needy Knife-grinder with:

I associate thee with sixpence! I will see thee in another association first!

But let us close our *florilegium* and attempt to illustrate Jargon by the converse method of taking a famous piece of English (say Hamlet's soliloquy) and remoulding a few lines of it in this fashion:

To be, or the contrary? Whether the former or the latter be preferable would seem to admit of some difference of opinion; the answer in the present case being of an affirmative or of a negative character according as to whether one elects on the one hand to mentally suffer the disfavour of fortune, albeit in an extreme degree, or on the other to boldly envisage adverse conditions in the prospect of eventually bringing them to a conclusion. The condition of sleep is similar to, if not indistinguishable from, that of death; and with the addition of finality the former might be considered identical with the latter: so that in this connection it might be argued with regard to sleep that, could the addition be effected, a termination would be put to the endurance of a multiplicity of inconveniences, not to mention a number of downright evils incidental to our fallen humanity, and thus a consummation achieved of a most gratifying nature.

That is Jargon: and to write Jargon is to be perpetually shuffling around in the fog and cotton-wool of abstract terms; to be for ever hearkening, like Ibsen's Peer Gynt, to the voice of the Boyg exhorting you to circumvent the difficulty, to beat the air because it is easier than to flesh your sword in the thing. The first virtue, the touchstone of a masculine style, is its use of the active verb and the concrete noun. When you write in the active voice, 'They gave him a silver teapot,' you write as a man. When you write 'He was made the recipient of a silver teapot,' you write Jargon. But at the beginning set even higher store on the concrete noun. Somebody—I think it was FitzGerald—once posited the question 'What would have become of Christianity if Jeremy Bentham had had the writing of the Parables?' Without pursuing that dreadful inquiry I ask you to note how carefully the Parables—those exquisite short stories—speak only of 'things which you can touch and see'—'A sower went forth to sow,' 'The kingdom of heaven is like unto leaven, which a woman took'—and not the Parables only, but the Sermon on the Mount and almost every verse of the Gospel. The Gospel does not, like my young essayist, fear to repeat a word, if the word be good. The Gospel says, 'Render unto Caesar the things that are Caesar's'—not 'Render unto Caesar the things that appertain to that potentate.' The Gospel does not say 'Consider the growth of the lilies,' or even 'Consider how the lilies grow.' It says, 'Consider the lilies, how they grow.'

Or take Shakespeare. I wager you that no writer of English so constantly chooses the concrete word, in phrase after phrase forcing you to touch and see. No writer so insistently teaches the general through the particular. He does it even in *Venus and Adonis* (as Professor Wendell, of Harvard, pointed out in a brilliant little monograph on Shakespeare, published some few years ago). Read any page of *Venus and Adonis* side by side with any page of Marlowe's *Hero and Leander*, and you cannot but mark the contrast: in Shakespeare the definite, particular, visualized image, in Marlowe the beautiful generalization, the abstract term, the thing seen at a literary remove. Take the two openings, both of which start out with the sunrise. Marlowe begins:

> Now had the Morn espied her lover's steeds:
> Whereat she starts, puts on her purple weeds,
> And, red for anger that he stay'd so long,
> All headlong throws herself the clouds among.

Shakespeare wastes no words on Aurora and her feelings, but gets to his hero and to business without ado:

> Even as the sun with purple-colour'd face—

(You have the sun visualized at once),

> Even as the sun with purple-colour'd face
> Had ta'en his last leave of the weeping morn,
> Rose-cheek'd Adonis hied him to the chase;
> Hunting he loved, but love he laugh'd to scorn.

When Shakespeare has to describe a horse, mark how definite he is:

> Round-hoof'd, short-jointed, fetlocks shag and long,
> Broad breast, full eye, small head and nostril wide,
> High crest, short ears, straight legs and passing strong;
> Thin mane, thick tail, broad buttock, tender hide.

Or again, in a casual simile, how definite:

> Upon this promise did he raise his chin,
> Like a dive-dipper peering through a wave,
> Which, being look'd on, ducks as quickly in.

Or take, if you will, Marlowe's description of Hero's first meeting with Leander:

> It lies not in our power to love or hate,
> For will in us is over-ruled by fate . . .,

and set against it Shakespeare's description of Venus' last meeting with Adonis, as she came on him lying in his blood:

> Or as the snail whose tender horns being hit
> Shrinks backward in his shelly cave with pain,
> And there all smother'd up in shade doth sit,
> Long after fearing to creep forth again,
> So, at his bloody view—

I do not deny Marlowe's lines (if you will study the whole passage) to be lovely. You may even judge Shakespeare's to be crude by comparison. But you cannot help noting that whereas Marlowe steadily deals in abstract, nebulous terms, Shakespeare constantly uses concrete ones, which later on he learned to pack into such verse as:

> Sleep that knits up the ravell'd sleeve of care.

Is it unfair to instance Marlowe, who died young? Then let us take Webster for the comparison; Webster, a man of genius or of something very like it, and commonly praised by the critics for his mastery over definite, detailed, and what I may call *solidified sensation.* Let us take this admired passage from his *Duchess of Malfi*:

Ferdinand. How doth our sister Duchess bear herself
           In her imprisonment?
Bosola.   Nobly: I 'll describe her.
           She 's sad as one long used to 't, and she seems
           Rather to welcome the end of misery
           Than shun it: a behaviour so noble
           As gives a majesty to adversity.[1]
           You may discern the shape of loveliness
           More perfect in her tears than in her smiles;
           She will muse for hours together;[2] and her silence
           Methinks expresseth more than if she spake.

Now set against this the well-known passage from *Twelfth Night* where the Duke asks and Viola answers a question about someone unknown to him and invented by her—a mere phantasm, in short: yet note how much more definite is the language:

Viola. My father had a daughter lov'd a man;
       As it might be, perhaps, were I a woman,
       I should your lordship.
Duke.   And what 's her history?
Viola. A blank, my lord.   She never told her love,
       But let concealment, like a worm i' the bud,
       Feed on her damask cheek; she pined in thought,
       And with a green and yellow melancholy
       She sat like Patience on a monument
       Smiling at grief.   Was not this love indeed?

Observe (apart from the dramatic skill of it) how, when Shakespeare *has* to use the abstract noun 'concealment,' on an instant it turns into a visible worm 'feeding' on the visible

---

[1] Note the abstract terms.
[2] Here we first come on the concrete: and beautiful it is.

rose; how, having to use a second abstract word 'patience,' at once he solidifies it in tangible stone.

Turning to prose, you may easily assure yourselves that men who have written learnedly on the art agree in treating our maxim—to prefer the concrete term to the abstract, the particular to the general, the definite to the vague—as a canon of rhetoric. Whately has much to say on it. The late Mr. E. J. Payne, in one of his admirable prefaces to Burke (prefaces too little known and valued, as too often happens to scholarship hidden away in a schoolbook), illustrated the maxim by setting a passage from Burke's speech *On Conciliation with America* alongside a passage of like purport from Lord Brougham's *Inquiry into the Policy of the European Powers*. Here is the deadly parallel:

BURKE

In large bodies the circulation of power must be less vigorous at the extremities. Nature has said it. The Turk cannot govern Ægypt and Arabia and Curdistan as he governs Thrace; nor has he the same dominion in Crimea and Algiers which he has at Brusa and Smyrna. Despotism itself is obliged to truck and huckster. The Sultan gets such obedience as he can. He governs with a loose rein, that he may govern at all; and the whole of the force and vigour of his authority in his centre is derived from a prudent relaxation in all his borders.

BROUGHAM

In all the despotisms of the East, it has been observed that the farther any part of the empire is removed from the capital, the more do its inhabitants enjoy some sort of rights and privileges: the more inefficacious is the power of the monarch; and the more feeble and easily decayed is the organization of the government.

You perceive that Brougham has transferred Burke's thought to his own page; but will you not also perceive how pitiably, by dissolving Burke's vivid particulars into smooth generalities, he has enervated its hold on the mind?

'This particularizing style,' comments Mr. Payne, 'is the essence of Poetry; and in Prose it is impossible not to be struck with the energy it produces. Brougham's passage is excellent in its way: but it pales before the flashing lights of Burke's sentences.' The best instances of this energy of style, he adds, are to be found in the classical writers of the seventeenth century. 'When South says, "An Aristotle was but the rubbish of an Adam, and Athens but the rudiments of Paradise," he communicates more effectually the notion of the difference between the intellect of fallen and of unfallen humanity than in all the philosophy of his sermons put together.'

You may agree with me, or you may not, that South in this passage is expounding a fallacy; but you will agree with Mr. Payne and me that he utters it vividly.

Let me quote to you, as a final example of this vivid style of writing, a passage from Dr. John Donne far beyond and above anything that ever lay within South's compass:

The ashes of an Oak in the Chimney are no epitaph of that Oak, to tell me how high or how large that was; it tells me not what flocks it sheltered while it stood, nor what men it hurt when it fell. The dust of great persons' graves is speechless, too; it says nothing, it distinguishes nothing. As soon the dust of a wretch whom thou wouldest not, as of a prince whom thou couldest not look upon will trouble thine eyes if the wind blow it thither; and when a whirlewind hath blown the dust of the Churchyard into the Church, and the man sweeps out the dust of the Church into the Churchyard, who will undertake to sift those dusts again and to pronounce, This is the Patrician, this is the noble flowre [flour], and this the yeomanly, this the Plebeian bran? So is the death of *Iesabel* (*Iesabel* was a Queen) expressed. They shall not say *This is Iesabel*; not only not wonder that it is, nor pity that it should be; but they shall not say, they shall not know, *This is Iesabel*.

Carlyle noted of Goethe 'his emblematic intellect, his never-failing tendency to transform into *shape*, into *life*, the feeling that may dwell in him. Everything has form, has visual excellence: the poet's imagination bodies forth the forms of things unseen, and his pen turns them into shape.'

Consider this, Gentlemen, and maybe you will not hereafter set it down to my reproach that I wasted an hour of a May morning in a denunciation of Jargon, and in exhorting you upon a technical matter at first sight so trivial as the choice between abstract and definite words.

A lesson about writing your language may go deeper than language; for language (as in a former lecture I tried to preach to you) is your reason, your λόγος. So long as you prefer abstract words, which express other men's summarized concepts of things, to concrete ones which lie as near as can be reached to things themselves and are the first-hand material for your thoughts, you will remain, at the best, writers at second hand. If your language be Jargon, your intellect, if not your whole character, will almost certainly correspond. Where your mind should go straight, it will dodge: the difficulties it should approach with a fair front and grip with a firm hand it will be seeking to evade or circumvent. For the Style is the Man, and where a man's treasure is there his heart, and his brain, and his writing, will be also.

LIEUTENANT LAPENOTIÈRE

THE night-porter at the Admiralty had been sleeping in his chair. He was red-eyed and wore his livery coat buttoned at random. He grumbled to himself as he opened the great door.

He carried a glass-screened candle, and held it somewhat above the level of his forehead—which was protuberant and heavily pock-marked. Under the light he peered out at the visitor, who stood tall and stiff, with uniform overcoat buttoned to the chin, between the Ionic pillars of the portico.

'Who's there?'

'Lieutenant Lapenotière, of the *Pickle* schooner — with dispatches.'

'Dispatches?' echoed the night-porter. Out beyond the screen of masonry that shut off the Board of Admiralty's forecourt from Whitehall, one of the tired post-horses started blowing through its nostrils on this foggy night.

'From Admiral Collingwood—Mediterranean Fleet off Cadiz —sixteen days,' answered the visitor curtly. 'Is every one abed?'

'Admiral Collingwood? Why Admiral Collingwood?' The night-porter fell back a pace, opening the door a trifle wider. 'Good God, sir! You don't say as how——'

'You can fetch down a Secretary or someone, I hope?' said Lieutenant Lapenotière, quickly stepping past him into the long dim hall. 'My dispatches are of the first importance. I have posted up from Falmouth without halt but for relays.'

As the man closed the door, he heard his post-boy of the last relay slap one of the horses encouragingly before heading home to stable. The chaise wheels began to move on the cobbles.

'His Lordship himself will see you, sir. Of that I make no doubt,' twittered the night-porter, fumbling with the bolt. 'There was a terrible disturbance, back in July, when Captain Bettesworth arrived—not so late as this, to be sure, but towards midnight—and they waited till morning, to carry up the dispatches with his Lordship's chocolate. Thankful was I next day not to have been on duty at the time. . . . If you will follow me, sir——'

Lieutenant Lapenotière had turned instinctively towards a door on the right. It admitted to the Waiting Room, and there were few officers in the service who did not know—and only too well—that Chamber of Hope Deferred.

'No, sir . . . this way, if you please,' the night-porter corrected him, and opened a door on the left. 'The Captains' Room,' he announced, passing in and steering for the chimney-shelf, on which stood a pair of silver sconces each carrying three wax candles. These he took down, lit and replaced. 'Ah, sir! Many's the time I've showed Lord Nelson himself into this room, in the days when he was Sir Horatio, and even after. And you were sayin'——'

'I said nothing.'

The man moved to the door; but halted there and came back, as though in his own despite.

'I can't help it, sir. . . . Half a guinea he used to give me, regular. But the last time—and hard to believe 'twas little more than a month ago—he halts on his way out, and says he, searchin' awkward-like in his breeches' pocket with his left hand, "Ned," says he, "my old friend"—aye, sir, his old friend he called me—"Ned," says he, pulling out a handful o' gold, "my old friend," says he, "I'll compound with you for two guineas, this bein' the last time you may hold the door open for me, in or out. But you must pick 'em out," says he, spreadin' his blessed fingers with the gold in 'em: "for a man can't count money who's lost his right flapper." Those were his words, sir. "Old friend," he called me, in that way of his.'

Lieutenant Lapenotière pointed to his left arm.   Around the sleeve a black scarf was knotted.

'*Dead*, sir?'   The night-porter hushed his voice.

'Dead,' echoed Lieutenant Lapenotière, staring at the Turkey carpet, of which the six candles, gaining strength, barely illumined the pattern.   'Dead, at the top of victory; a great victory.   Go: fetch somebody down.'

The night-porter shuffled off.   Lieutenant Lapenotière, erect and sombre, cast a look around the apartment, into which he had never before been admitted.   The candles lit up a large painting —a queer bird's-eye view of Venice.   Other pictures, dark and bituminous, decorated the panelled walls—portraits of dead admirals, a sea-piece or two, some charts. . . . This was all he discerned out in the dim light; and in fact he scanned the walls, the furniture of the room, inattentively.   His stomach was fasting, his head light with rapid travel; above all, he had a sense of wonder that all this should be happening to *him*.   For, albeit a distinguished officer, he was a modest man, and by habit considered himself of no great importance.   Albeit a brave man, too, he shrank at the thought of the message he carried—a message to explode and shake millions of men in a confusion of wild joy or grief.

For about the tenth time in those sixteen days it seemed to burst and escape in an actual detonation, splitting his head— there, as he waited in the strange room where never a curtain stirred. . . . It was a trick his brain played him, repeating, echoing the awful explosion of the French seventy-four *Achille*, which had blown up towards the close of the battle.   When the ship was ablaze and sinking, his own crew had put off in boats to rescue the Frenchmen, at close risk of their own lives, for her loaded guns, as they grew red hot, went off at random among rescuers and rescued. . . .

As had happened before when he felt this queer shock, his mind travelled back and he seemed to hear the series of discharges running up at short intervals to the great catastrophe.

. . . To divert his thoughts, he turned to study the view of Venice above the chimneypiece . . . and on a sudden faced about again.

He had a sensation that someone was in the room—someone standing close behind him.

But no. . . . For the briefest instant his eyes rested on an indistinct shadow—his own perhaps, cast by the candle-light? Yet why should it lie lengthwise there, shaped like a coffin, on the dark polished table that occupied the middle of the room?

The answer was that it did not. Before he could rub his eyes it had gone. Moreover, he had turned to recognize a living being . . . and no living person was in the room, unless by chance (absurd supposition) one were hidden behind the dark red window curtains.

'Recognize' may seem a strange word to use; but here had lain the strangeness of the sensation—that the someone standing there was a friend, waiting to be greeted. It was with eagerness and a curious warmth of the heart that Lieutenant Lapenotière had faced about—upon nothing.

He continued to stare in a puzzled way at the window curtains, when a voice by the door said:

'Good evening!—or perhaps, to be correct, good morning! You are Mr.——'

'Lapenotière,' answered the Lieutenant, who had turned sharply. The voice—a gentleman's and pleasantly modulated —was not one he knew; nor did he recognize the speaker—a youngish, shrewd-looking man, dressed in civilian black, with knee-breeches. 'Lapenotière—of the *Pickle* schooner.'

'Yes, yes—the porter bungled your name badly, but I guessed. Lord Barham will see you personally. He is, in fact, dressing with all haste at this moment. . . . I am his private secretary,' explained the shrewd-looking gentleman in his quiet, business-like voice. 'Will you come with me upstairs?'

Lieutenant Lapenotière followed him. At the foot of the great staircase the Secretary turned.

'I may take it, sir, that we are not lightly disturbing his Lordship—who is an old man.'

'The news is of great moment, sir. Greater could scarcely be.'

The Secretary bent his head. As they went up the staircase Lieutenant Lapenotière looked back and caught sight of the night-porter in the middle of the hall, planted there and gazing up, following their ascent.

On the first-floor landing they were met by a truly ridiculous spectacle. There emerged from a doorway on the left of the wide corridor an old gentleman clad in night-cap, night-shirt, and bedroom slippers, buttoning his breeches and cursing vigorously; while close upon him followed a valet with dressing-gown on one arm, waistcoat and wig on the other, vainly striving to keep pace with his master's impatience.

'The braces, my lord—your Lordship has them fore-part behind, if I may suggest——'

'Damn the braces!' swore the old gentleman. 'Where is he? Hi, Tylney!' as he caught sight of the Secretary. 'Where are we to go? My room, I suppose?'

'The fire is out there, my lord. . . . 'Tis past three in the morning. But after sending word to awake you, I hunted round and by good luck found a plenty of promising embers in the Board Room grate. On top of these I've piled what remained of my own fire, and Dobson has set a lamp there——'

'You've been devilish quick, Tylney. Dressed like a buck you are, too!'

'Your Lordship's wig,' suggested the valet.

'Damn the wig!' Lord Barham snatched it and attempted to stick it on top of his night-cap, damned the night-cap, and, plucking it off, flung it to the man.

'I happened to be sitting up late, my lord, over the *Aeolus* papers,' said Mr. Secretary Tylney.

'Ha?' Then, to the valet: 'The dressing-gown there! Don't fumble! . . . So this is Captain——'

'Lieutenant, sir: Lapenotière, commanding the *Pickle* schooner.'

The Lieutenant saluted.

'From the Fleet, my lord—off Cadiz; or rather, off Cape Trafalgaro.'

He drew the sealed dispatch from an inner breast-pocket and handed it to the First Lord.

'Here, step into the Board Room. . . . Where the devil are my spectacles?' he demanded of the valet, who had sprung forward to hold open the door.

Evidently the Board Room had been but a few hours ago the scene of a large dinner-party. Glasses, dessert-plates, dishes of fruit, decanters empty and half empty, cumbered the great mahogany table as dead and wounded, guns and tumbrils, might a battlefield. Chairs stood askew; crumpled napkins lay as they had been dropped or tossed, some on the floor, others across the table between the dishes.

'Looks cosy, eh?' commented the First Lord. 'Maggs, set a screen around the fire, and look about for a decanter and some clean glasses.'

He drew a chair close to the reviving fire, and glanced at the cover of the dispatch before breaking its seal.

'Nelson's handwriting?' he asked. It was plain that his old eyes, unaided by spectacles, saw the superscription only as a blur.

'No, my lord: Admiral Collingwood's,' said Lieutenant Lapenotière, inclining his head.

Old Lord Barham looked up sharply. His wig set awry, he made a ridiculous figure in his hastily donned garments. Yet he did not lack dignity.

'Why Collingwood?' he asked, his fingers breaking the seal. 'God! you don't tell me——'

'Lord Nelson is dead, sir.'

'Dead—dead? . . . Here, Tylney—you read what it says.

Dead? . . . No, damme, let the captain tell his tale. Briefly, sir.'

'Briefly, sir—Lord Nelson had word of Admiral Villeneuve coming out of the Straits, and engaged the combined fleets off Cape Trafalgaro. They were in single line, roughly; and he bore down in two columns, and cut off their van under Dumanoir. This was at dawn or thereabouts, and by five o'clock the enemy was destroyed.'

'How many prizes?'

'I cannot say precisely, my lord. The word went, when I was signalled aboard the Vice-Admiral's flagship, that either fifteen or sixteen had struck. My own men were engaged, at the time, in rescuing the crew of a French seventy-four that had blown up; and I was too busy to count, had counting been possible. One or two of my officers maintain to me that our gains were higher. But the dispatch will tell, doubtless.'

'Aye, to be sure. . . . Read, Tylney. Don't sit their clearing your throat, but read, man alive!' And yet it appeared that while the Secretary was willing enough to read, the First Lord had no capacity, as yet, to listen. Into the very first sentence he broke with:

'No, wait a minute. "Dead," d' ye say? . . . My God! . . . Lieutenant, pour yourself a glass of wine and tell us first how it happened.'

Lieutenant Lapenotière could not tell very clearly. He had twice been summoned to board the *Royal Sovereign*—the first time to receive the command to hold himself ready. It was then that, coming alongside the great ship, he had read in all the officers' faces an anxiety hard to reconcile with the evident tokens of victory around them. At once it had occurred to him that the Admiral had fallen, and he put the question to one of the lieutenants—to be told that Lord Nelson had indeed been mortally wounded and could not live long; but that he must be alive yet, and conscious, since the *Victory* was still signalling orders to the Fleet.

'I think, my lord,' said he, 'that Admiral Collingwood must have been doubtful, just then, what responsibility had fallen upon him, or how soon it might fall. He had sent for me to "stand by" so to speak. He was good enough to tell me the news as it had reached him——'

Here Lieutenant Lapenotière, obeying the order to fill his glass, let spill some of the wine on the table. The sight of the dark trickle on the mahogany touched some nerve of the brain: he saw it widen into a pool of blood, from which, as they picked up a shattered seaman and bore him below, a lazy stream crept across the deck of the flagship towards the scuppers. He moved his feet, as he had moved them then, to be out of the way of it: but recovered himself in another moment and went on:

'He told me, my lord, that the *Victory* after passing under the *Bucentaure's* stern, and so raking her that she was put out of action, or almost, fell alongside the *Redoutable*. There was a long swell running, with next to no wind, and the two ships could hardly have cleared had they tried. At any rate, they hooked, and it was then a question which could hammer the harder. The Frenchman had filled his tops with sharp-shooters, and from one of these—the mizen-top, I believe—a musket-ball struck down the Admiral. He was walking at the time to and fro on a sort of gangway he had caused to be planked over his cabin skylight, between the wheel and the ladder-way. . . . Admiral Collingwood believed it had happened about half-past one . . .'

'Sit down, man, and drink your wine,' commanded the First Lord as the dispatch-bearer swayed with a sudden faintness.

'It is nothing, my lord——'

But it must have been a real swoon, or something very like it: for he recovered to find himself lying in an arm-chair. He heard the Secretary's voice reading steadily on and on. . . . Also they must have given him wine, for he awoke to feel the warmth of it in his veins and coursing about his heart. But he was weak yet, and for the moment well content to lie still and listen.

Resting there and listening, he was aware of two sensations that alternated within him, chasing each other in and out of his consciousness. He felt all the while that he, John Richards Lapenotière, a junior officer in His Majesty's service, was assisting in one of the most momentous events in his country's history; and alone in the room with these two men, he felt it as he had never begun to feel it amid the smoke and roar of the actual battle. He had seen the dead hero but half a dozen times in his life: he had never been honoured by a word from him: but like every other naval officer, he had come to look up to Nelson as to the splendid particular star among commanders. *There* was greatness: *there* was that which lifted men to such deeds as write man's name across the firmament! And, strange to say, Lieutenant Lapenotière recognized something of it in this queer old man, in dressing-gown and ill-fitting wig, who took snuff and interrupted now with a curse and anon with a 'Bravo!' as the Secretary read. He was absurd: but he was no common man, this Lord Barham. He had something of the ineffable aura of greatness.

But in the Lieutenant's brain, across this serious, even awful sense of the moment and of its meaning, there played a curious secondary sense that the moment was not—that what was happening before his eyes had either happened before or was happening in some vacuum in which past, present, future, and the ordinary divisions of time had lost their bearings. The great twenty-four-hour clock at the end of the Board Room, ticking on and on while the Secretary read, wore an unfamiliar face. . . . Yes, time had gone wrong, somehow: and the events of the passage home to Falmouth, of the journey up to the doors of the Admiralty, though they ran on a chain, had no intervals to be measured by a clock, but followed one another like pictures on a wall. He saw the long, indigo-coloured swell thrusting the broken ships shoreward. He felt the wind freshening as it southered and he left the Fleet behind: he watched their many lanterns as they sank out of sight, then the glow of flares by the light of which dead-tired men were repairing damages, cutting away wreckage. His ship was wallowing heavily now, with the gale after her—and now dawn was breaking clean and glorious on the swell off Lizard Point. A Mount's Bay lugger had spied them, and, lying in wait, had sheered up close alongside, her crew bawling for news. He had not forbidden his men to call it back, and he could see the fellows' faces now, as it reached them from the speaking-trumpet: 'Great victory—twenty taken or sunk—Admiral Nelson killed!' They had guessed something, noting the *Pickle's* ensign at half-mast: yet as they took in the purport of the last three words, these honest fishermen had turned and stared at one another; and without one answering word, the lugger had been headed straight back to the mainland.

So it had been at Falmouth. A ship entering port has a thousand eyes upon her, and the *Pickle's* errand could not be hidden. The news seemed in some mysterious way to have spread even before he stepped ashore there on the Market Strand. A small crowd had collected, and, as he passed through it, many doffed their hats. There was no cheering at all—no, not for this the most glorious victory of the war—outshining even the Nile or Howe's First of June.

He had set his face as he walked to the inn. But the news had flown before him, and fresh crowds gathered to watch him off. The post-boys knew . . . and *they* told the post-boys at the next stage, and the next—Bodmin and Plymouth—not to mention the boatmen at Torpoint Ferry. But the country-side did not know: nor the labourers gathering in cider apples heaped under Devon apple-trees, nor, next day, the sportsmen banging off guns at the partridges around Salisbury. The slow, jolly life of England on either side of the high road turned leisurely as a wagon-wheel on its axle, while between hedge-rows, past farm hamlets, church-towers and through the cobbled

streets of market towns, he had sped and rattled with Collingwood's dispatch in his sealed case. The news had reached
London with him. His last post-boys had carried it to their
stables, and from stable to tavern. To-morrow—to-day, rather
—in an hour or two—all the bells of London would be ringing
—or tolling! . . .

'He's as tired as a dog,' said the voice of the Secretary.
'Seems almost a shame to waken him.'

The Lieutenant opened his eyes and jumped to his feet
with an apology. Lord Barham had gone, and the Secretary
hard by was speaking to the night-porter, who bent over the
fire, raking it with a poker. The hands of the Queen Anne
clock indicated a quarter to six.

'The First Lord would like to talk with you . . . later in
the day,' said Mr. Tylney gravely, smiling a little these last
words. He himself was white and haggard. 'He suggested
the early afternoon, say half-past two. That will give you
time for a round sleep. . . . You might leave me the name
of your hotel, in case he should wish to send for you before
that hour.'

'"The Swan with Two Necks," Lad Lane, Cheapside,' said
Lieutenant Lapenotière.

He knew little of London, and gave the name of the hostelry
at which, many years ago, he had alighted from a west country
coach with his box and midshipman's kit. . . . A moment later
he found himself wondering if it still existed as a house of
entertainment. Well, he must go and seek it.

The Secretary shook hands with him, smiling wanly.

'Few men, sir, have been privileged to carry such news as
you have brought us to-night.'

'And I went to sleep after delivering it,' said Lieutenant
Lapenotière, smiling back.

The night-porter escorted him to the hall, and opened the
great door for him. In the portico he bade the honest man
good night, and stood for a moment, mapping out in his mind

K

his way to 'The Swan with Two Necks.' He shivered slightly, after his nap, in the chill of the approaching dawn.

As the door closed behind him he was aware of a light shining, out beyond the screen of the fore-court, and again a horse blew through its nostrils on the raw air.

'Lord!' thought the Lieutenant. 'That fool of a post-boy cannot have mistaken me and waited all this time!'

He hurried out into Whitehall. Sure enough a chaise was drawn up there, and a post-boy stood by the near lamp, conning a scrap of paper by the light of it. No, it was a different chaise, and a different post-boy. He wore the buff and black, whereas the other had worn the blue and white. Yet he stepped forward confidently, and with something of a smile.

'Lieutenant Lapenotière?' he asked, reaching back and holding up his paper to the lamp to make sure of the syllables.

'That is my name,' said the amazed Lieutenant.

'I was ordered here—five forty-five—to drive you down to Merton.'

'To Merton?' echoed Lieutenant Lapenotière, his hand going to his pocket. The post-boy's smile, or so much as could be seen of it by the edge of the lamp, grew more knowing.

'I ask no questions, sir.'

'But—but who ordered you?'

The post-boy did not observe, or disregarded, his bewilderment.

'A Briton's a Briton, sir, I hope? I ask no questions, knowing my place. . . . But if so be as you were to tell me there's been a great victory——' He paused on this.

'Well, my man, you're right so far, and no harm in telling you.'

'Aye,' chirruped the post-boy. 'When the maid called me up with the order, and said as how *he* and no other had called with it——'

'He?'

The fellow nodded.

'She knew him at once, from his portraits. Who wouldn't?
With his right sleeve pinned across so. . . . And, said I : "Then
there 's been a real victory. Never would you see him back,
unless." And I was right, sir !' he concluded triumphantly.

'Let me see that piece of paper.'

'You 'll let me have it back, sir ?—for a memento,' the post-
boy pleaded. Lieutenant Lapenotière took it from him — a
plain half-sheet of note-paper roughly folded. On it was
scribbled in pencil, back-handwise, 'Lt. Lapenotière. Admiralty,
Whitehall. At 6.30 a.m., not later. For Merton, Surrey.'

He folded the paper very slowly, and handed it back to the
post-boy.

'Very well, then. For Merton.'

. . . . . .

The house lay but a very little distance beyond Wimbledon.
Its blinds were drawn as Lieutenant Lapenotière alighted from
the chaise and went up to the modest porch.

His hand was on the bell-pull. But some pressure checked
him as he was on the point of ringing. He determined to wait
for a while and turned away towards the garden.

The dawn had just broken ; two or three birds were singing.
It did not surprise—at any rate, it did not frighten—Lieutenant
Lapenotière at all, when, turning into a short pleached alley,
he looked along it and saw *him* advancing.

—Yes, *him*, with the pinned sleeve, the noble, seamed, eager
face. They met as friends. . . . In later years the Lieutenant
could never remember a word that passed, if any passed at all.
He was inclined to think that they met and walked together in
complete silence, for many minutes. Yet he ever maintained
that they walked as two friends whose thoughts hold converse
without need of words. He was not terrified at all. He ever
insisted, on the contrary, that there, in the cold of the breaking
day, his heart was light and warm as though flooded with first
love—not troubled by it, as youth in first love is wont to be—

but bathed in it; he, the ardent young officer, bathed in a glow of affection, ennobling, exalting him, making him free of a brotherhood he had never guessed.

He used also, in telling the story, to scandalize the clergyman of his parish by quoting the evangelists, and especially St. John's narrative of Mary Magdalen at the sepulchre.

For the door of the house opened at length; and a beautiful woman, scarred by knowledge of the world, came down the alley, slowly, unaware of him. Then (said he), as she approached, his hand went up to his pocket for the private letter he carried, and the shade at his side left him to face her in the daylight.

VOICES ON THE BANK

The May Races at Cambridge, 1913

VENATOR. Good Master, did you not promise me fish in this river?

PISCATOR. Methinks, Scholar, we tarried too long at the *Pike and Eel*. But since the fish have given over biting, what say you to stretching our limbs beneath yonder hawthorn?—where, while the many sweet-smelling flowers hold a creditable contention with the gas-works, I will teach you the best way to angle for the chavender or chub. . . . But what comes here? A boat! marry—and rowed by eight personable young men, with a ninth looking the other way and steering.

A COACH. *Ea*—sy, all!

PISCATOR. Well met, honest sir! . . . Will you tell me, who are these lads whose labours you compassionate?

COACH. (*Shortly.*) L.M.B.C.

PISCATOR. (*Puzzled.*) L.M.B.C.? . . . Ah! a clavender, or club! And this crowd that I see approaching?

COACH. [*Yet more shortly.*] Usual May binge. Forward, all! Look here, and remember your legs when you're paddling.

YOUNG AMERICAN LADY. [*First as usual.*] Say, poppa?

AMERICAN FATHER. [*Second as usual.*] He refers to their limbs, Sadie: they're going to *paddle*, didn't you hear? . . . Pleased to make your acquaintance, professor. [*To Piscator.*] This, sir, is my first visit to Oxford.

SADIE. [*Correcting.*] Cambridge, poppa.

AMERICAN FATHER. Sure!

> *Chorus of Aunts and Cousins approaching on towpath as other boats come down-stream.*

STROPHE.	Yon's
	John's.
ANTISTROPHE.	These
	Are Caius.
FULL CHORUS.	And *that's*
	CAT's!

SOCRATES. But it seems to me, Adeimantus, that the best boat on these occasions is the boat that goes fastest?

ADEIMANTUS. It seems so, indeed.

SOCRATES. And the boat which goes, or is propelled, faster than another boat, must necessarily overtake that other boat.

ADEIMANTUS. Most probably.

SOCRATES. But is not the 'head' boat, as you call it, presumably the fastest of all?

ADEIMANTUS. That is presumed, at least, until the contrary be proved.

SOCRATES. Then it would follow, O friend! that in a well-ordered state, having taken the gods into council and made ready our guns, and charged for admission and what-not, we should annually start our best boat at the bottom of the river, that so it might cover itself with glory by making the greatest possible number of bumps.

[He goes off to argue with a policeman.

STRANGER IN MOTOR LAUNCH. [*Drawing alongside the bank to Piscator.*] I hope, sir, we do not disturb your fishing? The fact is, we have left our tea-basket behind. Could you direct us to the nearest provender where we might get some pub— or, I should rather say, to the nearest pub, where we can get some provender?

PISCATOR. If, sir, you mean gravender or grub——

Aunts and Cousins interrupting :

STROPHE.	These
	Are Caius :
ANTISTROPHE.	There
	Goes Clare :
FULL CHORUS.	And *that's*
	Cat's!

PRAXINOË. My! what a crush!

GORGO. And the bicycles—don't run me down, my good man! They oughtn't to be allowed.

PRAXINOË. My new hat will be crushed to a jelly, at this rate. *Do* let us go on! [*She addresses a* STRANGER.] Could you tell us, sir, where we can get across to Ditton?

THE STRANGER. [*Who happens to be a Professor of Icelandic.*] Fiskr gekk oss at óskom eitrs sem ver haeofum leithath.

PRAXINOË. Thank you kindly, sir.

THE STRANGER. Gud-guthragud! Don't mention it.

PRAXINOË. [*Moving on.*] As I was saying, dear, parlour-maids you can replace, but a cook——

GORGO. [*Catching her arm.*] Do but look, though, at this boat approaching in the Lydian mode. How majestically it moves and how realistically the crew swing to and fro the while! One would say they were practising for the Royal Barge.

PRAXINOË. Why, have you not heard? They do say His Majesty is coming next year, and this is the King's boat. They will be in plenty of time, by the look of it.

GORGO. You don't say so! [*Sighs.*] And this year we have only Mr. Chesterton: though, to be sure, they are widening the Chesterton Road at the lower end. Is that necessary?

PRAXINOË. It is a compliment, at any rate, dear: and we in Cambridge like to be on the safe side.

GORGO. Yes, but look at that poor dear gentleman—such a fine figure too!—in his shirt-sleeves, trailing his coat behind him. Oughtn't we to draw his attention to it?

PRAXINOË. No, dear. That's the Professor of Archaeology, and it's his way of keeping cool.

A Rag-boat comes by, the crew singing :

> I wish I was in Dixie,
> Where the hens lay eggs in the stra-aw . . .
> [*Or words to that effect.*]

AMERICAN PARENT. [*Slowly.*] 'Might be better, now you mention it.

STILL, SMALL VOICE OF PUBLIC OPINION. And so say all of us.
[*Rag-boat moves off, to annoy somebody else.*]

A CAMBRIDGE POET:

> The sort of grass they grow at Grassy
> Is esculent but hardly classy:
>
> The sort of grass they grow at Ditton
> Is classier, but vile to sit on.
>
> Beware the men who work the grinds!
> They 'll pelt you with banana rinds. . . .

A PROFESSOR OF JARGON. [*Instructively.*] The races at Oxford and at Cambridge, while partaking in general of a similar character, are rowed under somewhat diverse conditions respectively. In the case of the former University the boats in all cases are of a uniform nature: in that of the latter a distinction is observed, those of the first division being rowed in boats of carvel construction, while the second is identified rather with the clinker build, in which the strakes have an overlapping tendency. Cases have occurred in which a so-called sandwich boat, having won its way to superior rank, finds itself matched against boats appertaining to that rank which owing to their construction are *ipso facto* of a speedier character. In that case the C.U.B.C. . . .

A Band plays :

> The flowers that bloom in the spring, tra, la,
> Have nothing to do with the CASE. . . .

DR. JOHNSON. [*Lifting his hat.*] Sir! Yours *per varios casus.* . . . The proficiency of this present age, as it is built on the slow labours of the past, should by privilege be elevated above concourse of the pert and upstart. Let the dogs sweat! . . . I remember at Oxford the young gentlemen of Christ Church challenged us of Pembroke to a rowing-match, and that I contributed somewhat to the losing of it half-way by drawing in my oar and honestly saying that I was tired.

BOSWELL. That, sir, showed great independence of spirit.

DR. JOHNSON. No, sir: stark insensibility!

> [*Noise of distant guns: sporadic explosion of suffragette bombs. Everybody cries:* 'They're off!' *except a Don in a Researcher's Hat, who says* 'Votes for Women!' *instead.*

GORGO. Are they really bumping, Praxinoë?

PRAXINOË. How silly of you, dear! Can't you *hear* them.

A LADY'S VOICE. [*Says equably but distinctly.*] And so, as the Colonel ab-solutely refused to extend his leave, dear Reggie had to go back. They are *very* strict in the Rifles; and he being only a savender——

> [*Noise of pistols. Several dull concussions are heard as the boats change places. Crowd shouts delirious: even the unoccupied houses take fire.*

A PHOTOGRAPHER. [*As two boats go by with a foot of daylight between them.*] One moment, gentlemen—please! If you could manage to smile——

> [*Tumultuous cheering.* 'Well rowed, all!' 'Well rowed, Hall!' 'Well rowed, everybody in general and Hall in particular!'

GORGO. And in this hot weather, too! [*As Lady Margaret's rows by.*] *Look* at those poor dears!—positively scarlet!

Chorus of Aunts and Cousins
(Tune: 'Johnny Crow's Garden')

So we 've done the Colleges, and done the Mays,
We 've lunched *seriatim* off the same mayonnaise;
But before we go our several ways,
Let 's all join together in a hearty vote of praise——

HERODOTUS, OF HALICARNASSUS. [*Button-holing a Pro-Proctor.*] Can you inform me, sir, in which direction this river happens to be flowing at the present moment? For amid much that is happening of equal or greater importance, this alone I am unable to detect.

*K

PRO-PROCTOR. You have arrived, nevertheless, in a fortunate hour, O stranger. For on 361 days of the year it cannot be confidently asserted to flow in any direction, albeit some say one thing and some another. But on these four days alone, under the propulsion you have witnessed, it makes a definite move in the direction of Ely, and even (so report goes) may ultimately reach the sea. There are indeed who assert that for this purpose and no other our May festival was instituted.

THE POET.

> Th' inhabitants of local inns
> Commit unmentionable sins:
>
> The Ordinances of Long Reach
> Are mostly honoured in the breach.
>
> The plants that in Glass Houses mate
> Cryptogamously propagate:
>
> Beneath the Bridge rot the remains
> Of old unhappy railway trains:
>
> But when we reach the *Pike and Eel*,
> O let me kneel! O let me kneel!

NOT HERE, O APOLLO!

A CHRISTMAS STORY HEARD AT MIDSUMMER

WE sat and talked in the Vicarage garden overlooking Mount's Bay. The long summer day lingered out its departure, although the full moon was up and already touching with a faint radiance the towers on St. Michael's Mount—'the guarded Mount'—that rested as though at anchor in the silver-grey offing. The land-breeze had died down with sunset; the Atlantic lay smooth as a lake below us, and melted, league upon league, without horizon into the grey of night. Between the Vicar's fuchsia-bushes we looked down on it, we three— the Vicar, the Senior Tutor, and I.

I think the twilit hour exactly accorded with our mood, and it did not need the scent of the Vicar's ten-week stocks, wafted across the garden, to touch a nerve of memory. For it was twenty years since we had last sat in this place and talked, and the summer night seemed to be laden with tranquil thoughts, with friendship and old regard. . . . Twenty years ago I had been an undergraduate, and had made one of a reading-party under the Senior Tutor, who annually in the Long Vacation brought down two or three fourth-year men to bathe and boat and read Plato with him, for no pay but their friendship: and, generation after generation, we young men had been made welcome in this garden by the Vicar, who happened to be an old member of our College and (as in time I came to see) delighted to renew his youth in ours. There had been daughters, too, in the old days. . . . But they had married, and the Vicarage nest was empty long since.

The Senior Tutor, too, had given up work and retired upon his Fellowship. But every summer found him back at his old haunts; and still every summer brought a reading-party to the Cove, in conduct now of a brisk Junior Fellow, who had read

267

with me in our time and achieved a 'first.' In short, things at the Cove were pretty much the same after twenty years, barring that a small colony of painters had descended upon it and made it their home. With them the undergraduates had naturally and quickly made friends, and the result was a cricket match—a grand Two-days' Cricket Match. They were all extremely serious about it, and the Oxford party—at their wits' end, no doubt, to make up a team against the Artists— had bethought themselves of me, who dwelt at the other end of the Duchy. They had written—they had even sent a two-page telegram—to me, who had not handled a bat for more years than I cared to count. It is delicious to be flattered by youth, especially for gifts you never possessed or possess no longer. I yielded and came. The season was Midsummer, or a little after; the weather golden and glorious.

We had drawn stumps after the first day's play, and the evening was to be wound up with a sing-song in the great tent erected—a marvel to the 'Covers,' or native fishermen—on the cricket-field. But I no longer take kindly to such enter-tainments; and so, after a bathe and a quiet dinner at the inn, it came into my mind to take a stroll up the hill and along the cliffs, and pay an evening call on the old Vicar, wondering if he would remember me.

I found him in his garden. The Senior Tutor was there too —'the grave man, nicknamed Adam'—and the Vicar's wife, seated in a bee-hive straw chair, knitting. So we four talked happily for a while, until she left us on pretence that the dew was falling; and with that, as I have said, a wonderful silence possessed the garden fragrant with memories and the night-scent of flowers. . . .

Then I let fall the word that led to the Vicar's story. In old rambles, after long mornings spent with Plato, my eyes (by mirage, no doubt) had always found something Greek in the curves and colour of this coast; or rather, had felt the want of it. What that something was I could hardly have defined: but the feeling was always with me. It was as if at each bend of the shore I expected to find a temple with pillars, or a column crowning the next promontory; or, where the coast-track wound down to the little haven, to happen on a votive tablet erected to Poseidon or to 'Helen's brothers, lucent stars'; nay, to meet with Odysseus' fisherman carrying an oar on his shoulder, or even, in an amphitheatre of the cliffs, to surprise Apollo himself and the Nine seated on a green plat whence a waterfall gushed down the coomb to the sandy beach. . . . This evening on my way along the cliffs—perhaps because I had spent a day bathing in sunshine in the company of white-flannelled youths—the old sensation had returned to haunt me. I spoke of it.

'"Not here, O Apollo——"' murmured the Senior Tutor.

'You quote against your own scepticism,' said I. 'The coast is right enough; it *is*

> Where Helicon breaks down
> In cliff to the sea.

It was made to invite the authentic gods—only the gods never found it out.'

'Did they not?' asked the Vicar quietly. The question took us a little aback, and after a pause his next words administered another small shock. 'One never knows,' he said, 'when, or how near, the gods have passed. One may be listening to us in this garden, to-night. . . . As for the Greeks——'

'Yes, yes, we were talking of the Greeks,' the Senior Tutor (a convinced agnostic) put in hastily. 'If we leave out Pytheas, no Greeks ever visited Cornwall. They are as mythical hereabouts as'—he hesitated, seeking a comparison—'as the Cornish wreckers; and *they* never existed outside of pious story-books.'

Said the Vicar, rising from his garden-chair: 'I accept the omen. Wait a moment, you two.' He left us and went across the dim lawn to the house, whence by and by he returned bearing a book under his arm, and in his hand a candle, which he set down unlit upon the wicker table among the coffee-cups.

'I am going,' he said, 'to tell you something which, a few years ago, I should have scrupled to tell. With all deference to your opinions, my dear Dick, I doubt if they quite allow you to understand the clergy's horror of chancing a heresy; indeed, I doubt if either of you quite guess what a bridle a man comes to wear who preaches a hundred sermons or so every year to a rural parish, knowing that nine-tenths of his discourse will assuredly be lost, while at any point in the whole of it he may be fatally misunderstood. . . . Yet as a man nears his end he feels an increasing desire to be honest, neither professing more than he knows, nor hiding any small article of knowledge as inexpedient to the Faith. The Faith, he begins to see, can take care of itself: for him, it is important to await his marching-orders with a clean breast. Eh, Dick?'

The Senior Tutor took his pipe from his mouth and nodded slowly.

'But what is your book?' he asked.

'My Parish Register. Its entries cover the years from 1660 to 1827. Luckily I had borrowed it from the vestry box, and it was safe on my shelf in the Vicarage on the Christmas Eve of 1870, the night when the church took fire. That was in my second year as incumbent, and before ever you knew these parts.'

'By six months,' said the Senior Tutor. 'I first visited the Cove in July 1871, and you were then beginning to clear the ruins. All the village talk still ran on the fire, with speculations on the cause of it.'

'The cause,' said the Vicar, 'will never be known. I may say that pretty confidently, having spent more time in guessing than will ever be spent by another man. . . . But since you never saw the old church as it stood, you never saw the Heathen Lovers in the south aisle.'

'Who were they?'

'They were a group of statuary, and a very strange one: executed, as I first believed, in some kind of wax—but, pushing my researches (for the thing interested me), I found the material to be a white soapstone that crops out here and there in the crevices of our serpentine. Indeed, I know to a foot the spot from which the sculptor took it, close on two hundred years ago.'

'It was of no great age, then?'

'No: and yet it bore all the marks of an immense age. For to begin with, it had stood five-and-twenty years in this very garden, exposed to all weathers, and the steatite (as they call it) is of all substances the most friable—is, in fact, the stuff used by tailors under the name of French chalk. Again, when, in 1719, my predecessor, old Vicar Hichens, removed it to the church and set it in the south aisle—or, at any rate, when he died and ceased to protect it—the young men of the parish took to using it for a hatstand, and also to carving their own and their sweethearts' names upon it during sermon-time. The figures of the sculpture were two; a youth and a maid, recumbent, and naked but for a web of drapery flung across their middles; and they lay on a roughly carved rock, over which the girl's locks as well as the drapery were made to hang limp, as though dripping with water. . . . One thing more I must tell you, risking derision; that to my ignorance the sculpture proclaimed its age less by these signs of weather and rough usage than by the simplicity of its design, its proportions, the chastity (there's no other word) of the two figures. They were classical, my dear Dick—what was left of them; Greek and of the best period.'

The Senior Tutor lit a fresh pipe, and by the flare of the match I saw his eyes twinkling.

'Praxiteles,' he jerked out, between the puffs, 'and in the age of Kneller! But proceed, my friend.'

'And do you wait, my scoffer!' The Vicar borrowed the box of matches, lit the candle—which held a steady flame in the still evening air—opened the book, and laid it on his knee while he adjusted his spectacles. 'The story is here, entered on a separate leaf of the Register and signed by Vicar Hichens's own hand. With your leave—for it is brief—I am going to read it through to you. The entry is headed:

'Concerning a group of Statuary now in the S. aisle of Lezardew Pish Church : set there by me in witness of God's Providence in operation, as of the corruption of man's heart, and for a warning to sinners to amend their ways.

'In the year 1694, being the first of my vicariate, there lived in this Parish as hind to the farmer of Vellancoose a young man exceeding comely and tall of stature, of whom (when I came to ask) the people could tell me only that his name was Luke, and that as a child he had been cast ashore from a foreign ship; they said, a Portugal ship. [But the Portugals have swart complexions and are less than ordinary tall, whereas this youth was light-coloured and only brown by sunburn.] Nor could he tell me anything when I questioned him concerning his haveage;[1] which I did upon report that he was courting my housemaiden Grace Pascoe, an honest good girl, whom I was loath to see waste herself upon an unworthy husband. Upon inquiry I could not discover this Luke to be any way unworthy, saving that he was a nameless man and a foreigner and a backward church-goer. He told me with much simplicity that he could not remember to have had any parents; that Farmer Lowry had brought him up from the time he was shipwrecked and ever treated him kindly; and that, as for church-going, he had thought little about it, but would amend in this matter if it would give me pleasure. Which I thought a strange answer. When I went on to hint at his inclination for Grace Pascoe, he confused me by asking, with a look very straight and good-natured, if the girl had ever spoken to me on the matter; to which I was forced to answer that she had not. So he smiled, and I could not further press him.

'Yet in my mind they would have made a good match; for the girl too was passing well featured, and this Luke had notable gifts. He could read and write. The farmer spoke well of him, saying: "He

---

[1] Lineage, descent.

has rewarded me many times over. Since his coming, thanks to the Lord, my farm prospers: and in particular he has a wonderful way with the beasts. Cattle or sheep, fowls, dogs, the wild things even, come to him almost without a call." He had also (the farmer told me) a wonderful knack of taking clay or mud and moulding it with his hands to the likeness of living creatures, of all sorts and sizes. In the kitchen by the great fire he would work at these images by hours together, to the marvel of every one: but when the image was made, after a little while he always destroyed it; nor was it ever begged by any one for a gift, there being a belief that, being fashioned by more than a man's skill, such things could only bring ill-luck to the possessors of them.

'For months then I heard no more of Grace Pascoe's lover: nor (though he now came every Sunday to church) did I ever see looks pass between the Vicarage pew (where she sat) and the Vellancoose pew (where he). But at the end of the year she came to me and told me she had given her word to a young farmer of Goldsithney, John Magor by name. In a worldly way this was a far better match for her than to take a nameless and landless man. Nor knew I anything against John Magor beyond some stray wildness natural to youth. He came of clean blood. He was handsome, almost as the other; tall, broad of chest, a prize-winner at wrestling-matches; and of an age when a good wife is usually a man's salvation.

'I called their banns, and in due time married them. On the wedding-day, after the ceremony, I returned from church to find the young man Luke awaiting me by my house door; who very civilly desired me to walk over to Vellancoose with him, which I did. There, taking me aside to an unused linhay, he showed me the sculpture, telling me (who could not conceal my admiration) that he had meant it for John and Grace Magor (as she now was) for a wedding-gift, but that the young woman had cried against it as immodest and, besides, unlucky. On the first count I could understand her rejecting such a gift; for the folk of these parts know nothing of statuary and count all nakedness immodest. Indeed, I wondered that the bridegroom had not taken Luke's freedom in ill part, and I said so: to which he answered, smiling, that no man ever quarrelled with him or could quarrel. "And now, sir," he went on, "my apprenticeship is up, and I am going on a long journey. Since you find my

group pleasing I would beg you to accept it, or—if you had liefer
—to keep it for me until I come again, as some day I shall." "I do
not wonder," said I, "at your wish to leave Lezardew Parish for the
world where, as I augur, great fortune awaits you." He smiled
again at this and said that, touching his future, he had neither any
hope nor any fear: and again he pressed me to accept the statuary.
For a time I demurred, and in the end made it a condition that he
altered the faces somewhat, concealing the likeness to John and
Grace Magor: and to this he consented. "Yet," said he, "it will
be the truer likeness when the time comes."

'He was gone on the morrow by daybreak, and late that afternoon
the farmer brought me the statuary in his hay-wagon. I had it set
in the garden by the great filbert-tree, and there it has stood for near
five-and-twenty years. (I ought to say that he had kept his promise
of altering the faces, and thereby to my thinking had defaced their
beauty: but beneath this defacement I still traced their first likeness.)

'Now to speak of the originals. My way lying seldom by Goldsithney, I saw little of John and Grace Magor during the next few
years, and nothing at all of them after they had left Goldsithney
(their fortunes not prospering) and rented a smaller farm on the coast
southward, below Rosudgeon: but what news came to me was ever
of the same tenor. Their marriage had brought neither children
nor other blessings. There were frequent quarrels, and the man had
yielded to drinking; the woman, too, it was reported. She, that
had been so trim a serving-maid, was become a slut with a foul
tongue. They were cruelly poor with it all; for money does not
always stick to unclean hands. I write all this to my reproach as
well as to theirs, for albeit they dwelt in another parish it had been
my Christian duty to seek them out. I did not, and I was greatly
to blame.

'To pass over many years and come to the 2nd of December last
(1718). That night, about 11 o'clock, I sat in my library reading.
It was blowing hard without, the wind W.N.W.; but I had forgotten
the gale in my book, when a sound, as it were a distant outcry of
many voices, fetched me to unbar the shutters and open the window
to listen. The sound, whatever it was, had died away: I heard but
the wind roaring and the surf on the beaches along the Bay: and I
was closing the window again when, close at hand, a man's voice

called to me to open the front door. I went out to the hall, where a lamp stood, and opened to him. The light showed me the young man Luke, on whom I had not set eyes for these four-and-twenty years: nor, amazed and perturbed as I was, did it occur to me as marvellous that he had not aged a day. "There is a wreck," said he, "in the Porth below here; and you, sir, are concerned in it. Will you fetch a lantern and come with me?" He put this as a question, but in his tone was a command: and when I brought the lantern he took it from me and led the way. We struck across the Home Parc southward, thence across Gew Down and the Leazes, and I knew that he was making for the track which leads down to the sea by Prah Sands. At the entry of the track he took off his coat and wrapped the lantern in it, though just there its light would have been most useful, or so I thought. But he led the way easily, and I followed with scarce a stumble. "We shall not need it," he said; "for see, there they are!" pointing to a small light that moved on the sands below us. "But who are they?" I asked. He strode down ahead of me, making swiftly for the light, and coming upon them in the noise of the gale we surprised a man and a woman, who at first cowered before us and then would have cast down their light and run. But my companion, unwrapping the lantern, held it high and so that the light shone on their faces. They were John Magor and his wife Grace.

'Then I, remembering what cry of shipwrecked souls had reached to my library in the Vicarage, and well guessing what work these wretches had been at, lifted my voice to accuse them. But the young man Luke stepped between us, and said he to them gently: "Come, and I will show what you seek." He went before us for maybe two hundred yards to the northern end of the beach, they behind him quaking, and I shepherding them in my righteous wrath. "Behold you," said he, and again lifted the lantern over a rock dark with seaweed (and yet the weed shone in the light)—"Behold you, what you have wrecked."

'On their backs along the flat of the rock lay two naked bodies, of a youth and a maid, half clasped one to another. He handed me the lantern for a better look, and in the rays of it the two wretches peered forward as if drawn against their will. I cannot well say if they or I first perceived the miracle; that these corpses, as they lay in the posture, so bore the very likeness of the two lovers on my sculptured slab. But I remember that, as John and Grace Magor screamed back and clung to me, and as by the commotion of them clutching at my knees the lantern fell and was extinguished, I heard the young man Luke say: "Yourselves, yourselves!'

'I called to him to pick up the lantern; but he did not answer, and the two clinging wretches encumbered me. After a long while the clouds broke and the moon shone through them; and where he had stood there was no one. Also the slab of rock was dark, and the two drowned corpses had vanished with him. I pointed to it; but there was no tinder-box at hand to light the lantern again, and in the bitter weather until the dawn the two clung about me, confessing and rehearsing their sins.

'I have great hopes that they are brought to a better way of life; and because (repent they never so much) no one is any longer likely to recognize in these penitents the originals upon whom it was moulded these many years ago, I am determined to move the statuary to a place in the S. aisle of our parish church, as a memorial, the moral whereof I have leave of John and Grace Magor to declare to all the parish. I choose to defer making it public, in tenderness, while they live: for all things point as yet to the permanent saving of their souls. But, as in the course of nature I shall predecease them, I set the record here in the Parish Register, as its best place.

'(*Signed*) MALACHI HICHENS, B.D.

'21st *Jan.*, 1719.'

'And is that all?' I asked.

'Yes and no,' said the Vicar, closing the book. 'It is all that Mr. Hichens has left to help us: and you may or may not connect with it what I am going to relate of my own experience. . . . The old church, as you know, was destroyed by fire in the morning hours of Christmas Day 1870. Throughout Christmas Eve and for a great part of the night it had been snowing, but the day broke brilliantly, on a sky without wind or cloud; and never have my eyes seen anything so terribly beautiful— ay, so sublime—as the sight which met them at the lych-gate. The old spire—which served as a sea-mark for the fishermen, and was kept regularly whitewashed that it might be the more conspicuous—glittered in the morning sunshine from base to summit, as though matching its whiteness against that of the snow-laden elms: and in this frame of pure silverwork, burning without noise and with scarcely any smoke—this by reason of the excessive dryness of the woodwork—the church stood one glowing vault of fire.   There was indeed so little smoke that at the first alarm, looking from my bedroom window, I had been incredulous; and still I wondered rather than believed, staring into this furnace wherein every pillar, nook, seat, or text on the wall was distinctly visible, the south windows being burnt out and the great door thrown open and on fire.

'There was no entrance possible here, or indeed anywhere: but, being half distraught, I ran around to the small door of the north aisle.   This, too, was on fire—or, rather, was already consumed; and you will say that I must have been wholly distraught when I tell you what I saw, looking in through the aperture through which it would have been death to pass. I saw *him*.'

'You saw the young man Luke?' I asked, as he paused, inviting a word.

'He was standing by the stone figures within the porch. . . . And they crumbled—crumbled before my eyes in the awful heat.   But he stood scatheless.   He was young and comely; the hair of his head was not singed.   He was as one of the three that walked in the midst of Nebuchadnezzar's furnace. . . . When the stone slab was crumbled to a handful of dust, he moved up the aisle and was gone. . . . That is all: but, as you accept your friend for a truthful man, explain, O sceptic!'

And again there fell a silence in the garden.

O MATRE PULCHRA

NEVER shaded
    Lovelier hand more lovely-ardent
Eyes than hers, my Ditton puntress,
Resting on her pole and gazing
    Up the waterway.

On the cushions
I her guardian loll recumbent,
While the transitory tumult
—Shouts and shots and straining galleys—
    Tears me past, to fade.

Eve composes
Soon again and smoothes a mirror
Low to which the swallow dips her
Daulian wound.—Yet Sweet-and-twenty
    Shades her lovely eyes.

Tense her brow as
Dian's bow!   The leading galley
Holds a youth, and ah! were wishes
Arrows, they would shoot him safely
    Past the Pike and Eel!

Fair-and-twenty!
Feebly middle age expostu-
lates, in sorrow not in anger,
'Here's but water in the teapot!
    I demanded Tea!'

Fair-and-twenty!
Four-and-twenty years agone as
Lovely hand as lovely eyebrow
Shaded, and your mother trembled
    As you tremble now.

Trust me truly;
Ere he passed, the race was over;
All was over bar the shouting . . .
Happy he shall steer you happy
    Through the dance to-night:

You triumphing
In his prowess tread the pavement.
So your mother, so your father
To *Die guten alten Zeiten*
    Heard the violins

Throb and tremble;
Heard their passion wake the nested
Bird and thrill a waking garden,
Whence, of three, one stole and sadly
    Left the twain to bliss . . .

Moor we softly—
Cross the haunted, scented meadows
Thither where her secret prelude,
Darkling in the grove of Jesus,
    Throats the nightingale,

As the Danube
Gurgling through a waltz of Strauss's
Brims a heart no longer hopeful,
Minds it of the merry, merry
    Days when it was young.

TO THE FRONT FROM THE BACKS

1915

MY DEAR DICK,
. . . I must now try to answer your questions about
'the old place,' as you call it with true Cambridge affection and
true Cambridge accuracy. 'What is it like in these days?'
Well, I will start by annoying you. It is still very much like
Oxford, and like no other place in the world.

At the same time it is curiously unlike Cambridge, even unlike the Cambridge of last term. We came up in October to
find the streets desolate indeed. The good soldiers who had
swarmed in upon town and college in August—a commander
of cavalry occupied my rooms; too busy, I hope, to curse the
dull contents of my shelves—had all departed for France. Nay,
already many of them slept in French earth. They had left an
historical piece of plate to the high table; and some photo-
graphic groups in Stearn's window. A head of a house halted
me before one of these groups and ticked off the cheerful reso-
lute faces of those fallen, by the Marne or the Aisne, since he
had entertained them a few weeks ago. In one row of a dozen
West Yorks he could find two survivors only.

These had come and gone like a summer cloud: and October
in Cambridge might have passed for the Long Vacation turned
chilly. In the courts and around the Backs the gardeners were
sweeping up the leaves, as ever; but no men passed on their way
to lecture 'with the wind in their gowns.' The University, one
heard, was 'functioning' still: the bell of Great St. Mary's still,
on degree days, suggested the hand of the ancient mother
smitten upon her chest mourning for her fee-paying children,
because they were not. In college one seldom met, never
heard, an undergraduate. A few would gather to hall, the

most of them in their O.T.C. uniforms after a strenuous afternoon out by Madingley. The scholar read grace with an unwonted reverence. 'Sic Deus in nobis et nos maneamus in Illo'—and we took our seats to a meal decently frugal. As I looked down the hall, this one undergraduates' table reminded me of a road in the west country I had followed a few days before, with the telegraph running beside it and on the wires the swallows gathering, discussing flight: the fire burning variously in each separate heart, but with the same call, to cross the Channel. . . . We in Combination Room talked of our depleted numbers as a matter for pride (very creditably too —if you understand college finance). One, who had been lecturing at the Examination Schools, likened the theatre there to the Pool of Bethesda.

I have to talk of it lightly, my dear Dick, because your letters, so constantly and undefeatedly cheerful, impose this tone. You must not suppose, however, that we do not think—and think all the while—of what the young are doing and suffering for us. . . . Well, thus it was in the Michaelmas Term; a suspended Cambridge; for which we were, on the whole, pretty well prepared. The Belgian refugees from their universities had found harbour with us. On the King's and Clare cricket ground lines of hospital sheds were growing up almost as silently as the Temple of Solomon in Bishop Heber's Newdigate; and the almost incomparable turf was selling (I am told) to some fortunate purchaser for incredible sums.

A notice-board at the entrance of Burrell's Walk advertised the 1st Eastern General Hospital, and on any afternoon you might see the Red Cross motor ambulances bringing in the wounded. A whole block of King's had been handed over to house the nurses. But here, as at the Research Hospital, the work had been so quietly and thoroughly organized that you had to go out of your way to find anything strange. For the rest, Cambridge life had merely been arrested. Youth had, for once, refused to revisit her with autumn, and was busy

elsewhere.   We, whom age or infirmity obliged to abide, laid our
account with the war and settled down to the dull streets, the
short unbrightened days, evenings without talk, the long nights
on depopulated staircases, our own heavy thoughts.   You will
think it queer, but the feeling of the change first broke on me
one day when, stepping incautiously off the pavement into the
road-way on this side of Magdalene Bridge, I recollected myself,
cast the old horrified glance behind, and found not a single
motor-cycle, not even a bicycle, in sight.

We returned in January to a vastly different Cambridge.
She had become a garrison town. . . .

At this point I was proposing to start a description of it all:
of the lines of artillery horses beside the Trumpington Road,
Adams Road, Jesus ditch; of the mud (but that is indescribable)
in which the poor brutes stand fetlock deep, each mournfully
chewing his neighbour's head-rope.   (You reported that head-
ropes wore out at a terrible rate in your brigade; and now I
understand, as you will understand, why the price of bitter aloes
has become prohibitive in Cambridge—not that I want to purchase any); of the mud on Midsummer Common, and the worse
mud on the road to the rifle butts, where the M.A. warriors
of the C.U.O.T.C. drill and improve their waists, though they
may never serve their country; of Whewell's Buildings occupied
by the Monmouths, who take it for an elementary school, and
Archdeacon C—— for its chairman of managers, faithful to
his post; of—most wonderful spectacle of all—the crowds of
Tommies navigating the Backs in Canadian canoes and other
bounding shallops.   The Welsh—for it is the Welsh Division
(Territorials) we have here—would seem to have lost some of
their celebrated skill with the coracle. . . .   I was going, I say,
to attempt a picture of all this, when the happy thought seized
me that I could convey it far more vividly by sending you a set
of photographs.   So forth I fared, and to my amazement was
told that no one had taken any photographs.   'It was a notion,
certainly: but, so far as was known, it had not occurred to any

one.' 'The omission should be repaired. . . . No, the military authorities would not refuse leave.' I hope the University Librarian will make a note of this. A bound volume of photographs, complete as his well-known enthusiasm can make it, would be at small cost a κτῆμα ἐς ἀεί, priceless in times to come, when the familiar streams flow again, *antiquos subterlabentia muros*; priceless as the Mercurius Aulicus or Aubrey's Gossip concerning Oxford in the Civil War.

The curfew no longer tolls the knell of parting day. It is not permitted. But when dusk has fallen and the Mayor and Corporation leave the world to darkness and to me, I walk in the Fellows' Garden, carefully hiding the ardent tip of my cigarette (lest it should attract a Zeppelin), and think upon those streams. . . . For who doubts they will flow again? 'Not the same.' . . . No, my dear Dick, I sincerely trust 'not the same!' In your last letter you observed brightly that 'it looks as if, before long, folks would be scrapping in every corner of this blessed planet.' Well, our wise men are already at it here, in corners of the *Cambridge Review*. They are concerned to regulate what is going to happen when the war is over. Well, I do not much believe in cooking an eagle before you have shot him. But suppose him shot. . . . Do these my reverend co-seniors actually believe that it will be left to us to put things right? What, to us?—who in our generation, in England and France and Germany, have allowed this thing to come to pass? No, my dear child: that responsibility, with the honour of it, must be yours. It is a heavy one (as a while ago we should have said distrustfully, but now say in solicitude, for the time it will steal from the natural joys of youth): but we left you youngsters to wipe up the mess, and you must restore the garden in which we shall walk humbly with you,

—ancients, musical at close of day.

You will come back, and those who return to the University will claim for youth a far larger measure of freedom, as they

have earned it ten times over.   But as you have always agreed
with me that Oxford and Cambridge are two of the loveliest
things in the world—each, but for the other, peerless—I can
trust you to deal reverently with this one; for she is your
mother, after all.

'THE TEMPEST'

'THE TEMPEST' is the first play in the First Folio of 1623; and this, for aught anybody knows—indeed almost certainly—was its first appearance in print. The Folio, at any rate, supplies our only text. Chronologically it is almost the last, if not the very last, that Shakespeare wrote. The Folio editors, Heminge and Condell, old friends of his and fellow-actors, may have given it pride of place for this pious reason, or possibly because it had won a striking success at Court when presented there in the winter of 1612–13, among many enter-tainments that graced the betrothal and nuptials of the Princess Elizabeth with the Prince Palatine Elector. John Heminge, as foreman of Shakespeare's old company, was paid by Lord Harrington, Treasurer of the Chamber of King James I, 'upon the councells warrant, dated at Whitehall xx° die Mai, 1613' his bill for producing 'foureteene severall playes' in the course of these festivities which were numerous and so costly as to embarrass His Majesty's exchequer. The entry (Vertue MSS.) specifies these plays, and *The Tempest* comes sixth on the list.

It is pleasant and certainly not impossible to believe that, as Heminge and Condell have preserved it for us, this play was written-up expressly for the betrothal—and presented on 27th December 1612, the betrothal night—of the incomparable Queen of Hearts whose name in story is Elizabeth of Bohemia,

> design'd
> Th' eclipse and glory of her kind.

For 'beauty vanishes, beauty passes,' but the charm of this woman still fascinates the imagination almost as in her life-time it won and compelled the souls of men to champion her sorrowful fortunes. That it did this—that it laid on the nobler

spirits of her time a spell potent to extravagance and yet so
finely apportioned as almost to serve us now for a test and
gauge of their nobility—no reader of early seventeenth-century
biography will deny.　The evidence is no less frequent than
startling.　It would almost seem that no 'gentleman' could
come within the aura but he knelt to Elizabeth of Bohemia, her
sworn knight: that either he followed thenceforth to the last
extremity, proud only to serve, or, called away, he departed
as one who had looked upon a vision which changed all the
values of life, who had beheld a kingdom of the soul in which
self and this world were well lost for a dream.　We may see
this strange conversion in Wotton; we may trace it in the
careers of Donne, of Dudley Carleton and (with a postscript of
morose disillusion) Lord Herbert of Cherbury.　We may read
it, youthfully and romantically expressed in this well-authenti-
cated story:

A company of young men of the Middle Temple met together for
supper; and when the wine went round the first man rose, and
holding a cup in one hand and a sword in the other, pledged the health
of the distressed Princess, the Lady Elizabeth; and having drunk, he
kissed the sword, and laying hand upon it, took a solemn oath to live
and die in her service.　His ardour kindled the whole company.
They all rose, and from one to another the cup and sword went
round till each had taken the pledge.

We may see this exuberance carried into steady practice by
Lord Craven, a Lord Mayor's son, who, having poured blood
and money in her service, laid his last wealth at her feet to provide her a stately refuge and a home.　Through all the story
she—granddaughter of Mary of Scotland, mother of Rupert
of the Rhine—rides reckless, feckless, spendthrift, somehow
ineffably great; conquering all hearts near her, that

> 　　　　—Enamour'd do wish so they might
> 　　　　But enjoy such a sight,
> 　　That they still were to run by her side
> 　　Thoro' swords, thoro' seas, whither she would ride,

lifting all those gallant hearts to ride with her, for a desperate cause, despising low ends, ignoble gain; to ride with her down and nobly over the last lost edge of the world.

We may take it almost for a certainty that—in whatever previous form or forms presented—this play *as we have it* was the play enacted at Court to grace the Princess Elizabeth's betrothal. No argument from internal evidence conflicts with this. Gonzalo's description of his ideal Commonwealth (ii. i. 146 *et seqq.*) comes out of Florio's translation of Montaigne, first published in 1603: and the name 'Caliban' suggests the essay 'Of the Canniballes' from which Gonzalo derived his wisdom. Ben Jonson most likely has a side thrust at *The Tempest* (and at *The Winter's Tale*) in his Introduction to *Bartholomew Fair* (acted in October 1614): 'If there be never a Servant-monster i' the *Fayre*, who can help it, he sayes: nor a nest of *Antiques*? Hee is loth to make nature afraid in his *Playes*, like those that beget *Tales, Tempests,* and such like *Drolleries*.' Further, we can easily allow the play to contain many passages suggested by the misadventure of the Virginian voyage of 1609, when a fleet of nine ships and five hundred colonists under command of Sir Thomas Gates and Sir George Somers was dispersed by a gale and the flagship, the *Sea-Adventure*, went ashore on the coast of Bermudas, her crew wonderfully escaping. That Shakespeare used at least one or two out of several pamphlets dealing with this wreck (by Silvester Jourdain, by William Strachey, and by 'advise and direction of the Councell of Virginia'—to mention no others) stands above question. But nothing of this is inconsistent either with the play's having been presented by the King's Players on Hallowmas, 1611, or with its having been recast and 'revived' for the festivities of the Princess Elizabeth's betrothal.

Nothing forbids our imagination to repeople the banqueting house and recall this bride, this paragon, to seat her in the front rank of the ghostly audience: to watch her, a moment before the curtain opens, a little reclined, her jewelled wrists, like Cassiopeia's, laid along the arms of her chair; or still to watch her as the play proceeds and she—affianced and, by admission, in love with her bridegroom—leans forward with parted lips to follow the loves of Ferdinand and Miranda.

Those who must always be searching for a 'source' of every plot of Shakespeare's (as though he could invent nothing!) will be disappointed in *The Tempest*. Thomas Warton (or rather, Warton misunderstood by Malone) started one false hare by a note in his *History of English Poetry*, vol. iii (1781), that he had been 'informed by the late Mr. Collins of Chichester'— that is, Collins the poet—that Shakespeare's *Tempest* was formed on a 'favourite romance,' *Aurelio and Isabella*, printed in 1586 (one volume) in Italian, French, and English, and again in 1588 in Italian, Spanish, French, and English; the Spanish of Flores being the original. But Collins's mind was darkening towards madness at the time: and *Aurelio*, when found, contained nothing in common with *The Tempest*. Others have followed the clue of a German play, *Die Schöne Sidea*, written by one Jacob Ayrer, a notary of Nuremberg, who died in 1605. There is a magician in this drama who is also a prince—Prince Ludolph: he has a demon or familiar spirit: he has an only daughter too. The son of Ludolph's enemy becomes his prisoner, his sword being held in sheath by the magician's art. Later, the young man is forced to bear logs for Ludolph's daughter. She falls in love with him, and all ends happily. The resemblances to *The Tempest* are obvious: and that there was some actual thread of connection appears the likelier when we note that 'mountain' and 'silver,' two names of the spirit hounds which Prospero and Ariel set upon the 'foul conspiracy' (iv. i. 256), occur in an invocation of Prince Ludolph's in the German play. It may be that Shakespeare used Ayrer's play; for the English Comedians were at Nuremberg in 1604, where they may have seen *Die Schöne Sidea*, to bring home the story. But it is just as likely that Ayrer's is a version of one they took from England to Germany. And, after all, what fairy-tale or folk-tale is commoner, the world over, than that which combines a witch, or wizard, an only daughter, an adventurous prince caught and bound to carry logs, etc., with pity and confederate love to counteract the spell and bring all right in the end?

When we turn to Shakespeare's handling of this story, we first admire that which all must admire, the enchantment wherein he clothes it, the poetic feeling wherewith he suffuses it. Magic and music meet in *The Tempest* and are so wedded that none can put them asunder.

> That was the chirp of Ariel
> You heard, as overhead it flew;
> The farther going, more to dwell
> And wing our green to wed our blue;
> But whether note of joy, or knell,
> Not his own Father-singer knew;
> Nor yet can any mortal tell,
> Save only that it shivers through;
> The breast of us, a sounded shell,
> The blood of us a lighted dew.

But when we have paid homage to all this, on second thoughts we may find the firm anatomy beneath the robe—the mere craftsmanship—scarcely less wonderful. For *The Tempest* accepts and masters an extreme technical difficulty. No one can react Shakespeare's later plays in a block without recognizing that the subject which constantly engaged his mind towards the close of life was *Reconciliation*, with pardon and atonement for the sins or mistakes of one generation in the young love of the children and in their promise. This is the true theme o *Pericles, Cymbeline, The Winter's Tale, The Tempest*, successively. But the process of reconciliation—especially when effected through the appeal of sons and daughters—is naturally a slow one, and therefore extremely difficult to translate into drama, which handles 'the two hours' traffic of our stage' and therefore must almost necessarily rely on the piling of circumstance and character upon one crisis and its swiftest possible

L

resolution. In attempting to condense such 'romantic' stories of reconciliation as he had in his mind, Shakespeare was in fact taking up the glove thrown down by Sir Philip Sidney in his pretty mockery of bad playwrights.

Now of time they are much more liberall. For ordinary it is that two young Princes fall in love. After many traverses she is got with child, delivered of a faire boy, he is lost, groweth a man, falls in love, and is ready to get another child, and all this in two hours' space; which how absurd it is in sence, even sence may imagine, and Arte hath taught, and all ancient examples justified.

The time supposed to be occupied by the action of *Pericles* is about sixteen years. *The Winter's Tale* has an interval of about sixteen years between its third and fourth acts. The chronology of *Cymbeline* is baffling and in places absurd; yet it must cover many months. The once famous Unity of Time is certainly no 'law': but it *is* a grace of drama. And after falling back on such makeshifts as ancient Gower in *Pericles* and Father Time himself in *The Winter's Tale*, of a sudden in *The Tempest* our artist triumphantly 'does the trick.' The whole action of the play, with the whole tale of ancient wrong un- folded, the whole company of injuring and injured gathered into a knot, the whole machinery of revenge converted to for- giveness—all this is managed in about three hours of imagined time, or scarcely more than the time of its actual representation on the stage.

The *clou* of this feat of stagecraft lies in the famous *protasis* of the second scene, where Prospero so naturally unfolds all the preliminaries to his daughter. For exquisite use of *protasis* this may be compared with the second scene of *Hamlet*. Many critics have praised it: but we hope that by a few simple stage directions we have managed to suggest a beauty which the most of them have missed—the abstracted mind of Miranda as she listens with a kind of *feyness* to the story so important on which her father, having chosen and prepared the moment, so im-

patiently insists.   It is, to our thinking, most necessary to
realize that Miranda is all the while less absorbed by this
important story than by the sea, out of which her fairy prince
is surely coming, though his coming be scarcely surmised as
yet.   We shall not understand this play, lacking to understand
how young impulse forestalls and takes charge, outrunning our
magician's deliberate contrivance.   When Ferdinand and
Miranda actually meet

> At the first sight
> They have changed eyes.

For another point, not over-subtle, which the critics would
seem to have overlooked: It is clear to us that the enchantment
of the island purposely makes its appearance correspond with
the several natures of the shipwrecked men who come ashore.
Gonzalo, the 'honest old councillor,' finds 'our garments rather
new dyed than stained with salt water.'   But Antonio and
Sebastian cannot see them so.   To him 'how lush and lusty
the grass looks! how green!'   Antonio, the total jaundiced
villain, sees it 'tawny,' the half-corrupt Sebastian detects 'an
eye of green in 't'—and so on throughout.   Gonzalo indeed
is one of Shakespeare's minor triumphs.   He is not left—as
Antigonus, his counterpart in *The Winter's Tale* was left—to
perish after his kind deed.   It was done long ago: but he survives, still in his character of loyal-hearted servant, still active
in loyalty, which in its turn advances the action of the play.
Is it not a delicate stroke that, when Miranda first hears the story
of her casting away, of all the shipwrecked company near at
hand, though she knows it not, this old councillor is the man
she (being heart-whole yet) most desires to see?   So in the end
he is not only one of the company that awakes Miranda's cry of

> O wonder!
> How many goodly creatures are there here!
> How beauteous mankind is!   O brave new world,
> That has such people in 't!

But for him is reserved the final blessing,

> Look down you gods,
> And on this couple drop a blesséd crown!

so unmistakably echoing Hermione's invocation in *The Winter's Tale*,

> You gods, look down,
> And from your sacred vials pour your graces
> Upon my daughter's head!

Caliban has been over-philosophized by the critics (with Renan and Browning to support them). The truth would seem to be that Shakespeare, like a true demiurge, had a tendency to love his creations, and none the less those whom he shows us as gross, carnal, earthy. If it be not unfair to drag Falstaff into the comparison, then even as none of us can help loving Falstaff, so few of us—shall we say?—if Caliban came fawning about our legs, would be disinclined to pat him on the head with a 'Good dog! Good monster!' Our sense of justice, too, helps this instinct: for, after all, Caliban has the right of it when he snarls,

> I must eat my dinner.
> This island's mine, by Sycorax my mother,
> Which thou tak'st from me:

—and we must remind ourselves that in 1611 and thereabouts this dispossession of the aborigine was a very present event, however feebly it might touch the imagination, to trouble the conscience, of our valorous circumnavigators and colonists. Shakespeare, as we conceive him, differed from Rousseau in most ways, and not least in immunity from any temptation to construct an ideal portrait of the 'noble savage.' But no man can be catholic as Shakespeare was without being fair, and so (as Hazlitt noted) while the nature of Caliban is the essence of grossness, there is not a particle of vulgarity in it. Few have remarked how admirably significant as a set-off to Caliban is Stephano, type of his predestined conquerors, the tarry, racy,

absolute British seaman, staggering through this isle of magic
with a bottle, staring, hiccoughing back against Ariel's invisible
harp:

The master, the swabber, the bos'n and I . . .

in extremity to be counted on for the fine confused last word of
our mercantile marine, 'Every man shift for all the rest.' It is
hard to over-estimate the solidarity of Stephano and the 'value'
it gives to the whole fairy picture.

Many critics have lost their hearts to Miranda and no one has
excelled Coleridge's praise in delicacy of insight. Let us add
but this—Shakespeare has contrived to mould her of frank
goodness and yet present her as fascinating, captivating by
touches so noble that one can hardly conceive the part adequately rendered save by a princess in real life as noble as she
—an Elizabeth of Bohemia, for example. She moves to her
appointed happiness with fairies and music about her; but she
sees no fairies, sings no song, simply walks straight as the
dictate of her heart directs, and, so walking, steps straight
beyond the magic her father has woven. This incomparable
play contains nothing more subtly simple than her unconscious,
quite fearless, outstripping of all Prospero's premeditated art.
He has drawn around the island a magic circle as that which
Ferdinand cannot step across. The play, like *A Midsummer
Night's Dream*, plainly celebrates a betrothal and marches to the
fruition of marriage joy. There is much music in both: in
both the fairies are made abetters. But whereas in *A Midsummer Night's Dream* the fairies were Warwickshire elves,
playing their pranks anarchically, at their own sweet fancy, to
befool mortals, the more rarefied spirits of *The Tempest* obey,
under threat, a mortal's compulsion. But Miranda is for the
world, gently but fearlessly; on the primal instinct that makes
homes, builds and populates cities, recreates and rules the race.
Some have objected that this play does not develop; that within
Prospero's charmed circle, for the space of three hours, all stands

still. In truth a great deal happens, and the ease of its happening is a trick of most cunning preparation.

Who is Prospero? Is he perchance Destiny itself; the master-spirit that has brooded invisible and moved in the deep waters of the greater tragedies, and now comes to shore on a lost nest of the main to sun himself; laying by his robe of darkness to play, at his great ease, one last trick before following the way of the old gods? Is he (as Campbell the poet was the first to suggest) Shakespeare himself, in this last of his plays breaking his wand and drowning his book 'deeper than did ever plummet sound'? The lights in the banqueting house are out: the Princess Elizabeth is dust: and as for the island conjured out of the sea for a night's entertainment:

> From that day forth the Isle has been
> By wandering sailors never seen.

Ariel has nestled to the bat's back and slid away following summer or else 'following darkness like a dream.' But still this play abides, after three hundred years, eloquent of Shakespeare's slow sun-setting through dream after dream of reconciliation; forcing tears, not by 'pity and terror' but by sheer beauty; with a royal sense of the world, how it passes away, with a catch at the heart surmising hope in what is to come. And still the sense is royal: we feel that we are greater than we know. So in the surge of our emotion, as on the surges rounding Prospero's island, is blown a spray, a mist. Actually it dims our eyes: and as we brush it away, there rides on it a rainbow; and its colours are chastened wisdom, wistful charity; with forgiveness, tender ruth for all men and women growing older, and perennial trust in young love.

AN ADDRESS AT THE OPENING OF
KEATS HOUSE, HAMPSTEAD

May 9th, 1925

Mr. Mayor, Ladies and Gentlemen,

I

BECAUSE this occasion is, for 'a little clan,' a monumental one: and because the memory of Keats seems to me in some danger of being over-laboured just now: I shall try to recall you to some of those simplicities which always best become a simple monument.

But first let me congratulate you, Mr. Mayor, upon the occasion:

> There may be cities that refuse
> To their own child his honours due.

But Hampstead is not one of these. Always in Hampstead, going by its walks or on the edge of its heath, any man of letters must be haunted by thoughts which seem to him almost memories: of a great literary tradition merging still—please Heaven!—into a great literary future. Still of the town, yet not of the town—but fragrant, on the country's rim—these ghosts, thoughts, memories, accompany or tread close on the musing mind. A statue or an obelisk were an offence to the *genius loci*; which pursues rather along the shade of a paling or under a tree that in a time before ours once

> in a drear-nighted December

showed a part of its frosted branches to the lamp-light, or in spring budded to arrest a poet's step on your pathways or broke into leaf and held, on this verge over London, an immortal nightingale captive.

II

And so, sir, it is surely to Hampstead's credit, that you have chosen, instead of obelisk or statue, to preserve this simple house in perpetuity for a memorial of John Keats. In this house he agonized with love and despondency: on a bed in a chamber above us he read in a drop of blood his death warrant: from the door beyond that passage he departed on his last journey—brave and hopeless as Henry Fielding on *his* last voyage. In the dim garden outside yonder pane of glass he heard the Hampstead nightingale and translated that song 'not born for death' into human speech as near to heavenly as any we can dare to snatch out of this transitory life to call immortal. . . . Still on the edge and shadow of that trench untimely digged we invoke that genius, fleet as water, 'writ in water.'

> Still are thy pleasant voices, thy nightingales awake:
> For Death he taketh all away: but them he cannot take!

'Men are we and must mourn.' *Mentem mortalia tangunt.* But here, sir, in this room—in this house—you preserve almost all that a decent, necessary piety can preserve.

III

Let me say frankly that your guest, whom you over-compliment by standing him here, could do very well without any memorials beyond the poems themselves—beyond the great odes (say), some sonnets, *La Belle Dame sans Merci*, *The Eve of St. Agnes*, *Hyperion*, and lines of *Endymion* chanted in the ear of his own youth. These and such things are to me the pure, the mere, the miraculous, the only considerable Keats.

I assert this in face of a most formidable company, far more learned than I: and I assert it in this haunted house. Through its chamber walks—and now must walk—the shade of Fanny

Brawne, by the favour of whose granddaughter, present to-night, many mementoes have been bestowed as its treasure. I shall say but a word of Fanny Brawne. She was young, sprightly (as she had, by virtue of her graces, a right to be), and as Touchstone said to Jaques

> if ladies be but young and fair,
> They have the gift to know it.

That Keats tortured himself over his passion for her is, of course, evident from his published letters. But one guesses that he would, in his febrile breaking health, have tortured himself almost equally in any passionate flame. She was not (if you will) the woman for him. But ask yourselves, of your experience of life, Who could have been? The few words she discreetly left of him in her later married life are sensible and most tender. Let us leave it at that. I wish, for my part, that the letters had never been exhumed. But they were: and they do *her* no harm.

IV

For we know—do we not?—that to any actual Keats any Fanny Brawne can never be the woman *we* criticize as sprightly or worldly or of breeding and self-possession, but is always an ideal creation in a lover's brain. Oh, believe me, ladies and gentlemen, you can as soon explain a play of Shakespeare's by imagining him in search along his shelves for his next plot, as you can explain Keats by Fanny Brawne, Fanny Brawne by Keats, or Dulcinea del Toboso by any process but that of Don Quixote's brain. There is a little of the poet in every man here: and if we did not all, rough men, poetize somewhat our selected mates, I ask you, How could the world go on? Who, above all, is to select mates for poets? What expert? What official? No, they must do it for themselves, and unhappily when they don't at first succeed they too often try, try again.

*L

V

Edward FitzGerald, to my thinking the best critic of his Victorian contemporaries, took up the love-letters of Keats straight after a study of Catullus: and (wrote he) to James Russell Lowell—but let me pause upon that name to regret that Miss Amy Lowell, whose two erudite massive volumes on Keats almost make me afraid to speak, weighing 'as an ox on my tongue,' cannot be here to-night as she intended. Let us all wish her a happy and speedy recovery!

To resume—Edward FitzGerald wrote (February 18, 1878):

When Keats came, I scarce felt a change from Catullus, both such fiery Souls as wore out their Bodies early; and I can even imagine Keats writing such filthy Libels against any one he had a spite against, even Armitage Brown, had Keats lived 2,000 years ago.

Yes, and for two other reasons I connect always in my mind these two Thalia's sons—Keats with Catullus: these two who died in their prime, died at apparently such spendthrift irreparable waste of the god's promise; died early because forsooth the gods loved them. For the first reason (which may seem trivial, but is not when searched) both passionately loved their family, their brothers. Catullus's *Frater ave atque vale* has come sighing to us down the ages, to be taken up and continued by Keats's devotional tears and lament over 'poor Tom': and who can forget that picture of little John Keats, aged seven or there-abouts, posting himself sentry in his night-shirt with a sword outside his mother's sick-room—that picture which FitzGerald so often and urgently begged Millais to paint?

VI

But records of children and brothers wildly devoted are common enough, you will say. Well then, for my second point of likeness, I say that of these two poets, when all the dross of their work has been sifted out, the residue is absolute gold, pure and proof against whatever touchstone brought. And therefore can any one name two stars in literature over whom we more wonder at—even though we upbraid not—the gods for slaying their darlings young, over whose twin trench we stretch more yearning impotent hands?   Says Robert Bridges:

If one English poet might be recalled to-day from the dead to continue the work which he left unfinished on earth, it is probable that the crown of his country's desire would be set on the head of John Keats.

An idle regret, on an idle speculation!   True: as all regrets, all speculations, wander around the foreknowing path of the gods—as Keats himself, for example, wanders in the maze of *Endymion*.

VII

An idle speculation!   It might have been that, relieved of personal disease and selfish torment (a part of it), Keats had opened the door wider on that larger vision revealed in *Hyperion*.

> 'High Prophetess,' said I, 'purge off
> Benign, if so it please thee, my mind's film'—
> 'None can usurp this height,' return'd that Shade,
> 'But those to whom the miseries of the world
> *Are* miseries, and will not let them rest.'

As idle the regret!

There are no voices, O Rhodope! that are not soon mute, however tuneful: there is no name, with whatever emphasis of passionate love repeated, of which the echo is not faint at last.

Catullus is dead: Keats is dead: and the ghost of the girl he idealized has gone out, somewhere, to dance and wear away, if she can, 'the everlasting flint.'   But here is the house inhabited, out yonder the tree, the garden, the listener to that song not born for death while poetry lasts.

VIII

I have personal reason to know, sir, the domesticity which guards and respects, for the mere sake, even quite modest literature in Hampstead.   I have real reason to know how far from this clearer height over London even a faint invalid voice can travel for the good of an uncounted many.   Hampstead is not a parade-ground of authors, nor a *campo santo* for tall monuments.   It is and has been, in gentle pre-eminence and dignity, a *home* of genius.   I like, sir, to think it our way to celebrate even our most illustrious poets in this modest, homely fashion: that as, a few days ago, Englishmen gathered in a country churchyard to honour Gray, so we to-night have gathered to this house of Keats as a shrine in your city.

A TOAST TO THE MEMORY OF SIR WALTER SCOTT

Given at the Twenty-seventh Annual Dinner of the Edinburgh
Sir Walter Scott Club, Nov. 26, 1926

My Lord Provost, My Lords, Ladies and Gentlemen,

I

YOU have cast far for a President this year, though you
might of course have found many nearer and more eminent
—better able certainly to acknowledge the honour which, at
this moment, naturally oppresses the heart and tongue. But
you could not (and this must be my justification), though you
flung your net in waters far remoter than the caves of Cornwall
where lies my home, have dragged up a more inveterate (shall
I say a more crustacean?) lover of that great man whose memory
an admitted Southron must presently, by the privilege of invitation, invite you to honour.

II

You know by report that I lecture at Cambridge and there
have sometimes to lecture upon Shakespeare. *That* is a career
to which, as few Professors can escape it, some evolutionary
instinct of self-protection has taught us to adapt ourselves.

But sometimes, dealing with Shakespeare, I have harked back
upon Scott; and have pondered upon the different ways which
history has chosen to assign her record of the two greatest
imaginative writers in our literature.

To Shakespeare, she has left 'a local habitation and a name.'
What else? Truly we know nothing apart from a very few
constated facts and a vast deal of trumpery gossip.

301

But of Scott, that other inspired charmer of souls, we know far more (probably) than has ever been recorded of any writer in history. Apart from his own industrious prefaces and notes and appendixes, we have not only the monumental *Life* by his son-in-law Lockhart—perhaps next to Boswell's Johnson the finest biography in our language (you Scots hold the palm in biography anyway)—but letters and journals, etc., line upon line, revelation upon familiar revelation of the actual man.

III

And there is the difference. Theoretically would you really wish—ought any of us really to wish—to know more of Shakespeare than we do? I ask, would you confidently wish it? I know this is a bold question. But I would ask you the like of Homer. Do we really want more for our image of Homer than the words of the hymn attributed to him?— 'Farewell, O maidens of Delos, and hereafter if any stranger landing on your beach should inquire "Who was the sweetest singer ever sung to you?" make answer to him modestly— "Sir, he was just a blind man and came (he said) from rocky Chios."' All the 'Lives' of Shakespeare when the pot is skimmed boil down to this—that there was a boy in Stratford who left it to try his fortune with the London theatre-people, learned to write superbly but still hankered after his native banks of Avon, and ended as a neighbour respected by his neighbours —a man not forgetting his roots. As Bagehot remarks in effect, of the passage in *Venus and Adonis* describing the tremors of a hare aroused at sound of his pursuers, 'Who says, after this, that we know nothing of Shakespeare? We know that he had once been after a hare.'

Now what I come to, my Lord Provost, is this, that of Scott —apart from the operation of genius, which is always a mystery —we are left with no mystery at all, and we want none.

We know that this Wizard of the North wore no Prospero's mantle, that he drew no cabalistic circle save that of the writing-lamp under which his figures—Di' Vernon or Jeanie Deans, Marmion or Richard of England, Edie Ochiltree or Dugald Dalgetty—weave their dance at his call. We know that he, too, had been after a hare: after a salmon too, and the running deer. But we see this man, alike in his poems and novels and in his own life so amply recorded, as almost the sincerest figure of a great Scots gentleman—'the Shirra'—*totus teres*: a figure so vivid, so sincere and simple, that only certain great simple characters in fiction—Don Quixote, My Uncle Toby, the Vicar of Wakefield, Mr. Pickwick—occupy in our affection a place comparable with this actual man, who rode Ettrick and survives to us, himself as romantic as any of the characters he created.

IV

A month or two since, sir—your Club's invitation giving me excuse to satisfy an old craving, one of those which conceived in boyhood are so often deferred to the lazier daily task which nevertheless must be done—I made pious pilgrimage through a good part of the Border. The weather was perfect, the sky clear blue above those enfolding hills; the hillsides were sheeted down in such green enchantment as ever ringed Thomas the Rymer beneath Eildon Tree. And I tell you, sir, that at every lap of the hills under circuitous Tweed I could see the Shirra riding down on his grey pony—a figure held somehow in the imagination of one's boyhood, inseparable even then between adoration of his writings and love of their author. On a return from some of these pilgrimages there followed a Sunday night o thunderstorm, memorable (I was told) even in these parts, and next day, visiting Lasswade for the site of his early farm-steading, I learned what Esk could do in spate, and knew again this younger man with his lame leg pressed to the saddle-flap daring (as Lockhart tells) the fords.

V

They tell us nowadays that Romance is dead and Scott neglected. Romance is never dead. As our greatest living Romantic puts it, Romance brings up the 9.15; and she always will. But there has been some neglect of Scott among lecturers and school masters, who still talk indefatigably of the Romantic Movement or a Romantic Revival, of which he and Byron were the tallest champions. Some while ago your new President, Professor Grierson, gave us a most vivifying lecture on the word 'Romantic' and I had shamefacedly to confess, when thanking him for it afterwards, I did quite recently advise my pupils that for a time we should give the words 'Romantic' and 'Classical' a rest. Of course I was wrong. We can never give even the word 'Romantic' a rest; but I was thinking of an admired lecturer who came to Cambridge and advertised a series of lectures on the Romantic Revival. Some of my pupils came to me to read some of the poetry of the early nineteenth century, and when I asked what passages of Byron had been recommended to them they admitted that Byron had not been included in the syllabus. I forget if Scott was. But Byron!—'God shield us, a lion among ladies!'

Nay, I regret to say that, but yesterday, I had read to me a chapter of my old friend Sir Walter Raleigh *On Writing and Writers*—the chapter was entitled *On the Decline and Fall of Romanticism in Nineteenth-Century Poetry*. Now as they used to say at Oxford 'Raleigh was a prince'; he was at any rate a man of his hands; above all Professors the man who despised lecturing, as he put it, 'for the school ma'am'; and although he had much to say for the impetus which made the Romantic Movement, I sought in vain for the name of Scott. Burns was mentioned. Many years ago I found myself in very hot water through asking innocently in a weekly paper why Scotsmen spent such a disproportionate amount of enthusiasm on Burns as compared with Scott. I shall not revive that controversy to-night, for fear of physical violence, save to say that had I the honour to be one of Scott's countrymen I would beat the racial tomtom in his honour above all other men of your jealous race.

But, sir, I remember here, that I am a Professor, and as such, perhaps, have my only justification for the honour of addressing you—if I can find it.

Well, to begin with, I do not see how any professorial talk consorts with an occasion like this, at so many of which Scott himself assisted and (according to Hogg) could out-toast all compotators, for the final toast standing with one leg on his chair the other (lame) on the table, after what I understand to have been a laudable national custom. It still is, maybe: but I hope to be excused presently from *that* challenge.[1]

VI

But of Scott as a writer let me just say three words and those very briefly:

In the first place few men, I think, unless or until their business obliges them to follow some way into English (I hardly dare add Scottish) literature, can realize how much this man had read, digested and known; in a word what a scholar he was, how careless in grace, yet how profound. I can only bring my own tribute of testimony to this, for what it is worth. But it happens that for some years I have been working on the comedies of Shakespeare, and always I am finding, in stray footnote or recollection or hint, that Scott somehow, somewhere, has been there before. It is not, as it is with Johnson, always a definite pronouncement of common-sense. I should compare it rather with Dante's search for a literary language among the Italian dialects of his time. Always ahead of us, as Dante says, is 'the panther of our quest'; in no province his abiding lair. So, in early literature, nowhere is Scott's abiding lair, yet

---

[1] The speaker was himself temporarily a cripple, through an accident.

always Scott has been that way—always in reading Scott, in almost any dozen pages, say of the *Talisman* or of *Nigel*, we are haunted by undertones, overtones of Shakespeare: so, reading Shakespeare, you catch, borne back out of somewhere on a whisper, the horn of elfland blowing, the music of the leading hound:

> Long I follow'd happy guides,
> I could never reach their sides;
> Their step is forth and, ere the day
> Breaks, up their leaguer and away . . .
> On eastern hills I see their smokes
> Mix'd with mist by distant lochs.

So it is with any one who has once surrendered his mind to these two, our most imaginative writers.

VII

He had, we know, an incomparable gift of verbal memory: comparable only in the next generation with that of your other countryman, Macaulay. All records attest it, even if we discount those of that egregious Shepherd (if in this company I may call him so) whose effigy to-day sits, as somebody ordained it to be, on a brae over sweet St. Mary's Loch, irremoveable as the Shepherd himself was when for the best part of two days and nights he sat attendant upon the conversation of Scott and John Murray, the publisher. But this gift of memorizing, while a respectable mystery to me, can be shared by any 'Calculating Boy.' The real mystery to me, sir, is the *understanding* that went with it, and communicated itself all over Europe.

Here was a man, intensely and actively conservative: a hater of the French Revolution and all it meant: a close clannish Scot, moreover—to whom his family ties and Tweed were Jordan and meant more than any Abana or Pharpar, rivers of Damascus. And yet from the circle of his writing-lamp radiated a something that made all European literature different. Even as, from a little monastery in Jarrow, Bede's candle cast its beam across fen marsh and channel fog to the Continent and Charlemagne's court, so the Waverley novels reached our dear enemy France and (more than ever Byron did, the more admired) rekindled romance over Europe. That is my second wonder—who talk to you as a man of letters: and I must leave it at that.

But let me fetch back the recollections from the far away nineties to which I suppose I must date myself. In those days our dear enemy France was getting back, as they say, something of her own, by opposing new Realism to the old Romance and uniting it with the anxious cultivation of style, the search for the exact word—*le mot juste*. Flaubert and de Maupassant were models in those days; with Tourguénieff, who was a Russian, but spent his life in exile in Paris. We sought back to Balzac and Stendhal too. But a man there was, to rescue us from the desert of Realism—one gallant Scotsman, the adored of us all, hopeless beyond our imitation, who kept the flag of Scott flying and carried it till he fell. I mean of course Robert Louis Stevenson.

My Lord Provost, while Scotland stands where it did it is impossible that Romance should die: this very gathering to-night testifies that it yet fervently lives.

VIII

For my third and last point of remark, I must (how shall I put it?) hitch up an old shooting-jacket between two wizard robes—that of the younger Scott, the poet, and the mature Scott of the novels (prolific, strong, then wearied, broken, but yet carrying through with honour, to the end). And I find, or try to find, some reconciliation of the two literary Walter Scotts in *this*—

All readers of all records, letters, anecdotes, must wonder, in these times, at the boisterous animal spirits of the man. He had always a fund of them—let me put it—more than sufficient for his immediate purposes, or for those of his friends over whose misadventures in his company he would laugh till the tears ran down his cheeks, whether he or they took a toss off horseback into a bog, or were sunk in a coracle at salmon-spearing and must swim for it in the perilous dark. So he would have rocked with laughter at the spectacle of a man pursuing his hat down the Canongate. There is a Homeric simplicity in all Scott's laughter; and to that same Homeric simplicity we owe and, criticizing, yet bless the rush and spate of his verse in *The Lay*, and in *Marmion*. Monckton Milnes, Lord Houghton, doubted in verse if our forefathers were really finer fellows than the best of later years: but he noted in verse one gallant difference:

> To them was life a simple art
>   Of duties to be done,
> A game where each man took his part,
>   A race where all must run;
> A battle whose great scheme and scope
>   They little cared to know,
> Content as men-at-arms to cope
>   Each with his fronting foe.
>
> Man now his Virtue's diadem
>   Puts on and proudly bears:
> Great thoughts, great feelings came to *them*
>   Like instincts, unawares.
> Blending their soul's sublimest needs
>   With tasks of every day,
> They went about their gravest deeds
>   As noble boys at play.

And I suggest to you that this same store of Homeric (or if you prefer it) of Sabine vigour carried Scott through. It is nonsense to say that in the novels he is no artist. Beginning with a wayward loose rein in *Waverley*, he runs loose again in *Guy Mannering*, and then, in *The Antiquary*, finds himself.

Who will say that *The Antiquary* is not great constructive art? Or that *Old Mortality*, *The Heart of Midlothian*, *Redgauntlet* are not master-works? Those prosperous happy years, by Lockhart with how delicate a familiarity described! Thenafter the tale of ruin, of 'all lost save honour' and still of honour winning through. I shall not touch on this, sir, save to suggest that even the bravest knight, not carried through on the almost spent tide of Scott's amazing vitality, must have gone down under the waves.

IX

At the very close almost—broken and near spent—he came to his native city, to make his will. A spell of most violent weather immured him, and his good friend Mr. Cadell persuaded him to remove to the hospitable house in Atholl Crescent, where for several days he wrote manfully at *Count Robert of Paris*. There, pestered by his publisher Ballantyne for an omitted motto, he moved to the window, gazed out on the whirl of the storm, and invented the few lines, subscribed *The Deluge*, that form the motto of Chapter V:

> The storm increases; 'tis no sunny shower
> Fostered in the moist breath of March or April,
> Or such as parchèd Summer cools his lips with.
> Heaven's windows are flung wide; the inmost deeps
> Call in hoarse greeting one upon another;
> On comes the flood in all its foaming horrors,
> And where's the dike shall stop it?

My Lord Provost, I have seen (I say) and could not help seeing the solid vision of this full-blooded high-mettled man riding down to dangerous fords by Tweed and Esk and Yarrow: I have heard the ripple of his river under Abbotsford and walked back up the meadow to assure myself that what Lockhart tells is not fable: it may well have been the last quiet music lulling him. But here, in the story I have quoted, is Mr. Valiant-for-Truth riding down to the last wildest ford of all, always the great man, bequeathing his sword to any that can deserve it, his great bow to any that can bend it.

And I say—speaking from my heart, and from my knowledge, such as it is—that no writer of this island has left at once so much of his genius abiding in the world for its clean delight, so much invention to entrance so many young and old, so gallant and good an example of good living, as has this exemplar of a great Scottish gentleman—whose most noble memory I now ask you, mesdames and sirs, rising to pledge.

My Lord Provost, my lords, ladies and gentlemen, I lift my glass with you to the well-beloved memory of Walter Scott.

A SEXAGENARIAN'S APOLOGIA
1928

I HAVE a knack, perhaps an ungrateful one, of forgetting my stories almost as soon as they are written; with an incurable habit of persisting on my own line, careless if my audience dwindle or no. I have still—and at my time of life it may be pardonably asserted—the assurance that I have been able, in various ways, to touch many hearts, and am still able to touch some.

They are few, perhaps, just now; and may yet dwindle, while professors talk of 'the Romantic Movement' as though a spirit enjoyed a period, to pass into a dead thing, to be classified.

It is not a dead thing. In the race that has bred Drake, Wotton, Peterborough, Scott, Gordon, it must ever revive and recur. And I ask to be remembered for no more than this —that, while he lived through a time of unpopularity, one man held on his way in that faith.

I might plead many things on behalf of romance, but will confine myself to one plea, taking Scott for my illustration— or Dickens, if you will. The worlds they drew were *kindly* worlds, if extravagant; worlds in which, as in the quieter worlds of Jane Austen or Trollope, it was a privilege to live. They, as did Goldsmith and Fielding before them, took our span of life as companionable, humorous, on the whole making for good.

Now—to drive at practice—any clever fellow can pull faces at humanity and deride it; as any one with little expense can invent mishaps and misunderstandings. A novelist who traffics with sex and suicide, domestic bickerings and disillusions, is playing the very easiest game in the world. Any illiterate can make a 'hit' with such a theme, if his mind be of the sort to descend to it. But to people a wide stage with characters at

once good (as most are) and brave, in patience or adventure—
that is the artist's test, as it seems to me. It means that in
growing he has learnt to judge his fellow-sinners charitably,
and to help them, before he leaves a world of all sorts in which
it has been worth while to live.

LECTURE ON W. S. GILBERT

I

I HAD parted, at the Cambridge Post Office, with a young friend of parts who 'deplores' (as he puts it) our whole heritage of English poetry and holds with reason that it ought to make a fresh start. Musing on this assurance of his, on my way to the Botanic Garden, and resigning myself, as my custom is, to grieving

> when even the Shade
> Of that which once was great is passed away,

I encountered two long lines of men on opposite sides of the thoroughfare; the one drawing, or seeking to draw, unemployment pay; the other taking, or seeking to take, tickets for Gilbert-and-Sullivan Opera.

'Ah, there,' thought I, 'after all, the last enchantment of the Victorian age has captured you, my lads, and holds you by the Achilles' tendon!' For I recognize your faces. You are the same that, the other day, were affecting to despise

> Come down, O maid, from yonder mountain height—

or

> O lyric love, half angel and half bird!

But as soon as it comes to 'Tit-willow!' or 'The Policeman's lot is not a happy one,' you are held and 'laid by the heel.'

Now I wish to inquire into this and the reason of it; and, believe me, not sardonically. My first introduction to Gilbert-and-Sullivan Opera dates back to an amateur performance of *H.M.S. Pinafore* that enchanted a child. The first play I ever saw in a London theatre was *Patience*, in the course of its first run at the Opéra Comique. As an undergraduate I have taken as much trouble as any of you to listen to *The Sorcerer, Princess Ida, The Mikado*; and my own two favourites, *Iolanthe* and *The Gondoliers*, still conjure up by association all manner of happy memories. I yet can surrender myself (at intervals) to Gilbert-and-Sullivan with an abandon you may ascribe to the natural gaiety of declining years, or to sentimentality—which you will. Let that pass: for, with your leave, the question affects not *me* but *you*. Why do you who expend so much cleverness in deriding the more serious contemporaries of W. S. Gilbert and Arthur Sullivan, yet experimentally confess to this one most typically late-Victorian enthusiasm which binds your spiritual contemporaries with your fathers and grandfathers?

You at any rate will not plead—you, who follow so eagerly all the many experiments of our Festival Theatre in substituting mechanics for drama—that you cling to a tradition of the provinces. That provincial audiences flock to these operas even as you do; that amateurs throughout England spend their winters in rehearsing one and another of them; that regularly, in the week following Easter, the railways convey down baskets of regulation wigs and costumes from Covent Garden to remote towns and Village Institutes—all this is certain.

II

Now this, when we consider how typically late-Victorian these operas are—how limited in range of idea, even of invention—how much of their quiddity (in *Patience*, for example) belongs to its hour in a past era; may well give us a shock. It might also give me occasion to ask, why some of you, and those not the least intelligent, haunt these operas, although in clever debate you think it not unseemly to deride Meredith for a mountebank and Tennyson for a maiden aunt.

But I seem to know you too well to believe that in your heart of hearts you cherish any such foolish opinions, at any rate ineradicably, or truly believe Gilbert and Sullivan to be the lone Dioscuri of our late-Victorian night. Let us start on the plain common ground that, after fifty years or so, their work continues to delight young and old, and try to account for it.

The appeal of music being, by virtue of its indefiniteness, so much more elusive of date than the spoken or written word, and especially if the subject be at all 'topical,' shall we hold that Gilbert survives mainly through Sullivan's music? Vaguely we may feel Sullivan's melody to be as Victorian as are Gilbert's plots and tricks and whole theatrical concept; but these, having to be framed in words and on lines of logic—and topsy-turvy logic is yet logic and the basis of Gilbert's wit—can be brought to tests which music airily eludes. They are written in words and can be attacked in words; and must continue to suffer this comparative disadvantage until critics of music find a method of expressing their likes and dislikes by musical notation.

But no; this explanation will not serve. For Gilbert, very much of his period and exposed to all the perils which must beset any man who would attract a theatrical audience by wit and song, was yet (if you will search his libretti) extremely wary of topical allusions that might date him. In *Patience*, to be sure (one of his earliest), he shot at, and winged, a passing mode. But save for a passing allusion to the late Captain Shaw of London's Fire Brigade and a somewhat pointed one in *Utopia, Limited* to the light refreshment provided for débutantes at Queen Victoria's Drawing-Rooms, you will seek his work in vain for topical references. To be sure, in *H.M.S. Pinafore* (his earliest success) he poked obvious fun at Mr. W. H. Smith, First Lord of the Admiralty: but there exists a most illuminating letter of his in which he hopes he has removed all suspicion of personal offence by indicating that the victim was a Liberal— a letter which should be a *locus classicus* for research into the ultimate obtuseness of wit. Dealing with his times as he knew them, he could not of course foresee that events would in time blunt the application of one of his neatest shafts—the sentry's song in *Iolanthe*. But I think we may agree that in this slow-moving country of ours Gilbert's raillery has worn as well as the absurd institutions against which he not too seriously aimed. They are accustomed to that sort of thing, and have allowed him to wear just as well as they have worn.

I suggest that if you mark and note this avoidance of topical allusion in Gilbert, you will come to the conclusion with me that the man considered himself as one writing for posterity, as carefully at least as Horace Walpole did in composing his familiar letters to Horace Mann. But on this point I shall presently have more evidence to bring. For the moment let his many years' survival stand for presumptive evidence that Gilbert wrote with intent to last.

This intention apart, it were unjust to hold that Gilbert lives by the grace of Sullivan. Offenbach's music was as tunable as Sullivan's and belonged to its age as closely. But Offenbach lacked good librettists, and for this reason you do not stand in long files to buy tickets for Offenbach. You may say that you do not for the more obvious reason that his operas are never presented in England nowadays; but the true reason, if you search for it, is that Offenbach never found his poet, his twin mind. Now Gilbert and Sullivan lived each by the grace of the other. Habitually, in actual practice, Gilbert wrote first, plot and lyric, and Sullivan followed; which is the only right order in the making of an opera, and was convincingly the right order in the making of these men's operas. For the contribution which Sullivan brought was not only his genius for melody, nor a wit that jumped with Gilbert's, nor a separate and musical wit which revelled in parody. Priceless as these gifts undoubtedly were, above them all (I think) we must reckon the quite marvellous sense of *words* in all his musical settings. You may examine number after number of his, and the more closely you examine the more will you be convinced that no composer ever lived with an exacter appreciation of words, their meaning, their due emphasis, their right articulation. A singer must be a fool indeed if you do not hear through Sullivan's notes the exact language of any song. Take, for example, the well-known Sentry Song in *Iolanthe* and attempt to unwed the wit of the air from the wit of the thought and words; or take the Lord Chancellor's song in the same play:

> The law is the true embodiment
> Of everything that's excellent,
> It has no kind of fault or flaw—
> And I, my Lords, embody the law,

and note how Sullivan subdues the air to something almost commonplace and almost silly, but just so as to bring out the intention of demure absurdity, with allowance for every syllable and room for the gesture in the fourth line. Yet should you think he is subduing himself to anything but his artistry, turn to the great duet in *The Sorcerer*, or to the robust Handelian burlesque that winds up 'He remains an Englishman' in *H.M.S. Pinafore*, and mark how riotously his own wit takes charge when Gilbert's gives it the rein.

IV

Gilbert had the advantage of setting the themes and dominating the stage-management of the operas. But before we call his the master-spirit (which by no means implies that it was the more valuable) in the combination, let us take a little evidence from the actors and singers they commanded. Remind yourselves that these two men, when they started at the old Opéra Comique, off the Strand, had to work with the cheapest material. The 'brassiness' of the orchestra during the first run of *Pinafore*—the combined incompetence in *Patience* of the vocalists as actors and of the actors as vocalists—would be incredible to-day even if faithfully reproduced to eye and ear. In that first run of *Patience* one or two of the cast could act a little, one or two could sing a little; Miss Rosina Brandram alone, asserting that there would be too much of her in the coming by and by, could do both.

But these two men, combining upon an idea, turned even

shortness of means to their service. They found themselves in the position long and vainly required by a neighbour of mine, a great gardener—'I want an intelligent fellow ready to plant a cabbage upside down without questioning.' Having at first a stage so inexpensive, a cast which had to listen and obey, they imposed their idea, or ideas, with a tyranny to which countless anecdotes bear witness.

The most of these anecdotes are of Gilbert: but Sullivan, if less irascible in rehearsal, appears to have been almost as ruthless. Here is the musical procedure, as related by George Grossmith—who knew it if any man did:

The music is always learned first. The choruses, finales, etc., are composed first in order; then the quartets, the trios; the songs last. Sometimes, owing to changes and re-writing, these are given out to the singers very late (so late that the singer sometimes found less difficulty in learning the new tune than in unlearning the old one). The greatest interest is evinced by all as the new vocal numbers arrive . . . Sullivan will come suddenly, a batch of MS. under his arm, and announce that there is something new. He plays over the new number—the vocal parts only are written. The conductor listens and watches and, after hearing them played over a few times, contrives to pick up all the harmonies, casual accompaniments, etc. Sullivan is always strict in wishing that this music shall be sung exactly as he has written it. One of the leading performers was singing an air at rehearsal, not exactly dividing the notes as they were written, giving the general form as it were. 'Bravo!' said Sullivan, 'that is really a very good air of yours. Now, if you have no objection, I will ask you to sing mine.'

But the little finger of Gilbert at rehearsal would be thicker than Sullivan's loins. He kept at home a small model stage, made to scale, and a box or boxes of tiny bricks varying in height and colour. These he would group and re-group in endless patient stage-management until satisfied just where and just how at any given moment any actor should be standing. Then he would come to the theatre and, moving everybody about as on a chessboard, start to bully them into speaking to his exact wish. To quote Grossmith again:

The music rehearsals are child's play in comparison with the stage rehearsals. Mr. Gilbert is a perfect autocrat, insisting that his words shall be delivered, even to an inflexion of the voice, as he dictates. He will stand on the stage and repeat the words, with appropriate action, over and over again until they are delivered as he desires.

Add that Gilbert, on top of a detestable temper, had a tongue like a whip-lash: and—well, you see, as any of you who wish to be artists must learn in some way, sooner or later, that there is not only a pleasure in poetic pains but a tax upon human pains for poetic pleasure.

V

If I have established that Gilbert's is a dominant, even tyrannical, brain in these plays which you find so delightful, let us go on to deal with them a little after the manner of Aristotle. Obviously they obey Aristotle in preferring plot to character, even though by inversion: for, his plots being always legal rather than moral in their topsy-turviness (Gilbert, you know, was a barrister and made his first success as a playwright in *Trial by Jury*), his characters behave always on a topsy-turvy legal logic—a logic as mad as Lewis Carroll's or madder; they transfer their affections, or reverse their destinies, by insane rational process:

> Quiet peaceful contemplation
> Disentangles every knot.

A captain in the Royal Navy turns out to have been changed at birth with a common seaman: it follows that, the revelation made, they change places and stations. A promising lad has, by a lapse of terminological exactitude, been apprenticed to a pirate instead of to a pilot; a love-philtre works the wrong way (as it did in *A Midsummer Night's Dream*); a drummer ascends the throne of Barataria on the affidavit of a foster-mother in eight lines of *recitative*.

Within these limits of absurdity you will notice that all the operas have limits also in ethic, and are built on an almost rigid convention of design.   There is usually an opposition of the Victorian real against the fanciful: of a House of Peers, for example, in robes, against a chorus of fairies under Westminster clock-tower: of a body of Heavy Dragoons against Bunthorne and his lackadaisy maidens.   There is almost always a baritone singer, more or less loosely connected with the story, introduced with some sort of patter-song—the First Lord's song in *Pinafore* (which, by the way, started its success), the Major-General's in *The Pirates*, the Lord Chancellor's in *Iolanthe*, and so on. There is also a lady with a contralto voice, who deplores her mature years.   The more you examine the operas to compare them, the closer you will get to a severe and narrow model. And the model in its ethical content is no less straitly laced. It invites you to laugh at the foibles of kings, soldiers, lawyers, artists, and faddists of all sorts.   But it touches no universal emotion, no universal instinct even (such as conviviality).   Still less does it allow us to think of the base on which society is built, or admit a thought on it to intrude in any way upon our tomfooling.   We all belong to the upper or upper middle class, or to the class which apes these two.   We are all conscious of class distinctions, are a little too consciously snobbish even while we enjoy the exposure of snobbery.   The general moral, in fact, is that of the song which he characteristically entitled *King Goodheart*:

> There lived a King, as I 've been told,
> In the wonder-working days of old,
> When hearts were twice as good as gold
>   And twenty times as mellow.
> Good temper triumphed in his face,
> And in his heart he found a place
> For all the erring human race
>   And every wretched fellow.

When he had Rhenish wine to drink
It made him very sad to think
That some, at junket or at jink,
    Must be content with toddy:
He wished all men as rich as he
(And he was rich as rich could be),
So to the top of every tree
    Promoted everybody. . . .
That King, although no one denies,
His heart was of abnormal size,
Yet he 'd have acted otherwise
    If he had been acuter.
The end is easily foretold,
When every blessed thing you hold
Is made of silver, or of gold,
    You long for simple pewter.
When you have nothing else to wear
But cloth of gold and satins rare,
For cloth of gold you cease to care—
    Up goes the price of shoddy:
In short, whoever you may be,
To this conclusion you 'll agree,
When every one is somebody,
    Then no one 's anybody!

VI

That, you may say, is all very well—or would be well enough
if Gilbert could be cleared as a writer who genuinely sym-
pathized with some things, or with one class, and just happened
not to sympathize with others. That is common enough with
authors, and especially with comedians and writers of light
verse. Their business being to apply the touch of common
sense to human affairs, one may even allow a certain hardness

M

to be a part of their outfit (I am ungrateful enough even to find
a certain hardness of surface in that favourite of us all, C. S.
Calverley). But Gilbert had a baddish streak or two in him;
and one in particular which was not only baddish but so
thoroughly caddish that no critic can ignore or, in my belief,
extenuate it. The man, to summarize, was essentially cruel,
and delighted in cruelty. I lay no heavy stress on his addiction
—already glanced at—to finding fun in every form of torture
and capital punishment. This indeed persists in his work from
The Bab Ballads right through the plays:

> Oh! listen to the tale of little Annie Protheroe;
> She kept a small post office in the neighbourhood of Bow,
> She loved a skilled mechanic, who was famous in his day—
> A gentle executioner whose name was Gilbert Clay.
>
> I think I hear you say, 'A dreadful subject for your rhymes!'
> O reader, do not shrink—he didn't live in modern times!
> He lived so long ago (the sketch will show it at a glance)
> That all his actions glitter with the limelight of Romance.
>
> In busy times he laboured at his gentle craft all day—
> 'No doubt you mean his Cal-craft' you amusingly will say—
> But, no—he didn't operate with common bits of string,
> He was a Public Headsman, which is quite another thing.
>
> And when his work was over, they would ramble o'er the lea,
> And sit beneath the frondage of an elderberry tree;
> And Annie's simple prattle entertained him on his walk,
> For public executions formed the subject of her talk.
>
> And sometimes he'd explain to her, which charmed her very
>   much,
> How famous operators vary very much in touch,
> And then, perhaps, he'd show how he himself performed the
>   trick,
> And illustrate his meaning with a poppy and a stick.

It persists (I repeat) through *The Bab Ballads* and into play after play; until, if you are tired and seek a *terminus ad quem*, I suggest this, from *The Mikado*, where an artless maiden sings:

> He shivered and shook as he gave the sign
>   For the stroke he didn't deserve;
> When all of a sudden his eye met mine,
>   And it seemed to brace his nerve.
> For he nodded his head and kissed his hand,
>   And he whistled an air did he,
>   As the sabre true
>   Cut cleanly through
>   His cervical vertebrae!
>   When a man's afraid
>   A beautiful maid
>   Is a charming sight to see.
>   And it's O, I'm glad
>   That moment sad
>   Was soothed by sight of me!

Or—

> To sit in solemn silence, in a dull dark dock,
> In a pestilential prison, with a life-long lock,
> Awaiting the sensation of a short, sharp, shock
> From a cheap and chippy chopper on a big black block.

On this cheap and chippy chopper business I merely observe that Gilbert revelled in it; as any one else may, so long as I am not asked to join the party.

But Gilbert's cruelty took an uglier twist upon one incurable and unforgivable vice — that of exposing women to public derision on the stage just because they are growing old and losing their beauty. We can forgive Horace or Catullus (if hardly) for venom against their cast-off mistresses. We should all think the better of them had they refrained. But the revulsion, even the vituperation, of a wearied amorist—unpleasant as one may think it—consists with our experience of men and women. It is *humanly* vile. What disgusts one in Gilbert, from the beginning to the end, is his insistence on the physical odiousness of any woman growing old. As though, great Heaven! themselves did not find it tragic enough—the very and necessary tragedy of their lives! Gilbert shouts it, mocks it, apes with it, spits upon it. He opens with this dirty trump card in *Trial by Jury*, where the Judge tells how, as a briefless Barrister,

> I soon got tired of third-class journeys,
>   And dinners of bread and water;
> So I fell in love with a rich attorney's
>   Elderly, ugly daughter.
>
> The rich attorney, he wiped his eyes,
>   And replied to my fond professions:
> 'You shall reap the reward of your enterprise,
>   At the Bailey and Middlesex Sessions.
>
> 'You'll soon get used to her looks,' said he,
>   'And a very nice girl you'll find her—
> She may very well pass for forty-three
>   In the dusk, with a light behind her!'

He follows it with 'Little Buttercup' in *Pinafore,* in *Patience* with

> Fading is the taper waist—
>   Shapeless grows the shapely limb,
> And, although securely laced,
>   Spreading is the figure trim!
>
> Stouter than I used to be,
>   Still more corpulent grow I—
> There will be too much of me
>   In the coming by and by!

—in *The Mikado* with

> The flowers that bloom in the Spring, tra la,
>   Have nothing to do with the case:
> I've got to take under my wing, tra la,
> A most unattractive old thing, tra la,
>   With a caricature of a face.

—and so he proceeds until the end, in *The Mountebanks*, to a scene which almost drove one from the theatre in nausea.

But I dare say the best rebuke of this was the gentle one administered by his favourite actress, Miss Jessie Bond. When she told Gilbert she was going to marry, he burst out, 'Little fool!' 'I have often,' she answered, 'heard you say you don't like old women. I shall be one soon. Will you provide for me? You hesitate. Well, I am going to a man who will.'

VII

Mr. Rudyard Kipling has observed somewhere that in the life of every happily married man there must come a moment when the sight of his wife at the head of the table suggests the appalling thought that this must go on for ever. Without going so far as this, one may say that even in the happiest marriage one or both of the partners has an occasional sense of some ambition missed. So it happened, we know, in the immensely successful partnership of Gilbert and Sullivan, and it led to frequent quarrels, endeavours on Sullivan's part to break away, finally to estrangement, though happily to no such deadly feud as closed the almost equally successful partnership of MM. Erckmann-Chatrian. Sullivan dreamed that he was capable of High Opera; and so perhaps he was, had he attempted it sooner. But few men can usefully resolve to embrace a new and higher career on their silver wedding-day, and when Sullivan produced *Ivanhoe* at the Royal English Opera House in 1891 it was evident that his resolve had come too late.

But Gilbert, who had bound him to his task, in latter days so sorely against his protestations, also cherished a soaring dramatic ambition. Of men so irascible as he it may usually be observed that they have a bee in their bonnet. (I may use that expression because Gilbert once wore a bonnet as officer in the Gordon Highlanders Militia and had a photograph taken —reproduced in his *Biography*—in the full costume of that gay regiment.)　And the very queer bee in Gilbert's bonnet was a violent antipathy against the name and fame of Shakespeare, particularly against the public appreciation of *Hamlet*. It sounds incredible, but there it was. He not only lampooned the great tragedy in a play, *Rosencrantz and Guildenstern*: he never could get away from Hamlet and Ophelia; he had to go on and befool their story, as in *The Mountebanks*, in a silly dumb show—and again to drag the very weeds and the mud out of Ophelia's end:

> When she found he wouldn't wed her,
> In a river, in a medder,
> Took a header, and a deader
> 　　　　Was Oph-e-li-a!

Levity, vulgar and blatant!—Yes, and almost we might call it incredible in the man, even if explicable by that same strain of insensitiveness which deadened him to all charity for women past their first youth. It has indeed a like suggestion of impotence.

But insensitiveness will not cover this fault, which actually lay very near the raw. Reading his 'Life' and his plays together, we perceive that this neat rhymer, neat wit, neat barrister, neat stage-manager, nursed at the back of his head a conception of himself as a great and serious dramatist—even as Sullivan, with better excuse, nursed the conception of himself as a great composer in oratorio. Nor did Gilbert fail to realize this conception for want of trying. He has left a number of 'serious' dramas behind him—dramas in prose and verse—all more or less unsuccessful on the stage. He even essayed one on the *Faust* theme, fated to allure and defeat all but great souls. He could not see that, whilst genius may be versatile and many-sided, there are certain talents which naturally *exclude* greatness. In his workshop, maybe, he was happy to deem himself possessed of high seriousness. When his efforts came to be produced, the public quite accurately divined that he was not. The discovery cost a not very critical generation of audiences no

Alice in Wonderland, a province of it in which all had been kindly.

For *The Bab Ballads*—if you are wise, you will treat them as wise men treat *Tristram Shandy*. You will not argue, but either like them or leave them alone. I do not compare them as achievements, but simply as they are unsusceptible to criticism; and, however wrong I may be about Gilbert, I have read enough miss-the-mark criticism of Sterne by eminent persons, from Thackeray down, to assert that there are some writings for which criticism has found little guidance between 'I Like It' and 'I Like It Not.'

For my part I rejoice in *The Bab Ballads*, and find them on the whole considerably superior to the lyrics with which Gilbert diversified the operas. Nor can I easily believe that, being the man he was, he deliberately and artistically keyed down his wit to the requirements of the music and of stage-presentation. He may have done so half consciously. The possibility, however, suggests a question on which we may conclude.

x

An examination of Gilbert's and Sullivan's success in some-times wedding, sometimes alternating, words with music to produce a genuine, if narrow, form of light opera may be of some use to those who accept, as to those who on its results feel a little doubtful about accepting, the Wagnerian and post-Wagnerian claims for grand opera. I feel some timidity in advancing so much as a foot over this ground; since of all hierophants those of music are the most scornful of intruders who would ally their pet art with others that make life enjoyable. I observe also that the majority of these apostles of harmony are as intense in vendetta as incapable of explaining what it is all about; so that one wavers in amaze between the 'interpretations' in the programme of any symphony concert

* M

and the Billingsgate in which these critics pursue their sacerdotal loves and hates.

But I suppose that, after all, it works out to this:

(1) Grand opera, like any other opera, is an artificial thing; a lovely form of art if its components of drama, words, and music be intelligently blended, yet always so artificial that the audience's imagination and intelligence must be invited together to assist in their own captivation.

(2) If these three elements (to omit scenery) of drama, words, and music could be captured, each at its highest, *and perfectly blended*, we should have perfection in one combined form of art.

(3) But this combination implies that each contributory has its due place, each giving its best and yet subduing it to the others' best, at the right moment: that suppose, for example, one could enlist Shakespeare and Beethoven together for an opera of *Lear*, or Molière and Mozart for a *Don Giovanni*, still the composing authors must each submit his genius to the total result.

(4) Now the trouble is that such things don't happen in this world.

(5) But suppose the theory sound. Of all men of genius Wagner was perhaps the worst equipped with those concomitants which his theory demanded. Therefore, being one of the most arrogant of men, he put music in supreme command and tortured our divinest of gifts—the modulated speaking voice for which Sophocles and Shakespeare wrote—to speak *through* music; which is to say, largely *against* it. It is not for me to do more than marvel at the genius for orchestration which stunned or mesmerized sensible men into accepting a megalomaniac theory. The temperate voice of the eighteenth century may whisper something salutary at this point: for, after all, Joshua Reynolds *could* paint.

I believe [says Reynolds] it may be considered as a general rule, that no art can be grafted with success on another art. For although they all profess the same origin, and to proceed from the same stock, yet each had its own peculiar mode of imitating nature and of deviating from it, each for the accomplishment of its own particular purpose. These deviations, more especially, will not bear transplantation to another soil.

Now Reynolds may easily be wrong if we apply this observation to opera in general, as presumably Hazlitt would have applied it. 'The opera,' says Hazlitt, 'is the most artificial of all things . . . it is an illusion and a mockery. . . . A headache may be produced by a profusion of sweet smells or sweet sounds; but we do not like the headache the more on that account. Nor are we reconciled to it, even at the opera.'

But the Attic Theatre proved, centuries ago, that speech and music, with dancing and scenery, could be brought together to produce one of the very highest forms of art, *provided that each of the contributories were kept in its proper place*. Aristotle recognized this, of course; and, to use our immediate subject for an illustration, Gilbert and Sullivan prove that the difficulty of bringing together accomplished pedestrian speech and accomplished music can be solved *ambulando*, if the rule of keeping them in their proper places be observed more or less as the Greeks observed it. As I have said, a combination of supreme poetry with supreme music and a variety of the other arts at their very best is not granted by the gods to the generations of men; but it seems evident that in some happy moments the co-operation of poet and musician, neither of the first eminence, may almost chemically produce a new thing which, if not transcendent, is extremely pleasing, at once novel and reasonably permanent in its appeal. Opera is an artificial thing. It is not made less artificial on a theory of 'realism' which disguises nature under a new artificiality such as the *leit-motif*, this *leit-motif* being actually as much of a convention as the label enclosing words which primitive painters and caricaturists drew as issuing from the mouths of their figures. It is, I suggest, greatly to Sullivan's credit that with his incomparable talent for articulating speech in music, he resisted all temptation of that talent to obscure or deafen by music the spoken words which must be the backbone of all drama since they carry and advance the plot.

And—for a last word—it may even be that your delight in Gilbert and Sullivan testifies to a natural unconscious revolt against the theory of opera so prevalent in our time. We know from the history of the theatre—from the tyranny, for example, laid upon it so long by the theories of Castelvetro and his followers—that a barbarous mistake can be ferociously enforced by pedantry. Against such pedantry a childlike instinct may sometimes usefully assert itself, insisting 'But the Emperor *has* no clothes!'

TWO EPIGRAMS

TO CYNTHIA

THE sculptor's chisel slid askance
       And dinted Aphrodite's cheek:
But ah! the blemish woke a glance
   So lively-lovelier than the Greek
   That Nature, copying, forebore
   The smooth perfection to restore
   And left the dimple I adore.

II

THE CHRYSALIS

Cupid, in letters yet untaught,
Captured a scroll in a cobweb caught
And duteous to his Mother brought.

His face upturning for a kiss,
'Mother,' he panted, 'read me this!'
His clasp unclosed a chrysalis:

From which escaped, as fell apart
The two halves of a broken heart,
An aria—Capture it, Mozart!

LECTURE ON
TRADITION AND ORTHODOXY
CAMBRIDGE, 16 MAY, 1934

I

IN February last we in England had our first opportunity of reading under the title *After Strange Gods: A Primer of Modern Heresy*, a series of three 'Page-Barbour' Lectures given by Mr. T. S. Eliot before the University of Virginia. Anything written or spoken by Mr. Eliot is eagerly awaited: and because his conclusions, if I accepted the premises, would strongly enforce, or by selected quotation might be used to enforce, some warnings I addressed to you the other day (and, as it happens, while he was speaking some thousands of miles away) against the prevalent individualism in modern writing, and the worship of originality for its own sake, as of an idol; I could be grateful for support so powerful, as in a degree I am. But the subject is to me a serious one; so serious that I should hate to invoke the support of any rhetorical enthymemes which seem unsound to me, or to use such for my purpose on any man's *ipse dixit*, whatever my esteem for the man himself. And so I shall take leave, this morning, to question some two or three of Mr. Eliot's pronouncements.

II

He, to be sure, in his Preface very frankly disclaims and rejects argument.

'I am not arguing or reasoning,' he says, 'or engaging in controversy with those whose views are radically opposed to such as mine. In our time controversy seems to me, on really fundamental matters, to be futile. It can only usefully be practised where there is a common understanding. It requires common assumptions, and perhaps the assumptions that are only felt are more important than those that can be formulated. The acrimony which accompanies much debate is a symptom of difference so large that there is nothing to argue about. We experience such profound differences with some of our contemporaries that the nearest parallel is the difference between one epoch and another. In a society like ours, worm-eaten with Liberalism, the only thing possible for a person of strong convictions is to state a point of view and leave it at that.'

Now this, reduced to plain terms, amounts to no more than 'I am not arguing with you: I am just telling you.' It takes up an attitude which, however politely assumed, I find hard to differentiate from that of Thrasymachus in the *Republic*; who (if you remember) having drenched his audience with a pailful of his own opinions on Justice, was for 'leaving it at that' and walking off, when Socrates plucked him by the sleeve: 'O Thrasymachus, excellent man, how suggestive are your remarks! And are you really going to move away before you have fairly taught or learned whether they are true or not?' Mr. Eliot's is, at any rate, the attitude of a dogmatist: and in one who is addressing (as he announces) the 'possibly convertible' about the least likely to succeed: since, the 'convertible' being by hypothesis un-regenerate as yet; and since in my experience the unregenerate, if intelligent at all, are prone to ask questions; any claim or suspicion of a claim that you have access to wells of inspiration denied to the rest of mankind is apt to repel at the start.

I am particularly sorry that a critic so finely equipped as Mr. Eliot, and just now possessed of so much influence, should be in successive books so evidently hardening into this oracular attitude, because I feel sure that it can only end in ossification. Already, while elaborately endeavouring to define tradition and orthodoxy, to separate them, in practice he is mixing them up, and confusing both with religion and politics. And I am the sorrier over these lectures of his because, when talking of tradition, he sharpens and betters many points I tried to put to you, gentlemen, in a couple of lectures last

Michaelmas Term on 'The Poet as Citizen.'   Up to a point
I am greatly his debtor for the improvement: and if at that
point I must part company with him I shall, before we part
to-day, submit my reasons.

III

Since his concept of Orthodoxy concerns me less than his
concept of Tradition—though it puzzles me more—let us, for
our present purpose, first get that conception cleared out of the
way, if we can.

It puzzles me more because while careful, and even more
than careful, to define what he means by Tradition, when he
comes to Orthodoxy he seems to me to wander around the word
without fixing it at all until we come to his third and last lecture.
In the first he gives it a 'similar inclusiveness' with Tradition,
and proceeds 'though of course I believe that a right tradition
for us must be also a Christian tradition, and that Orthodoxy
in general implies Christian orthodoxy, I do not propose to
lead the present series of lectures to a theological conclusion.'
Yet after a dozen words he dives off into an attack on liberalism
in Church and politics with illustrative quotations, the worth
of which I shall presently examine.

The interposed sentence, or half-sentence, runs: 'The relation
between tradition and orthodoxy in the past is evident enough.'
But 'the past,' so used, is surely the vaguest of terms.   For
example, Orthodoxy *in the past*, before and after the Council of
Trent—before and after 1563, its last sitting—carried for
Catholic Europe two very different meanings: the newer one
restricting it in sundry ways and fencing the restrictions with
anathema.   Up to that date the Medieval Church had been
moving.   For a single instance—Many of its churchmen hitherto
allowed as orthodox did not receive as canonical all the Apocrypha
or accept with an equal devotion the Second Book of Maccabees

with St. Mark's Gospel.   As my friend Mr. Bernard Manning
has put it:

The Roman Church after the sixteenth century was less corrupt,
freer from scandals, more devoted to its spiritual work, more efficient
in its administration; but it was less free intellectually, less bold, in
all its uses of the Christian tradition, more fearful of exploring into
the unsearchable riches of Christ, than it had been before the Council
of Trent.   It definitely refused to carry with it into modern times
some part of its ancient and medieval heritage.   This happened
partly from reaction against Protestantism.

Well, after the Reformation what happens to Orthodoxy under
Protestantism?   We find one Orthodoxy narrowing itself into
the Lutheran, another (fiercely) in the Calvinistic Church.   A
third, through the polemics of the seventeenth century, despite
the gentle efforts and gentle examples in living of such men as
Herbert, Jeremy Taylor and the Cambridge Platonists, econo-
mized its allowance of Orthodoxy to the Church of England
in the eighteenth century—an Orthodoxy in part political, in
part asleep on formularies, in spirit inert, in daily practice lazy,
choleric only when some intrusive evangelist rang the bell disturbing the afternoon doze: while—to infringe with respect
upon Mr. Eliot's native soil—scarcely had the Pilgrim Fathers
landed on Plymouth Rock before they started to build an
Orthodoxy of their own at least as repressive and rigidly
tyrannous as anything they had fled from.   Escaping across
the Atlantic for liberty of conscience, they found a New
England, cast there the anchor of their souls, landed, and
ran to and fro burning 'witches.'

   I am sorry to have been led even so far as this into ecclesiastical
story: but Mr. Eliot's method so far compels me.   For in my
search after what he means by Orthodoxy in literature I find
him continually sliding off into theology.   Pursuing, I learn
that a *Tradition*, in so far as it differs from Orthodoxy, is a way
of feeling and acting which characterizes a group throughout
generations; and that it must largely be, or that many of the

elements in it must be, unconscious—and here I do not think Mr. Eliot will quarrel with me if I interpret this a little more definitely as 'good manners inherited through breeding,' 'manners' as a term carrying just that moral significance which William of Wykeham intended and bequeathed in his noble motto '*Manners makyth Man*';—'whereas,' Mr. Eliot proceeds, 'the maintenance of Orthodoxy is a matter which calls for the exercise of all our conscious intelligence.' The *maintenance*, then, will be conscious; but Orthodoxy itself 'exists, whether realized in any one's thought or not.' Orthodoxy, again, is 'continuous'; and yet, in Mr. Eliot's words, 'a whole generation might conceivably pass without orthodox thought, or, as by Athanasius, Orthodoxy may be upheld by one man against the world.' These sayings, dropped in the course of a spoken lecture, must have puzzled his audience somewhat; and merely dropped and 'left at that' they *are* puzzling, though not irreconcilable. Still pursuing, I come, in his third and last lecture, to a pronouncement clear enough. 'What I have been leading up to,' he says, 'is the following assertion: that when morals cease to be a matter of tradition and orthodoxy—that is, of the habits of the community formulated, corrected, and elevated by the continuous thought and direction of the Church—and when each man is to elaborate his own, then *personality* becomes a thing of alarming importance.'

(But has it ever been less, in human history?)

IV

Now let me be equally definite in taking up the separate parts of the above composite assertion. I agree, of course, that 'when morals cease to be a matter of tradition . . . and when each man is to elaborate his own, then personality becomes a thing of alarming importance.' It was this, and just this, I was trying to preach to you in my lectures before Christmas on 'The Poet as Citizen'; and if Mr. Eliot uses the tone of authority while I can only attempt persuasion, I must be the more indebted to authority for his backing.

But when he goes on to insist that Tradition requires to be 'formulated, corrected, and elevated by the continuous thought and direction of the Church,' I must cry halt.

To begin with, I doubt if the tradition of any community can ever be 'formulated'—if even its minor unconscious habits can be 'formulated' save in books of etiquette, the rules of which for one generation tend to be a laughing-stock for the next. (Should a man for example wear his hat at table when dining with the King?)   But tradition more vital—tradition in matters which deeply concern the moral, physical, intellectual health of a society—is at once too various and too delicate a thing to be caught, constricted within formulas or creeds by any Church. Take, for instance, poetry; with which and its traditions we have been specially concerned.   When, as a historical fact, have the traditions of poetry been usefully formulated, or even, with the great exception of Dante, considerably directed, by any Church?   Elevated by religious fervour poetry may be, of course, and often has been; as by other passionate convictions theologically orthodox or unorthodox in their day.   The real answer to Mr. Eliot's question 'Why is most religious verse so bad?' is, I should contend, precisely in so far as it has submitted to his own theory.   He accounts for it by the ingenious suggestion that people who write devotional verse are usually writing as they want to feel rather than as they do feel.   I rather believe the great mass of what is called in editorial offices 'Vicarage Verse' to be quite sincere, and bad only because the people who write it are not poets.   Poetry in short is poetry: it has known many creeds and survived them all.   One after another they have discredited and cast down his altars, but Apollo survives.   Whoso would recruit him from one category into another is mixing up things that differ: whoso would enslave him to any flock, be it of Admetus or of the Archbishop of Canterbury, is weaving nets for the wind.

V

But to pass over many questions raised by this claim that 'the Church' should exercise control over our literature, and over poetry in particular—as for example the question put to Dogberry 'How if a will not?' and if so, how punishable, and by whom? We come to the fatal question '*What and which Church?*'

Well, we know from previous declarations of his creed or creeds in religion and politics how Mr. Eliot would like this to be answered. And here I must simply say that, as I read it, literature in England has never in fact submitted to a control so narrow, and (in my hope and belief) never will.

I am sorry, I repeat, to have been dragged by him even so far into the confines of dogmatic theology: but his views of right literature and his illustrations constantly slide off into that; as, to do him justice, they logically must. And, if I may say it without acrimony, those views seem to be largely coloured by a particular hatred of what he calls Liberalism: and I must most seriously protest against the device by which, to present the Liberalism of a century ago, he imposes upon a foreign audience, presumably unacquainted with the story he is telling, a passage of inventive by a writer whose name, if not wholly forgotten, any serious critic to-day would either pass over as negligible among the great antagonists, or select only as a curiosity of forgotten spite. This is how Mr. Eliot adduces his testimony—'There was certainly (he says), a hundred years ago, a relation between the Liberalism which attacked the Church and the Liberalism which appeared in politics.' According to a contemporary, William Palmer, the former group of Liberals

Were eager to eliminate from the Prayer Book the belief in the Scriptures, the Creeds, the worship of Christ. They called for the admission of Unitarian infidels as fellow-believers. They would eviscerate the Prayer Book, reduce the Articles to a few deistic formularies, and reduce religion to a state of anarchy and confusion, etc.

'It is well to remember,' adds Mr. Eliot, 'that this sort of Liberalism was flourishing a century ago; it is also well to remember that it is flourishing still.'

VI

But fair and softly! Who was this William Palmer, whose denunciation of the Liberals in 1843 Mr. Eliot tosses before an audience in Virginia, U.S.A., as true contemporary description, capped by his own *ipse dixit* that 'this sort of Liberalism is flourishing still'? The short footnote in his printed lecture says merely 'Quoted in *Northern Catholicism*, p. 9.' I look up that work (a collection of Anglo-Catholic papers) and find on p. 9 the passage just quoted as testimony, and again 'left at that.' Pursuing, I get at the works of William Palmer, and some contemporary evidence concerning him. He was, admittedly, a very learned man, an Irishman, a violent Anti-papist: who, coming across to Oxford, latish, considerably helped the beginnings of what is called the Oxford Movement by his liturgical information. 'But,' says Newman after a tribute to his gifts, 'he was deficient in depth, and besides'—you must forgive me, gentlemen—the words are Newman's, not mine—'coming from a distance, he had never really grown into an Oxford man.' In brief he was impracticable, positive, irascible as a bull at a hint of the Scarlet Woman: and his methods of controversy invited rebuke for themselves in a pamphlet attributed to M. Renouf and politely, beyond their worth, condescended to by Hurrell Froude. I have studied the work from which Mr. Eliot took his quotation at second hand (*Narrative of Events connected with 'Tracts for the Times'*), and, if you have not guessed it from the very style of the quotation, can only add that his arguments strike me as those of a learned but rather vulgar disputant, originally by nature, provincially by habit, deficient in self-control.

Now had it not been fairer if Mr. Eliot, addressing in Virginia, U.S.A., an audience presumably unacquainted with the story of this eccentric cleric, had quoted against the Liberalism of a hundred years ago the testimony of its foremost contemporary opponent; a voice infinitely more authoritative, a book not only accessible, but now classical? I mean, of course, Newman and his *Apologia*. It had surely been more to his right purpose to take the famous note on 'Liberalism' towards the end of that book. I invite you, gentlemen, to read the whole of Newman's note, the manner of which I have here but time to illustrate by a few sentences.

When [says Newman] in the beginning of the present century [that is, the last century] after many years of moral and intellectual declension, the University of Oxford woke up to a sense of its duties, and began to reform itself, the first instruments of this change, to whose zeal and courage we all owe so much, were naturally thrown together for mutual support, against the numerous obstacles which lay in their path, and soon stood out in relief from the body of residents, who, though many of them men of talent themselves, cared little for the object which the others had at heart. These Reformers, as they may be called, were for some years members of scarcely more than three or four Colleges; and their own Colleges, as being under their direct influence, of course had the benefit of those stricter views of discipline and teaching, which they themselves were urging on the University. They had, in no long time, enough of real progress in their several spheres of exertion, and enough of reputation out of doors, to warrant them in considering themselves the *élite* of the place.

Thus was formed an intellectual circle or class in the University—men, who felt they had a career before them, as soon as the pupils, whom they were forming, came into public; men, whom non-residents, whether country parson or preachers of the Low Church, on coming up from time to time to the old place, would look at, partly with admiration, partly with suspicion, as being an honour indeed to Oxford, but withal exposed to the temptation of ambitious views, and to the spiritual evils signified in what is called the 'pride of reason.'

Nor was this imputation altogether unjust; for, as they were following out the proper idea of a University, of course they suffered more or less from the moral malady incident to such a pursuit. The very object of such great institutions lies in the cultivation of the mind and the spread of knowledge: if this object, as all human objects, has its dangers at all times, much more would these exist in the case of men, who were engaged in a work of reformation, and had the opportunity of measuring themselves, not only with those who were their equals in intellect, but with the many who were below them. In this select circle or class of men, in various Colleges, the direct instruments and the choice fruit of real University Reform, we see the rudiments of the Liberal party.

Now Newman's main argument may be right or may be wrong. But I invite you, remembering that the above sentences were penned by one who had already admitted—to use his own words—that 'from the age of fifteen dogma has been the fundamental principle of my religion: I know no other sort of religion: cannot enter into any other sort of religion'—I invite you to contrast that passage, simply as an example of style in controversy with that other quotation from Mr. William Palmer, and then turn to these few of Newman's own words from his well-known 'Definition of a Gentleman':

If he engages in controversy of any kind, his disciplined intellect preserves him from the blundering discourtesy of better, though less educated, minds; who, like blunt weapons, tear and hack instead of cutting clean, who mistake the point in argument, waste their strength on trifles, and leave the question more involved than they found it. He may be right or wrong in his opinion, but he is too clear-headed to be unjust: he is as simple as he is forcible, and as brief as he is decisive.

It is—as a lawyer would say—'not for me to advise.' Yet think, in Mr. Eliot's place and with his intention, I should have chosen to prefer and present Newman before W. Palmer as a descriptive writer.

VII

But when Mr. Eliot speaks of Tradition I am grateful to him; and the more beholden because, in a voice that carries far beyond mind and in a tone I could not imitate, he was uttering to his audience in Virginia the very caution that I was suggesting here to you—and, as it happened, at the very moment; a warning, that is, and a protest, against the exploitation of self, the intrusion of an author's 'personality' or 'individuality' upon his work; an egoism of late years in fashion, accepted and applauded by critics, by many if not most as a merit in itself, by some as even the first of merits: my contention being rather that in writing as in other arts—as evidently as in social life— self-assertiveness almost infallibly suggests some defect of breeding. In a familiar 'essay,' to be sure, a man may unbosom himself; the more pardonably in proportion as his confessions are worth while. But the familiar essay is a delicate business demanding a curious tact of its own: and success in it carries no warrant for use in larger spheres of writing—in epic, tragedy, history, or the novel. In these the true writer (if I may put it vulgarly) sticks to his job, is immersed in it, and lets his 'personality' take care of itself—which it will certainly do whether he forget it or even, should he be writing history, take pains to exclude it. Consider Thucydides, for example. He begins: 'Thucydides, an Athenian, composed an account of the war between the Peloponnesians and the Athenians. He considered from the beginning that such an account would be valuable.' Thenceforward we have an austere narrative, bonebare even when he himself was mixed up in the events and condemned for failure. He allows no pause for justification or self-excuse. Still in its stride the detailed unemotional inflexible narrative moves on to the terrible climax in the caves of Syracuse — this, even, told austerely. *Then* we realize the whole composition as at once true and a work of art; *then* the power suppressed, the genius commanding it and at length disclosed, the man as characteristic, a giant among historians.

Holding this poor opinion of self-assertiveness obtruding upon art, I was heartened, of course, on reading such passages as these in Mr. Eliot's lectures:

The general effect in literature of the lack of any strong tradition is twofold: extreme individualism in views, and no accepted rules or opinions as to the limitations of the literary job.

That and:

It is true that the existence of a right tradition, simply but its influence upon the environment in which the poet develops, will tend to restrict eccentricity to managable limits: but it is not even by the lack of this restraining influence that the absence of tradition is most deplorable. What is disastrous is that the writer should deliberately give rein to his 'individuality'; that he should even cultivate his differences from others; and that his readers should cherish the author of genius, not in spite of his deviations from the inherited wisdom of the race, but because of them.

Well, this passage might stand as text before some arguments of mine. But there was one which lack of time compelled me to shorten; and I am glad of this opportunity to recall it with a little more insistence: for it concerns a prevalent temper among writers of to-day in most forms of creative work, and in criticism too.

You may or may not remember my inviting your attention to one trap among several baited for artists and critics by this worm of personality—this *eidolon omphalou*, as I may call it. I mean the lure toward self-conceit; expressed in practice by condescension, writing down to one's audience, or (worse) choosing an ignoble subject and writing down to that. On this pretentiousness in contemporary criticism I shall not here dwell. Even when Delphi claimed to be the whole world's navel the voice of Apollo disguised itself in ambiguity, through smoke. With a score or two of Pythians each drawing inspiration from the centre of his own unbelted personality, the hum of the Oracles passes into a noise not less hideous because confused and dissipated.

But for lack of time I must hasten past the critics and come to writers engaged just now upon creative work, whether in poetry or fiction: for these after all are the primary ones in any important age. Whether it belong to post-war disillusionment, or to a curious deflection of our old aristocratic tradition in literature to adapt itself to democracy and instinctively to patronize it—more or less in the style of a grand lady opening a Women's Institute—I think that few students of contemporary poems and novels will deny the almost universal tendency of such writers as this generation has seriously taken, to choose unheroic themes, sordid environments, characters to be dangled as marionettes from aloft and condescendingly explained through commentary.

I shall not ask you to take any assurance of mine about that sort of thing as being about the easiest scamping of real art and to that extent contemptible, however popular. I prefer to quote a passage I came upon, a few weeks ago, in the *Spectator*. A reviewer, Mr. H. E. Bates, wrote thus of a certain novel:

[The writer] is not a great writer but a precious one. His attitude throughout the book is one of superiority. Whereas the great writer credits the reader with an intelligence equal to his own, the lesser writer credits him with less; the great writer keeps himself detached and unseen, never stepping between himself and the picture; but the lesser writer keeps holding himself up, Sir Oracle fashion, with what he considers are vital explanations or remarks of profound philosophical importance.

It may seem pedantic to enforce this by going back to Aristotle and his insistence on nobility of character ($\tau\grave{o}$ $\beta\epsilon\lambda\tau\acute{\iota}o\nu$) as a necessary apanage of the true Tragic Hero. But consider Shakespeare's tragic heroes, and how even their enemies salute them, dead. Recall Antony's grand words over the corpse of

Brutus, with Octavius' echo of them: recall Antony's own last claim:

> a Roman by a Roman
> Valiantly vanquish'd—

and Octavius' coda over him and Cleopatra:

> No grave upon the earth shall clip in it
> A pair so famous.   High events as these
> Strike those that make them: and their story 's
> No less in pity than his glory which
> Brought them to be lamented.

Even poor Timon ends as noble Timon; for Coriolanus the drums are bidden to beat, the pikes to be trailed, for

> the most noble corse that ever herald
> Did follow to his urn.

So, of Hamlet:

> Let four captains
> Bear Hamlet, like a soldier, to the stage;
> . . . and, for his passage,
> The soldiers' music and the rites of war
> Speak loudly for him.

That is the accent by which great writers communicate their magnanimity and teach the rest of us that 'we are greater than we know.'

VIII

I have dwelt at some length on this particular tendency of ego-worship; to belittle the author's theme, patronize his subject, parade what in himself is what an Athenian would have called 'the idiotic,' and to hang (if I may adapt a phrase of Henry James) our frail humanity as a beaten rag upon a clothesline: and have dwelt on this vice, among traps of egoism indicated in my last lecture, because in proportion to its prevalence just now we should thank Mr. Eliot alike for his vigour and his opportuneness in denouncing it.

But I do not thank him for the rhetorical sleight of hand or series of ambiguities by which he palms off this ego-worship as identical with 'Liberalism.' We must remember, of course—and the more vividly for his insistence upon the indelibility of early training—that he is a New Englander addressing an audience in America's conservative South, whose prejudices on a local issue he starts, as a converted missionary, to enlist for his general attack on what he calls 'Liberalism.' What he means by 'Liberalism,' except that it is something he dislikes, one must use patience to discern, so dexterously he shuffles religion into politics, politics into literature, tradition into dogma, to and fro, until the reader—let alone a listener—can scarcely tell out of what category the card (so to speak) is being dealt. Still, if one keeps gripping, as Menelaus and his comrades did upon the Old Man of the Sea, this may be squeezed out—that 'Liberalism' is anything which questions dogma: which dogma, to be right dogma, is the priestly utterance of a particular offset of a particular branch of a historically fissiparous Church.

IX

Well, as Mr. Eliot wisely hints in the course of his lectures, we can none of us escape the shadow of what we learned at our mother's knee. And as my own Alma Mater insisted (perhaps too austerely) upon logic, I find it hard to call myself off from such a roaring scent after the fallacy of the 'Undistributed Middle' as he here puts up. But perhaps the simplest way to go to work is to define what Liberalism means to *me*. Whether you agree or not, we come to a point, and so our business is advanced.

I define 'Liberalism,' then, first as a *habit of mind*. This at once disengages it from formulas, party cries, vestments, or 'shirts' in religion or politics. It is neither a separate stick nor a faggot of opinions out of which, if one be dropped, brand and faggot be involved together and cast as heretical to the fire.

Further, it is a habit of mind which exercises, and claims to exercise, man's right, on this planet in this mysterious universe, surrounded on all hands of ignorance, to lift some veil of that curtain if he can: in short, to think for himself. As I see it, a man owes that effort to his own dignity as well as to the help of his fellows. But at any rate that effort must find itself—as Columbus found it at Salamanca before he could start on discovering the outpost of Mr. Eliot's nativity—in direct opposition to dogmatic clerical assurance that there was not, nor could be, any such place.

And—yet further—let me say that this claim for the free operation of man's mind has been, if you will consider it, gentlemen, the fount and inspiration of the greatest literature bequeathed through centuries to civilized Europe—and our inheritance yet to be nursed in increase, not for our sake alone (since charity lies at its emotional base), but for others until the comity of Europe recover its balance. Go farther back than Plato if you will: but start, if you will, with Plato and the dogmas upon which his thought operated for enlightenment. Follow literature down—But no! What has Newman himself, the fairest upholder of dogma, to admit of the Western world's literature?—

He must confess, surveying it in a series of *Lectures to the Roman Catholic University of Ireland*, that the contribution of dogmatic writers to it has been negligible: in Italy, France, England alike—all but null. He faces the admission of England that 'a literature, when it is formed, is a national and historical fact; it is a matter of the past and the present, and can be as little ignored as the present, as little undone as the past.' If his co-religionists have to build a new literature upon dogma, they must start upon a new one. And who, reviewing the great names in our own literature, however curiously, can hold that as a solid phalanx they do not stand for this free play of the human mind?—Chaucer, Langland, Spenser, Shakespeare (I dare say I may claim through age and circumstance, to have heard as much as any of you to Shakespeare's discredit, while never yet that he was illiberal), Milton, Dryden, Blake, Coleridge, Shelley, Byron, Landor; Bacon, Locke, Berkeley, Newton, Butler, Darwin; Fielding, Johnson, Scott, Dickens. . . . Which of these do we not connect, as part of our indebtedness to them, with the unhampered play, imaginative or strictly 'scientific,' of man's mind?

And so—and if we read the story right—this 'Liberalism' which Mr. Eliot arraigns as a worm, eating into the traditions of our society, reveals itself rather as Tradition itself, throughout literature (which is thought worth setting down and recording) the organic spirit persisting, aerating, preserving, the liberties our ancestors won and we inherit.

x

All great principles have their risks: else they were not worth fighting for.   No one disputes that a man's liberty to think his own thoughts and express them in words can be abused, even as the liberty of the Press is daily abused among us: that it may be pleaded as condoning, if not justifying, much that is eccentric, even frantic.   Such is the price; and in this world the inestimable jewel of freedom can only be had at a price.   For my part I cannot see how any one can study our English literature—for six centuries now a 'glory of our blood and state' and yet a most 'substantial thing'—without feeling that in his blood and state this liberty of thought is not only a tradition but its dominant tradition, web and woof; or mistrust the sleight that would pass it off on us for bastard, as a sophism offending fact, repulsive to intelligence.   I turn to Milton:

Fool! he sees not the firm root out of which we all grow, though into branches.

Here, in this your University, the field of our literature is spread before you for your judgment. To that I leave it, reminding you only that Milton and Wordsworth were her sons who is now your mother: that Milton wrote this:

Lords and commons of England, consider what nation it is whereof ye are and whereof ye are the governors; a nation . . . not beneath the reach of any point that human capacity can soar to.

And Wordsworth:

> We must be free or die, who speak the tongue
> That Shakespeare spake: the faith and morals hold
> Which Milton held—

Trite words: but as true to-day and imperative as when they were written. For—and to conclude—what is the alternative? What the dirty trump card ever up dogma's sleeve is to be slid down and sneaked, upon opportunity? It is suppression; tyranny (as Pascal defined it 'the determination to get in that way what you cannot in another'); in its final brutal word— force. Look around Europe to-day and consider under what masks dogma is not feeling for, or openly shaking, this weapon to cow the minds of free men; and ask yourselves if it be not the inherited duty of our race to vindicate the tradition of that liberty which was the ark within the citadel of our fathers' souls.

THE SCHOLARLY DON

LET me start with the simple proposition that there is such a thing in the world as a love of learning.

I suppose that a university in these days should serve two main purposes. It should (1) be a seat of learning, and (2) it should educate youth. On these apparently simple postulates the friends and foes of Oxford and Cambridge usually agree to start, and I shall take them in their order.

For the first, then, I would meet any direct attack with a straight challenge. If any man deny that Oxford and Cambridge to-day are seats of learning—nay of great learning—one can only suppose that he does not know what he is talking about. In the matter of information alone (and information alone is but a handmaid to culture) no two cities in this land or in any other possess a larger stock; and that not only stored in libraries, but available from the lips of men variously eminent in knowledge and generous to impart it: since the more a man knows the tenderer he will be as a rule to ignorance, himself aware of the little his own industry has won from the vast amount of ignorance surrounding us all. 'Knowledge,' says Bacon, 'be it in quantity more or less, if it be taken without the true corrective thereof, hath in it some nature of venom or malignity; and some effects of that venom which is ventosity or swelling. The corrective spice, the mixture whereof maketh knowledge so sovereign, is charity.' A resident in Oxford or Cambridge must be either exceptionally shy or exceptionally self-confident if he have missed finding this charity of knowledge at his service. 'Freely ye have received; freely give.' It is one of the pleasures of life in either place that, if you lack some information for your purpose on any particular point, there is always a friend down the next street to supply or help you to it.

The adversary, however, is usually too wise to risk a frontal attack. He will grant the learning but assert (among other objections presently to be considered) that the mass of it is 'useless'; that it deals with past history, dead languages, etc., that it 'doesn't pay'; and he will point to the admitted fact that a number of the most learned professors fail to fill their lecture rooms. But this, to start with, begs the question. It assumes the value of learning to correspond with its immediate market price, whereas in the whole world there is no greater fallacy, or string of fallacies, than can be hung round the question 'Does it pay?' Even the blessed word 'efficiency' is a relative term, at once inviting the question 'Efficiency *for what*?' A generous mind (which, as I understand it, a university exists to cultivate) knows that a number of the very best things in the world do not pay—for the simple reason that they are priceless. Tempted to stray for a moment beyond my immediate subject, I might ask if it paid Columbus to insist that the earth was round, or Galileo that it rotated, or Harvey that the blood circulates.

But I must confine myself here to the favourite object of attack—Greek and Latin, the 'Classics.' Now the most difficult assailant to meet on this ground is the self-made man who proclaims, 'Sir, I had never a smattering of either, and look at Me!' Well, you do; and precisely because a polite education has given you a smattering (say) of both, your tongue is tied, the *argumentum ad hominem* which he challenges is just what a different training forbids.

To the wiser I would suggest that Greek and Latin have no rivals in cultivating a certain *habit of mind*, which, being slow of acquisition, cannot (any more than fine manners) be tied up with string and delivered over the shop counter in a parcel. It is not only not 'Woolworth's'; it has nothing to do with mass production or quick returns. No genuine work for man's lasting health can ever be produced in that way. We may go on amusing ourselves with cinematic sketches of civilization's slow past and equally popular advice on making existence move quicker and faster—always faster, but to what end? We may employ a hundred specialists to vie in discovering the last

N

refinement in poison gas.   That again would be 'practical'—but for what final purpose save to obliterate decent society?   In Greece, and in Athens especially, there happened to emerge a habit of mind which, united with a disinterested curiosity in the scheme of creation, has set the example to all European 'culture'; in Rome there grew up two systems—of jurisprudence and of government—which to-day enshrine all the principles of law and order.   No doubt the ancients knew less of astronomy, of geometry, of mathematics than we knew, less of painting and perhaps less of poetry.   But I speak of the habit of mind which laid the foundations.

Moreover, let no one contemn Greek and Latin as dead languages, spent and therefore *not dangerous*.   Twice already in what is labelled as 'Modern History,' Greek has revived, to explode and blow, first a realm of Papacy and, next, a whole chain of Bourbon dynasties sky-high.   Let the simple narratives of Plutarch, for example, once get out of control by the educated and into the heads of the community—as in the French Revolution and the Italian *risorgimento*—and you never can tell what may happen.

But (continues the objector) your eminent Professors of Greek and Latin do not *spread* their learning; do not publish world-compelling books; do not attract large classes; are not even sociable in conversation.   It were idle, perhaps, to refer one who falls back upon this ground to Browning's *A Grammarian's Funeral* as probably hinting a part at least of the answer.   He would be perplexed.   So after pointing out that the ground *has* been shifted—away from the value of knowing for its own sake to the vulgar presumption that universities exist—not primarily alone, but wholly for the instruction of youth—I will take him on this ground also.   Be it admitted that the more deeply a man explores his subject, the further he will be led to consider the views of those who have studied and thought upon it before him; the more conscious he will feel of his own fallibility in the fog of ignorance encompassing us all.   He will read on and on, and a growing modesty (weighted maybe with a touch of scorn) will deter him from seeking such positive assertions as are made by hastier, less-informed men. Be it further admitted that in some the very weight of their knowledge induces timidity. They start on a Preface or Introduction, and are forthwith daunted by the crowd of pros and cons, through which the argument has to cut its way, while yet accounting for them. Moreover, in the pursuit of much reading they have missed the knack of lucid writing, which can only be won by practice; and so many of our great scholars have died with the *magnum opus* unwritten, left but in note-books, scraps, hieroglyphics, of which their executors can make nothing.

But, as a fact, the 'output' (as our critic would phrase it) of Classical scholarship by Oxford and Cambridge will stand against that of any two universities in the world, and is continuous, as the critic might assure himself by a study of current book-catalogues, together with listed reports and 'proceedings' of learned societies. On top of these he might consider (say) the *New English Dictionary* and ask himself how that monument of our time could have been based or built save on the trained judgment and patient industry of classical scholars: in which industry, he might, if generous, detect also something of the *noblesse oblige* of their order.

As for the sneer that few pupils attend the lectures of these eminent ones, a brief reflection should tell him that the higher the learning the narrower will shrink the number of those qualified to listen to it with profit—a rule of common sense that applies, one might imagine, to most occupations in life. The universities provide other lectures, diverse and plenty—informative or stimulating, as the subject requires or the student needs. Waiving that simple but important fact, let me assure the critic of my own young experience and later daily observation, that these eminent men are privately, constantly, at the call of any undergraduate, however elementary his attainment, to discuss, instruct, advise. A very few weeks ago, in a letter to

The Times, the present Master of Trinity, having to point out a general proposition, modestly (as he would) disclosed—'let out' as it were—how he had once helped a pupil in mathematics.

One who came to us in his third year was described by his tutor as idle, stupid, and very unlikely to get through his Tripos. I agreed with his tutor until we began to study the mathematics of collisions between spheres. I knew he was fond of billiards and I pointed out to him that the mathematics we were doing gave reasons why he should play certain shots in the way he did. The effect was remarkable. He had never before had any conception that mathematics could have any connection with anything that could interest a rational being. He began to work like a nigger and in one year's work got a good place among the Senior Optimes.

Now this is but a striking example of what in a less striking way daily happens in every 'School' or Faculty in Oxford and Cambridge; and in it lies the familiar, though seldom advertised, virtue of the tutorial system—that easy intercourse connoted by the phrase 'I am reading with So-and-so'; in either place a *habit*, a quiet system, in which old and young keep their places, but meet in friendly understanding.

The dons naturally do not talk about this; seldom or never trouble to defend themselves; in fact, do *not* talk much, and are consequently arraigned as dull fellows by the outside world. This is a trifling matter; but, having some experience of what our most persistent denouncer can do when he shares our hospitality, I can affirm that he at any rate has never given our powers of conversation a chance; never allowing our grave interest to stray from the fascinating theme of himself. To be sure the play of talk at a table from which women are excluded must, in the nature of things, lack much of civility and charm. But we do our best: and Hazlitt's remark that 'You will hear more good things in one day on the top of a coach, going and coming from Oxford, than in one year from all the residents in that learned seminary' seems to me, apart from its extravagance, at once obvious and stupid—so obvious, indeed, that its stupidity may be left without comment. As a pendant to it, equally without comment, I will leave to my supposed adversary on this point a small story as a present. Entertaining a distinguished guest at my own present college, in Combination Room after dinner the Senior Fellow (an eminent classic, now defunct) politely inquired, 'I suppose, Mr. Astronomer Royal, the old notion prevalent in my youth, that the moon had some influence on the tides, has in these days been *quite* exploded?'

Now, without going into details—innumerable and not to be embarked upon in a short paper—of the training offered by Oxford and Cambridge to their undergraduate members, I invite the reader to draw some general conclusions with me.

First, it cannot be denied that Oxford and Cambridge are venerable, were it but historically for the sake of the illustrious host that have taught and learnt, resided in or passed through them; on that the mind of a newcomer, so it be of any gentle quality, will yield to this impression:

> I could not print
> Ground where the grass had yielded to the steps
> Of generations of illustrious men
> Unmoved. I could not always lightly pass
> Through the same gateways, sleep where they had slept,
> Wake where they waked, range that inclosure old,
> That garden of great intellects undisturbed . . .

And this veneration is not merely retrospective. It and its virtue continue alive and active, hospitable to each new generation. It was a proud thing (I must not speak of to-day) for a boy to belong to a society which included a Thomas Hill Green, a Robinson Ellis, an Ingram Bywater; or a Munro, a Westcott, a Henry Maine, a Clerk-Maxwell. These men were as lanterns attracting youth to receive the light and carry it on. Prestige is a word open to unworthy connotation; but no snobbery can be attached to the prestige these conferred. Where would our electricians be to-day but for Clerk-Maxwell? In what measure inconsiderable the influence of Jowett on minds that have ruled large dominions under the Crown? Or, to take a man who neither knew nor courted publicity—Who can count the many diverse debts owed by students to Henry Bradshaw, some time University Librarian of Cambridge—of whom Mommsen said: 'If I'd had a shorthand-writer with me, I could have got in half an hour's talk enough materials to have made an interesting volume.'

Of the beauty of the two gardened places and what it means —of what the Bodleian, for instance, or Magdalen Tower, or King's College Chapel and the nigh river bridges, have meant through life to those who have passed, during three years or so, under their shadow, I need not speak. 'But they are medieval.' Yes, as I put it once in a lecture: 'As they stand, Oxford and Cambridge—so alike while they play at differences and both so unlike anything else in the world—do by a hundred daily reminders connect us with the Middle Ages, or, if you prefer Arnold's phrase, "Whisper their lost enchantments." The cloister, the grave grace in hall, the chapel choir, the men hurrying into their surplices or to lectures "with the wind in their gowns," the stair-case, the nest of chambers within the oak—all these softly rever-berate over our life here, as from belfries, the medieval mind.' Yes, and transmuted through the medieval, the classical mind also, to modern uses.

It is because these two universities are not *devised* institutions, constructed by theorists or by politicians (Laud himself reformed of inner knowledge, though he imposed his reforms from with-out), but have grown and grown slowly with the national character, that external interference, however well intended, has so often defeated its own object.

Let me conclude with one instance of development by this process of growth. Simply because men of eminent learning set up their desks in these two places, young scholars flocked to them from north and south and from all over Europe; because this young multitude was naturally turbulent, wise authority used a model at hand, the monastic system, to separate it into colleges under rule.   As the experiment succeeded, the colleges multiplied; every poor scholar being assigned to a senior for advice and supervision.   All this, of course, is elementary: but not everybody recognizes that out of this grew the flower of university life, which is friendship.

For the dons (you say) are dumb fellows, and on this point they certainly are.   One has to live long and intimately among them before realizing, and then with difficulty, their innumerable acts of kindness, help over young troubles, self-sacrifice, quiet and secret benevolence; and they are not rich men.   As for the undergraduates, let Bagehot speak, no sparing critic:

There is nothing for young men like being thrown into close neighbourhood with young men; it is the age of friendship; and every encouragement should be given—every opportunity enlarged for it. Take an uncollegiate Englishman and you will generally find that he has *no friends*.   He has not the habit.   He has his family, his business, his acquaintances, and these occupy his time.   He has not been thrown during the breathing-time of human life into close connection with those who are also beginning or thinking of beginning to enter on its labours.   School friendships are childish; after-life rarely brings many; it is in youth alone that we can engrave deep and wise friendships on our close and stubborn texture.   If there be romance in them, it is a romance which few would tear aside.

Be it added as an advantage of university life over that of any training college, that as this concourse of youth is taught in various subjects and for different careers, its intercourse gives a catholicity to its friendships and, albeit insensibly, a grasp on one of the most useful truths in life—that it takes all sorts to make a world.   In disputation—and 'dialectic' has ever been traditional at Oxford and Cambridge, once a serious academic exercise, now a half-serious sport—it is no bad thing for a youngster to talk some folly, very good for him to have the froth blown off by a cheerful exhortation not to make an ass of himself, or 'Tell us something you know something about.'

But I am being tempted beyond my theme; and shall end by asserting that if learning be valuable for its own sake and beyond any price to be put in ledgers; if it be a reward of life to live in the affectionate remembrance of men whom he helped as youths, and another to have spent his days in guarding a high tradition while stewarding a beautiful estate; then the Scholarly Don has no call to answer for himself.   But, though

The gratitude of men has oftener left him mourning, he and the shades of many I have walked with beside the perpetual streams of Isis and Granta will let pass this tribute with a smile.

SEA STORIES: A CHANCE CATALOGUE

THE reader, at this time of year supposed to be on holiday, is invited to visit a certain room overlooking the sea. It served the family once on a time as day nursery.

> He that hath found some fledg'd bird's nest may know
> At first sight if the bird be flown . . .

The toys have gone—some relegated upstairs to the attics, others parted with (and, when it came to the tailless rocking-horse, not without some natural tears) to endow the infants' department of the elementary school up the hill. But the room keeps its mementoes in pictures on the wall, some bits of pottery on the mantelshelf and, specially, a plain table covered with a cloth of check red-and-blue, its pattern by no means beautiful but recovered, after a religious search through London, as ancestrally 'the proper one for the children' and since from time to time renewed as their affection for it insisted.

But the real monument of this bared room remains: its long and large bookcase, to which paterfamilias has, even yet, to resort sometimes in desperate hunt after a book missing from the library. Sometimes he discovers it, oftener not more than once—to interrupt the narrative for a moment—he has been caught, held up in his search, by a wild surmise—a stab, so to speak, of wonder at the mysteries of childhood, of contrition perhaps for some thorn he might have extracted, some seated inward trouble he should have guessed but did not. How or why in the world, for instance, or when, did Law's *Serious Call to a Devout and Holy Life* come to be wedged here between *The Three Musketeers* and *Mr. Midshipman Easy*? Did it mark some intermittent resolve 'to be good'?—something, for example, having happened with the catapult, as in the Nicomachean Ethics? No such hypothesis, at any rate, will account for the close companionship of *Epipsychidion* and Mr. W. W. Jacobs's *Many Cargoes* — admirable compositions both, but seldom associated in the grown-up mind as next-door neighbours or even as on visiting terms.   Maternal suggestion—its sagacity admitted, its profundity not—is that Miss X, late governess, probably left it (*Epipsychidion*) behind her.   Well, to be sure, Miss X had her off moments, or so at least one was assured. But so have children for that matter: mighty odd ones and hours of them.   As a rustic philosopher once remarked: 'You can usually account for a cheeld afore he comes; but once he's here—good Lord!'

> A boy's will is the wind's will
> And the thoughts of youth are long, long thoughts.

It should have been announced earlier that the proprietors of the bookcase came of old seafaring stock, its later blood tinged —not tainted, one hopes—with some infusion of literature. Therefore, of course, Longfellow is here, well thumbed.   And why not?   'A white man, but no poet'—one has heard it said of him.   But surely it must be a superfoetation of culture (and how Blake, for instance, would have scorned it!) which forbids a poet to move the simple simply and denies the title to one who can awake the young heart to romance with such a verse as

> Sails of silk and ropes of sendal,
>   Such as gleam in ancient lore;
> And the singing of the sailors,
>   And the answer from the shore.

Mrs. Alice Meynell, including *The Ancient Mariner* in her anthology *The Flower of the Mind*, added a note: 'This poem is surely more full of a certain quality of extreme poetry—the complete flower of the mind, the most single magic—than any other in our language.   But the reader must be permitted to call the story silly.'   He may also go a bit farther and hit on the reflection that in this very 'silliness' lies no small part of the secret of the poem, its essence, its 'poetry'; in short,

> The silly buckets on the deck,
>   That had so long remained,
> I dreamt that they were fill'd with dew.

A certain divine foolishness belongs to the true sea-story, is as proper to it as to a fairy-tale. Take up almost any story of Marryat's, of Ballantyne's, and you find this the inspiration of the young runaway, its hero. If romantic poetry sprang in Coleridge's time from a 'renascence of wonder,' here in observable fact, in the person of 'the small apple-eating urchin whom we know,' is renascence perpetual with the race; a restless instinct often incurable by age, hardship, repeated disillusion; seized upon and interpreted by many writers under many personifications—Robinson Crusoe, Simon Danz, who, at home among his tulips in a landscape dotted with water-mills,

> thinks he shall take to the sea again,
> For one more cruise with his buccaneers,

Ulysses (Tennyson's), Mr. Kipling's mariners in heaven 'plucking at their harps, and they plucked unhandily' to the Last Chantey:

> And the ships shall go abroad
> To the Glory of the Lord
> Who heard the silly sailor-folk and gave them back their sea.

'Wonder' would seem to be the nerve of it. 'They that go down to the sea in ships, and occupy their business in great waters, these men see the works of the Lord and his wonders in the deep. . . . This great and wide sea also. . . . There go the ships: there is that Leviathan. . . .'

This wonder, operating upon simplicity as in a fairy-tale, is best served in a sea-story, as in a fairy-tale, by perfectly plain straightforward narrative. The horizon lies straight, level, open as the palm of your hand: the marvels begin over the drawn line of it, and on that edge belief or disbelief will hang suspended. For this reason, for some time to their parents' surprise, the children declined to get excited over Conrad—save by *Youth*, that little masterpiece. They not only wanted more sea and less psychology: they complained against a kind of story that was always filling and backing; as one of them observed idiomatically, it was like steering a monkey by the tail. Paterfamilias, skirting Conrad, surmised another snag ahead. Parents are apt to take it for granted that the idols of their own youth will be acceptable to their offspring, and to choose books for birthday and Christmas presents accordingly. A little to the left of Conrad lay a shoal of these with affectionate inscription on their fly-leaves—*Tom Cringle's Log, The Cruise of the 'Midge,'* Dana's *Two Years Before the Mast,* and others—long-winded yarns composed by seamen in days of long-winded voyages for readers as patient as themselves in expectation of port. Would the young of a hastier generation be as patient? The worn condition of the books is reassuring. 'Soiled copies,' too, are the scattered Marryats—*Easy, Peter Simple, Snarleyyow, Frank Mildmay, The King's Own* (the tears of an aunt, long ago, had bedewed an earlier copy of this last), and a few of Herman Melville's, down to *White Jacket.* The belated 'discovery' of Melville by our intelligentsia had not lacked comment at the time in a household the head of which had lost in the early nineties, by the toss of a coin with a friend, the delectable name 'Fayaway,' coveted by each for his own small yacht.

On evidence of the bindings, interest in Kingston's famous tetralogy, passionate over *The Three Midshipmen,* declined almost mathematically between it and *The Three Admirals.* (But do not nine-tenths of us grow less interesting with advancement, if not with age? How could Dumas have achieved that last triumph, the *Vicomte de Bragelonne* but by weaving incident around a great heart which had lost its companions and missed promotion?) In the works, too, of 'Ballantyne the Brave' a like decline of interest becomes painfully convincing if one takes them down from their haphazard jumble on the shelf and rearranges them in chronological order as they were written; the reason for it apparent even more painfully. Increasing doses of pietism, of 'improvement,' of talky-talky; too, too much powder in the jam! The clean, unconsciously cruel, instinct of childhood rejected this as it had rejected *Masterman Ready,* and as it would have rejected any intrusion of the schoolmaster upon a fairy-tale. But Ballantyne at his best, as in *The Coral Island*!

In *The Swiss Family Robinson* this intrusion or infection by the schoolmaster—in guise of a papa capable of everything as Habakkuk and in botany omniscient as Solomon, who 'spake of trees, from the cedar-tree that is in Lebanon even unto the hyssop that springeth out of the wall,' not to mention the rum shrub of Burnand's parody—had been confessedly deterrent to the children's zest; in their language he was 'a whale': was, in fact, very like a whale, and overpowering. Barring papa the book had all the best ingredients—the wreck, salvage, hunt for provisions, carpenter's work with necessity mother to invention—the house in the tree, a superlative stroke. It was Defoe, of course, who first discovered the fascination of carpentry in such a tale, of improvising a hut with stockade complete. *The Coral Island*, taking this over, raised the young mud-pie sand-castle-building imagination to its proper *n*th by employing three boys for its wrecked castaways. On top of this the story worked in a ferocious pirate and an escape. What nearer to the real thing was ever devised until Sir James Barrie came along and in *Peter Pan* subtilized Scottish with Scottish, the rather heavy fun of Ballantyne's Peterkin with his own wistful finer wit?

For a sustained narrative of castaway contrivance, with the open boat business thrown in, Charles Reade's *Foul Play* can be as highly commended, and to middle age more highly. One can scarcely name a prose novelist superior to Reade when he forgets for a while his fads, propaganda, petty squabbles, besetting vulgarities, and fairly lets his genius loose on a sustained epic narrative, such as (among others) that of the homeward voyage of the *Agra* in *Hard Cash*. Invention again, with carpentry turned scientific and its tools beaten into piston-rods, is the motive-power in Jules Verne: his special literary gift a power over what Aristotle called the 'probable impossible.' He commands a vessel carefully equipped with every appliance for hunting the snark; with the latest thing in sextants he finds the sun a trifle wide of due north at noon, reports this, and the reader as chief officer 'makes it so' without a twinge; for the ship's log has been forewarning this or something like it all along, with entries of 'corroborative detail intended to give artistic verisimilitude' to a narrative which, however, is neither bald nor unconvincing, but rather so convincing in its logical flow of detail that a young student of *The English at the North Pole* from this bookcase did once, on hearing of its reported discovery by a lot of Americans, stand up and indignantly protest that it had been done some years before and it was a dirty trick to sneak the credit of it off Captain Hatteras just because he happened at present to be in a lunatic asylum and could not contradict this rumour.

Jules Verne, then, is fairly well represented; and here are *Treasure Island,* of course, *The Master of Ballantrae, The Cruise of the 'Cachalot'*; a row of W. W. Jacobs, another of Frank Stockton (blessings on Mrs. Lecks and Mrs. Aleshine!), another of Clark Russell headed by *The Wreck of the 'Grosvenor,'* of which the legend is that one member of the family sat up all night to finish it by the ray of a smuggled candle. Indeed you will meet in it a thrill to match Crusoe's discovery of the footprint—a thrill conveyed in seven words:

At this moment I missed the carpenter.

The array of fiction on the shelves, it should be said, includes many of the old and tried novelists (Dickens, for instance, in a row almost complete, with, possibly to the visitor's surprise, sets of Disraeli, Mrs. Gaskell, even Jane Austen; nursery books, 'Lears,' 'Alices,' Miss Potters, Leslie Brookes, Andrew Lang's multicolour fairy books, all in a right profusion and confusion. But the sea-faring books predominate: and lest this chance catalogue be held to have favoured fiction beyond all proportion, let us hastily weigh in James's *Naval History,* Brassey's index to the same, half a dozen other volumes of the Navy Record

Society, an Oppenheim or two, Captain Cook's Journals, Dampier, Shelvocke, a Hakluyt condensed 'for the young'; and top these with a full armful of strictly practical—*The Channel Pilot, Yachtsman's Guide, Textbook of Navigation and Nautical Astronomy, The Sailing Boat,* stray numbers of *The Mariner's Mirror,* in publications of the old (now the Royal) Cruising Club, *Hints for Navigation:* these and their like in plenty to choose from.

Add to them a selection of 'single-handed' books, full of practical stuff set down by solitaries who loved the sea, avoided their fellows, and yet by exploring out-of-the-way creeks, channels, havens, and charting them, have left, beneficently if not benevolently, whole stacks of helpful soundings, with hints and cautions. As notable among these we may choose McMullen's *Down Channel* and five volumes of *Sailing Tours,* by the late Frank Cowper ('Tom Allalone'). Internal evidence hints broadly enough that McMullen could never get along with any crew he shipped; while Cowper, as any one's shipmate, would start with rancour and continue it ashore. But each was a redoubtable man of his hands. Cowper closed his career as a Beaufort Brother in the famous Hospital of St. Cross, *juxta* Winchester; McMullen met an end more to his liking; he was found, dead and cold, in mid-Channel, his hand still stiff on the tiller of his boat *Perseus,* apparently holding her close up and along the stairway of the moon:

> —for my purpose holds
> To sail beyond the sunset and the baths
> Of all the western stars until I die.
> It may be that the gulfs will wash us down,
> It may be we shall touch the Happy Isles.

But dearest, perhaps, of all the books in the case—rich treasuries of equal excitement for old and young—have been Mr. Basil Lubbock's epical yet scholarly books on the great sailing clippers, *The China Clippers, The Colonial Clippers,* with *The Log of the 'Cutty Sark,'* and their great homeward races with

their cargoes of tea or of wool. Could ever a finish be more
thrilling than that neck-and-neck one, all the way up the
Channel, between *Taeping* and *Ariel*, leaders of the China fleet
of eleven in 1866? All Mincing Lane and half the City had
bets on the result:

All day the two ships surged up Channel together going 14 knots,
with royal stunsails and all flying kites set, the wind being strong
from W.S.W.

The Lizard lights were abeam at 8 a.m. and Star Point at noon.
Towards 6 p.m., when off Portland both ships were compelled to
take in their Jamie Greens in order to get the anchors over. At
7.25 p.m. St. Catherines bore north one mile, and soon after midnight Beachy Head was abeam, distant five miles. All this time
there had been no alteration to speak of in the distance between the
two vessels—*Ariel* kept her lead, gaining a little as the wind
freshened, and letting *Taeping* up again as it took off.

For the issue, suspended until the last moment, the reader of
this extract must go to the book itself, as also for details of the
Homeric rivalry between *Thermopylae* and *Cutty Sark* and their
great duel of 1872. *Cutty Sark*, after many and moving vicissi-
tudes, has come to anchor and honourable old age in Falmouth
Harbour. *Thermopylae* has passed into a name, a shade. The
youngsters know *Cutty Sark*, therefore, and worship every line
of her; but because the present writer has talked with survivors
from the service of both, as an elder he keeps up his end for
Thermopylae, with the gilt 'Cock of the Sea' on her truck: the
pride of our Merchant Service, 'justly considered by most seamen,' says Mr. Lubbock, 'the fastest sailing ship ever launched':
a witch in conjuring speed out of light airs. She has been
known to have gone along seven knots an hour when a man
could have walked round her decks with a lighted candle; in a
steady quartering breeze she would reach thirteen comfortably,
her helm amidships and a small boy steering:

> Men are we, and must grieve when even the shade
> Of that which once was great is passed away.

Even the shades of these, of their Australian trade sisters, of the Clyde-built rounders of the Horn, their last successors, have passed—the final death warrant dates back to the cutting of the Panama Canal. A Dutch story, *The Johanna Maria*, nobly solemnizes the close of a noble era. It is a love story: the beloved a ship, her life-long lover and pursuer a simple sail-maker; and when at length he wins her and as a bridegroom brings her home he is old and she a 'museum-piece':

With topmasts and yards struck the ship lay moored in the Dijksgracht, near the place where she had first taken the water. Boys from the training-ship and from the navigation school who came to row stopped to look at her from bow to stern. . . . The people walking over the Mariniersborg stood still, pointed and said, 'a sailing ship, the old days.' Rarely was any one seen on board, only two grizzled men and a negro and sometimes in the evening there was the sound of music.

Yet it remains a consolation for some of us to have known the sailing ship as she trod the waters in that sunset of which the last rays lie up her achieved perfection. *Et vera incessu patuit dea.* . . . Even goddesses die, and many queens have gone to execution: none more royally than this one in all her high-piled pride.

TWO EPIGRAMS

I

A GARDEN SPEAKS
(After Arabius)

WATERS and orchards are mine, trellis of apple and vine
    Ordered, and bordered below the sea caresses my wall;
Plenty of all that I lack pours from the farm at my back,
    Tribute of fish at my feet from the smack unlading her haul.
Ye that of me are possest nightly securely may rest
Lulled, with the song-weary bird in his nest, by the ferryman's
    call.

II

ON THE CNIDIAN VENUS
(App. Planud: Author unknown)

'Wretch!'—by her statue in Cnidos soliloquized Aphrodite—
'When did Praxiteles catch me without a chemise, or a nightie?'

OBITUARY OF GUSTAVE DAVID
1936

AMONG vanished and fast vanishing features of the Cambridge Market Hill, none will be searched for by habitual eyes and missed with a keener sense of loss than he.

Gustave David was born in 1860 in Paris, where his father kept a small antique-shop. Four years later the family—of French descent crossed with Hebrew—moved to Switzerland, where the child received his early education in three languages; thence in the seventies, under what mysterious direction is not known, migrated to England, to start a book-trade in Gorleston. 'At that time,' says Boswell, writing of 1709, of Lichfield and of Dr. Johnson's father, 'booksellers' shops in the provincial towns of England were very rare "and might only earn with assiduity" a reasonable share of wealth.' One may guess that in one hundred and fifty years or more Gorleston had scarcely overtaken Michael Johnson's Lichfield as a literary mart. At any rate another move was made, this time to London; where Gustave, now a grown man, set up in a small business of his own. Whether it wilted, or a narrow street in the capital palled on him, or (let us believe) urged by the daemon of his genius, one day he put up his shutters, headed for Cambridge, and erected a stall; and there for many generations (as generations are counted here) was a centre of his own amid ancient colleges, accepted as belonging to a 'University' which, literally translated, means 'all of Us.'

There it just *was*. And there he stood on all working days save Thursday and Saturday; always smoking but at your service; inscrutable with a subdolent smile which lit up something like affection on the approach of some tried favourite among his clients. (His greeting of the late Charles Whibley, for instance, had to be witnessed to correct any one's estimate of his own worth in the scale of David's.) On Saturdays, when the merry costers invaded the market, like some grave Tyrian trader he withdrew to the neighbouring eminence of Pease Hill, and there, among the fried-fish stalls, undid his corded bales. Also, if you had hesitated over a purchase, or passed in too great a hurry to snap it up, the odds were you would miss it for ever. It had been swept back overnight into his shop, in which to recover it was to search for a needle in a haystack. Legend even held that he disposed each day's surplus stock under the *hic jacets* of St. Edward's churchyard. On Thursdays he attended the book sales in London. His method of bidding and buying there must have obeyed some steady system into which it is no business of ours to inquire. But his system of pricing and selling, long tested, could be accepted as an honest conspiracy of help between dealer and purchaser. It was based (if I understand it) on the working out in the long run of a simple, modest, and reasonable percentage. He must have been wise enough to know the money's worth of many a *trouvaille*, but sacrificed that knowledge to his noble reputation for probity.

A spice of vanity may have mixed itself into this, as into most men's high purposes: but it once led to the defeat of a lower one. A few years ago some friends and admirers planned a luncheon in his honour, and would have decorated the front of the menu card with a photogravure of David, singular and familiar personification of something in the *genius loci*. Unhappily, getting wind of this, he faced the photographer in a 'gent's boater,' frock coat, light trousers, and white spats. At the subsequent luncheon in the hall of Trinity his emotion, expressed in manner rather than in words, went straight to the hearts of all the large company gathered.

An obituary notice in the *Cambridge Daily News* tells us that 'his great ambition was to retire and collect old books.' This to many will suggest a possible parallel with Omar Khayyám's wonder:

> What the Vintners buy
> One half so precious as the stuff they sell.

May the stall he founded, and so curiously made his own and the University's, long stand on Market Hill!

MONUMENTS

BY all means practise thou to live alone,
  Hardening thy talent to a monument
On a high moor, impervious, a stone
Whereby the reverent pilgrim, pitching tent
    Shall kneel to trace
The legend on its lichened northern face,
And say 'Here was a Master, by God's grace.'

But in the valley, where thy brothers keep
  And sisters, that in duty grow—as trees
O'ercharging ladders where the salmon leap,
Or shading cattle, or sheltering cottages—
    Their temporal race
Continues in the plowman's steady pace
To grave a deeper legend, by God's grace.

FAITHFUL JANE

A CHRISTMAS STORY

I

JOHN BERRYCOMBE having crossed the public ferry (on a Sunday twopence for foot passengers, there and back) took a path which led up through and along the woods to descend and join the high road by Reselda Creek, thereby shortening his journey by half a mile.

Reselda Creek (locally Reselda 'Pyll') is actually a creek no longer. Detritus from the mines inland began to choke its navigable channel long years ago; and what was once an estuary is now a green level of apparent but treacherous pasture, through which at low water a stream trickles to be met half-heartedly by the neaps, and where a branch of it washes round the eyot a pair of swans nest annually—original ones or progeny, and never more than one pair, forbidding the creek to intruders. But stray herons come to fish there and at intervals whole flocks of gulls will stud the level. Twice a year maybe, at the equinoxes, a spring tide with a sou'wester behind it will flood Reselda Pyll to cover the roadway and suck at the timbers of a broken lock-gate, relic of a canal, planned in the eighteen-thirties and abandoned on the threat of a mineral railway, which in turn never came to birth. The high woodlands on either side of Reselda belong legally to an impoverished landlord, but towards nightfall the curlews claim tenantry, later the owls.

At a turn of the road—on this Sunday afternoon the goal of John Berrycombe's walk, as for twenty-five years it had been—one house stood solitary; an inn: one-storeyed, thatched, cleanly whitewashed, with a signboard 'The Norseman's Arms,' and over the door lintel:

JANE TREWMAN, SHIPPING GAZETTE,
LICENSED TO SELL ALES, SPIRITUOUS LIQUORS
AND TOBACCOS

The explanation why a public-house, and one so oddly named, should occupy this unlikely spot is simple enough. In the earlier years of Queen Victoria's reign, while the mines worked and before their refuse had silted up its channel, vessels of light draught and strings of barges too, at times, had frequented Reselda Pyll, unloading timber for mine-props. The vessels with their cargoes—and their skippers and quite often the skipper's family for crew or part of it—were all from Norway; and it was Jane Trewman's grandfather Christopher who had planted an inn here as a house-of-call, run almost on domestic lines, but without stint of drink. It had attracted the miners, too, from 'up above'—staid men for the most part, and Methodists, whose wives (as they put it) 'didn't mind getting a man out of the way for a bit, so long as one knows where he's *to*.' So Christopher had put by a tidy pile of money and left it with the inn to his only child, Christopher the Second: a cautious man, who, when the mining collapsed in the late forties, and the young men emigrated to America, and the kindly Norwegian timber-carriers came no more, resigned himself to dwindled custom, lived sparingly on his income and left the capital to his only child, Jane, then seventeen.

II

As John Berrycombe took the woodland footpath the ferryman jerked a thumb after him:

'Sure as three o'clock strikes—Sunday—rain or shine. 'Wonder how long 'tis old Hardy's been at it.'

Indeed neither he nor the other man, idling by the quayside, could tell; nor even why they spoke of John as 'old Hardy.' Years ago some wag had put the nickname 'Hardy Norseman' upon him, but the second word had dropped out of memory.

'Before you and I were much better than christened, I reckon. "Marry in haste," the saying is. Well, maybe the both of us done it in our hot days, and I'm not askin'; but seemin' to me old Hardy's trying of it t'other way about.

'And the trouble is'—the ferryman lit his pipe slowly—'that neither you nor me will likely see it out. . . . Well, soce, there's only one life to live, here below; and, Sunday or week, *that's* a comfort.'

John Berrycombe, of course, heard nothing of this, nor if he had would he have heeded. By habit he was one who took all talk with his fellows as meaning just so much as 'Good day.' No one ever called him surly, but his mind worked slowly, and, unless sharply recalled, blind as a mole's, unobservant of any but its own track. So this afternoon, whether the path changed its carpet from moss to larch-needles under his large feet, or his heavy shoulders brushed past yellowing beech, or the sun rayed through gaps over and across patches of rhododendron, no sense of any difference touched him. His mother, as always, had provided an ample midday dinner: Selina had cooked and served it well; and here was September, latish and the usual sort of thing.

But where this footpath descended and met the road a sharp musketry of sound fetched him to a standstill—of children's voices shrilling, and volleys of excited laughter. It came from 'The Norseman's Arms,' too, not fifty yards ahead; and this was Sunday afternoon.

John halted and pulled out his watch; pocketed it slowly and went forward.

Just beyond a point where the road turned up to the inn's main door, and below its long back garden, there ran a 'hoist' (raised footway), years ago built as a protection against the high spring tides. A few yards beyond the inn's abutment a wicket-gate gave access to the garden—a gate John habitually used on wet days, entering the house by its back door.

(It should be explained that at the date of our story the law laid on public-houses a Sunday restriction against all customers save 'bona fide travellers,' but no one—not even the police—

ever thought of measuring the distance of the 'Arms' from the paper-mills where John lived and did his business; it being understood that he came for purposes of courtship, and, more-over, paid nothing for what he consumed.)

John Berrycombe, then, halted again at this wicket-gate and stared upon the garden. On its stretch of turf, hands joined, a circle of children danced wildly to the game of Kiss-in-the-Ring, Jane Trewman, in the middle of the chain, directing it. When the chain was broken for a boy to walk around to choose his partner, peals of clapping and laughter greeted bride and bridegroom as they stepped into the centre to be danced around.

In one of these intervals Jane caught sight of John at the gate.

'There! that will do. . . . Now run, all of you, and play tig in the orchard. Twenty minutes, and then time for good-bye.'

She came towards John, flushed and panting a little; but turned midway to call to a middle-aged woman busy at clearing a set of deserted tea-tables aligned under the brick wall against a border of hollyhocks, phloxes, Michaelmas daisies.

'Emma!'

'Yes, mistress.'

'Gather what's left of the cake and splits—anything left of the cream, too, and hand 'em up to they Methody children peekin' over the hedge there. No jam or treacle, mind—or their mothers will be crying out when they get home.'

She faced John and pointed to a low bench that, over a fence of low-trimmed euonymus, overlooked pathway and creek.

'You can sit here with your back to it all.' As John settled himself, she dropped, still panting, upon the bench beside him. John slowly felt for his pipe.

'Oh, yes, I know what you're thinking. But I went to Parson, and he approves. Being new to parish—all things to all men as yet, as you might say, he didn't turn up. But they poor Methody children, forbidden, and hanging over the wall with their tongues fairly watering—well, come what may, I hadn't the heart . . .'

John lit his pipe and puffed at it.

'It rained cats and dogs on Anniversary Day, and the poor mites had to stay in the schoolroom, in their gay dresses, too. So I took a fancy, and with Parson's leave and to-day turning out so fine, thank God. . . . But you 're thinking I 'm over fond of children.'

'I haven't said so.'

'But you were thinking so, John, and at that very moment. Lord sakes! do you reckon I can't read your thoughts in all this time, and you so slow of speech? Well, I dote on children: and all the more, maybe, because I 'm past having 'em.'

She rose up and called to Emma to run and boil up a fresh pot of tea for Mister John.

'I didn't take your meaning,' said John as she came back to her seat.

'I don't suppose you do,' she snapped, 'and wouldn't, if you put it into your pipe and smoked it. But your mother would understand, and glad enough of small mercies.'

She left him to kiss the returning children good night. While they trooped away, and she saw them off to rejoin the small, envious non-Anglicans in the road, Emma Peascod brought his tea and set it beside him, with home-made bread, honey of Jane's own hiving, cream of Jane's own dairying. John absorbed it all, lit another pipe and sat ruminating, his gaze upon the creek.

By and by (as he knew she would) Jane came and dropped into the seat beside him. He had not stirred.

'Yes,' she said, 'but it won't interfere.'

'Eh?'

'That pole t' other side. The Post Office reckons to run the wire across. They want to put up its pillar at the end of the orchard. One-and-six way-leave, and I 've given permission as it won't interfere.'

'I was just wonderin' . . . But how you guessed——'

'Hasn't it ever struck you, John'—she laid a hand on his

sleeve, to rest there—'how often I run ahead of your thoughts and answer before you speak 'em?'

'Can't say I have.' John stirred at last, a trifle uneasy.

'Oh, it's never anything to count—leastway not much. Because, John, I know them to be clean always, thank God.' (There, however, half a sigh escaped her.) 'But about that pole—they got it up last Thursday, and I'm glad you noticed it. There's a notion that folk living up in a place like this, year in and year out, don't take heed of changes. But I do, down to the teeniest-weeniest things—birds' nests we'll say, and whether 'tis the old birds or a new pair mating. And so with Emma Peascod. She woke me up at six o'clock to tell me they were cutting a clearing across there: and when the pole went up you'd have thought 'twas the end of the world come. Naught but bad news, she holds, ever comes by telegraph.'

John made no answer. Yet this was the same oaken bench on which they had exchanged their first kiss.

III

It had happened when John, rising twenty-two and always slow of development, had fared up Reselda Creek on command of his father, who owned and ran a prosperous paper-mill well on the left shore above Ridmouth, and wellnigh in the narrows above its wide harbour. Samuel Berrycombe, ageing but alert, had received news of a trader due to discharge at the head of Reselda Creek a cargo of limestone and nitrate with other general cargo, including a truss or so of esparto grass, picked up at Plymouth in a sample sent by some Algerine enterprise as bait for a marker. Advertised of this and alert for a new line in paper-making he had sent his son up to Reselda to bring back a sample.

So John, always in terror of his father's temper, had risen before cockcrow and sought the creek head, long ago, by the path trodden by him this afternoon.

But then it happened to be May morning: a festival when village maids are allowed (or were) to rise before daybreak, fare to the meadows and dabble their naked feet in the dew, afterwards to troop and eat clotted cream under hedges over which the May sun rises.

So it happened at the bend where the footpath first joined the road John found himself caught up in a swirl of young women, naked legged, who, in all innocence but excited, surrounded and chivvied him up the road to the 'Norseman,' where tables heaped with splits and clotted cream awaited them in the sunrise. And then—John could never tell how—the troop had faded away into silence, and he had found himself on a bench beside a girl who, stretching her ankles for the young sun to dry, suddenly struck on his sense as the dearest possession in the world. So somehow they had exchanged a first kiss.

It need not be added that John, returning home with his samples of esparto grass, reported nothing of this to his parents.

Silence on the garden bench lasted until the September dusk began to gather. Then, as if timed by clock, the two rose and passed by the garden door into Jane's parlour, where Emma Peascod had already lit the hanging lamp and set out decanter and apparatus for brandy-grog, also a plate of apples with finger bowl and napkin beside it, on a small table by the fire. A brass kettle shone and sang gently on the hob.

John sank into his accustomed chair on the right of the hearth. Jane moved the kettle from hob to fire, and set about peeling an apple. He contemplated her — this dark-haired woman, broad of brow, deep of breast—as she bent in the cross rays of lamp and firelight. She was his, had been from first avowal and plighting; secure as his money invested or in the bank, to be drawn upon on Sundays with satisfying interest without touching capital.

Jane, having peeled his apple, dipped and wiped her finger-tips, then took off the steaming kettle and mixed his brandy-grog for him. He took it with the plate. For a while they sat by the hearth in the usual opposite chairs and in a silence broken only by John's heavy breathing between bite and sup. Then as he pulled out pipe for his final smoke: 'I doubt you were annoyed this afternoon?' said Jane.

'Eh? Oh, then,' John answered between puffs, 'when I came on you from the gate—and you among them children caperin' just like—a—a——'

'Capering?'

'—like as you was a fairy—or wanted to be.' John, having found his simile, was not to be put off.

Half a minute's silence followed. Then said she, looking straight across under dark brows: 'Look here, John. Wasn't it *ever* like that to you, not even to begin with? Well, it was to me—often. And now I'll tell you something you won't understand—but you may tell it to your mother. A woman at my time o' life takes fancies. Goes off the rails, as they say. Sometimes it runs to bad temper, but easier when the ewe runs lamb-like, for a bit. You may go home and tell that to your mother if you choose.'

'Mother and I——' This after a pause.

'—never mention me. Don't I know that? And well, John, that's over. I've told you; and when 'tis over, 'tis over, as Joan said by her wedding.'

She laughed, as John pulled out his watch. They rose together and went to the front door, on their way passing the glass window of the bar-room, within which, on a stool, Emma Peascod sat with Bible open on the zinc counter. It was Emma's custom of a Sunday evening, and (gossip said) with the book upside down as often as not. Anyhow, Emma was a teetotaller, and it may have been her vicarious sacrifice upon this altar for the sins of the week.

In the porch John and Jane exchanged their customary kiss. He did not feel how her lips trembled.

IV

John's mother awaited him at home, at the end of a long dining table of the family house built alongside and here and there into the paper factory, at every point so close that on work-days the chant of its water-wheel droned through every room. On Sunday, the wheel stayed, the sound changed to that of a straight waterfall.

Religiously as Emma Peascod sat by the counter of 'The Norseman's Arms,' old Mrs. Berrycombe (Honoria by name) was sitting by *her* Bible open before her—a copy of the last issue but one of Debrett's Peerage. The bookseller at Ridmouth at due intervals sought these volumes for her—'a lady, if ever there was one'—and they lined almost a third of a shelf in the 'study' where her late husband had always room alongside ledgers.

The explanation lies in her story; a strange one, only to be summarized here. She came direct of high lineage—eldest of three daughters of a family rectory on the edge of a deer-park, the acres of her uncle, no less a person than Earl of Molton, in Devon, Baron Carminowe of Carminowe (a lost estate in Cornwall), with some lesser titles. This good Earl's eldest son, Lord Carminowe, had died young in the fifties, hopelessly in debt which his father honourably shouldered, living himself on an income of scarce three hundred a year, and leaving, when he died, the bulk of his estate intact but still heavily encumbered. His second son, succeeding to the title and upon it retiring from Her Majesty Queen Victoria's Guards, was a dilettante who collected dubious masterpieces, and had divorced his wife after begetting a son whose career in the Army remained a question as dubious as the value his father set upon the masterpieces he crowded into Berry Regis. The third son, the Rev. the Hon. Eustace Carminowe, was a widower with three daughters—Honoria, Georgiana, and Charlotte.

They had to share a great part of the rectory housework and to stitch their own dresses for the county balls.

Charlotte, the youngest, had a sharp tongue. One day as the three sat sewing in the converted 'nursery' she asked amiably:

'Honoria! When must we ask to tea the young man you are walking out with?'—a question for which Honoria never in life forgave her.

(Charlotte, it may be explained, knew all the twists and corners of a maze of clipped yew for which the rectory was famous; and also as the youngest daughter she occupied an attic chamber which not only overlooked the maze but neighboured on the servants' quarters and within earshot of backstairs gossip incautiously and too loudly spoken.)

But the 'young man' had proved a determined wooer. From Honoria's surrender he straightway laid siege to the rector and —her father's poverty rather than his will consenting—won his bride and carried her off to the great house beside his paper factory.

There she had borne him four children, three sons and a daughter. With John he had his way—from the first even to choice of the child's name, and John must be bred and brought up to the business. For Samuel Berrycombe showed himself in those early days as dominating in wedlock as he had been in courtship. With Radical notions, moreover, he nursed no little resentment at the Carminowe airs and graces—as he called them—which he had endured. He had won, but had been wounded. He seldom revealed this to Honoria (though of course she knew well enough), being in love with her, as she with him, to the end; she admiring his strength of brain, success, and mastery among men, he secretly proud of the 'noble connection,' never confessedly, of possessing a wife with 'quality' in her every word and movement. Therefore they agreed perfectly in her keeping aloof from the other ladies of Ridmouth. But with the second and third son the mother's gentle obstinacy had prevailed. Miles, the second, received a name

of frequent recurrence to the table of the Carminowe pedigree:
the third son had been christened Samuel Coningsby on a compromise; but, to save confusion, the 'Samuel' had always been
dropped, and 'Coningsby' shortened (by his father) to 'Con.'
And whereas their elder brother had picked up his reading,
writing, and arithmetic as a day boy in the local academy, these
two had been wheedled off to a public school of repute: whence
Miles had proceeded to Oxford, Coningsby to Cambridge.
Matilda, the last-born, after a restless girlhood under governesses,
with aid from such instructors in music and water-colour as
Ridmouth provided, had accepted with joy her aunt Charlotte's
invitation to spend six weeks in London and be presented at
Court, and had there, making the best of her time, found
opportunity of betrothal and marriage to a prosperous young
ironmaster in the Midlands, much to her aunt's disgust and
every one's annoyance in the family except her father's.

Anyhow Matilda could now fend for herself, and did.   Miles,
called to the Bar, had withered to a dry and pernickety Chancery
lawyer, domiciled in bachelor chambers within Lincoln's Inn.
Coningsby had taken orders, married, and was now vicar of
Bagworthy Regis, in Devon, a poor benefice under Exmoor.
For their two sons their father had made a passable allowance
of £240 apiece, which John maintained without question.

But on John himself, heir and successor to the business, from
childhood his father had expended little but abuse by way of
licking him into shape; obstinate in purpose, irascibly scolding
morning-to-night at a sloth of mind he could never understand.
For how could it have happened in a boy so begotten and yet
not corrigible?   As a result John grew up cowed, uncouth, all
filial love concentrated upon his mother, to whom he looked
up with a dumb, dog-like devotion; while she—disappointed
too, yet preferring her first-born to the others and protectively
answering that dumb love in his eyes—had as vainly striven to
correct his dress, bearing, speech, social manners, and mould
him to a gentleman of the Carminowe stamp.   She never

realized that her own aloofness was in part responsible, cutting him off from the rudiments that the despised social life of Ridmouth might have taught him. Into the *petits soins* of indoor life she had patiently drilled him; in other ways she had poorly succeeded; but in all but one thing had enslaved him. From his word once given John could never be turned.

Happily for her she had never learned the exact details of her husband's end; how that, after storming upon John for a round two minutes, he had turned upon a dilatory workman, had been seized with apoplexy, in the act of cursing, and had died betwixt being lifted and carried into the house.

V

So when John this evening, having shed his boots for a pair of shoes laid out within the front door, had gone through the ritual of a wash and a brushing-up, he found his mother seated at her end of the long mahogany table with Debrett open before her at the page of 'Collateral Branches,' every word of which he knew by heart. His Sunday supper, cold but ample, lay spread at the other end. Two candles shone there. Selina, having timed his footsteps, entered punctually with his jug of beer, removed two candles from beside Debrett, set them to make four for John's meal, and poked the fire to a blaze while he helped his mother to a chair on his right. At seventy-eight she yet enjoyed watching his good appetite.

The meal over, he armed her to her usual chair by the hearth and took his own. Given the rooms' difference, their disposal nearly resembled that of John's and Jane's a couple of hours back. But here the candlelight shone, the firelight flickered, upon over-tall walls, papered in dark crimson, decorated with long engravings in maplewood frames—'The Waterloo Banquet' (the Earl, Honoria's grandfather, had led his squadron of the 16th Light Dragoons under Vandaleur at Waterloo, and lost an arm in the final charge), 'The Meeting of the Duke and

o

Blücher' at the 'Auberge Rouge,' an extended view of Berry Regis and its surroundings (after Tintoretto and the farther the longer) with a portrait in oils of Samuel Berrycombe over the swing table at the far end.

'Coningsby came down this afternoon,' said Honoria, breaking the long silence, 'in that rattletrap car of his. He was in a hurry. Of course, he was prepared not to find you at home.'

John lit his pipe before answering. 'I'll bet he was. Queer day, Sunday, for him to leave his parish—costing him two guineas for a hired locum, if that's the price . . . 'must be in some hurry, too. . . . How much did he stick you for this time?'

'I gave him another fifty pounds—or rather I shall send it to-morrow, for you know I never write cheques on Sunday. He spoke of his two daughters growing up——'

'Families commonly do, don't they?'

'—and he does so need a new car for his rounds in that scattered parish.'

'So he wore the old one out, eighty miles good, to raise fifty pounds out of you. If you care to know, he raised a hundred off me, scarce three months ago. Reason, maybe, why he reckoned on finding me away from here, seeing as——'

'Yes, John.'

'Anything more?'

'He thought—well, he has been wishful for a long time, as you know, to change that expensive barrack of a vicarage for something, as he put it, more cosy and central. His suggestion was that there's an advowson for sale at—I forget the name of the parish, but somewhere nearer Exeter, more convenient for the girls' education, and with our help——'

'Which he won't get——' John, for once, was quick of speech.

His mother dropped the subject. A long silence fell.

'John.'

'Yes, mother.'

'I want to speak to you very seriously. I am seventy-eight, as you know, and in the nature of things could not count on more than a very few years. But I saw Dr. Fleming yesterday, and I must not count on months, even. Heart it is—and a long time since it woke me at night to read the warning. 'Tis not about myself, though . . . John, you 'll want looking after when I 'm gone, and what I 've done I thought to be for your best, or so I persuaded myself. I doubt now there was selfishness mixed up in it: for I loved you, John—I couldn't help it, right or wrong—above the others, as you must have known; and I wanted to keep you to myself. But now—now that all is slipping away—you with it'—she commanded her voice —'I want something for you that I cannot grudge . . . I want you to marry Jane Trewman.'

'Mother!' John's mouth opened wide. Between it and his fingers his pipe slipped, fell, and clattered against the fender. He bent as if to recover it.

'She 's a wonderful housekeeper by all accounts—for her station——'

But the great, clumsy fellow had dropped forward on his knees, and his face was buried in her lap.

'As it was in the beginning . . .' Honoria murmured, stroking his hair. 'And now, dear, rise and close the book over there, and before Selina clears away you shall lift and carry me upstairs as I used to carry you!'

VI

On a night less than three weeks later death took Honoria Berrycombe in her sleep. In the afternoon John walked up to Reselda and broke the news.

Jane heard it in silence, then went upstairs and put on her hat. By consent she and John left the house and took the path above the creek, alongside the deserted canal.

'I 'm sorry, of course—for you, John.'

'It must have been quite sudden, *and* peaceful,' said John, for the third time since his arrival. 'And now——'

'And now, I suppose . . . Don't be harried, John, by what comes at long last. 'Tisn't seemly.'

'I don't take the meaning of that. I was going to tell what my mother said to me about us two, scarce three weeks agone.'

They halted and he told her, while she stared at him.

'So now,' he wound up, 'we can feel easy about it. That's what I wanted to tell you—no weight is on our minds ever —in that respect.'

'Thank you,' Jane managed to say, after choking down something in her throat.

'It has been a long wait, of course,' he went on, 'and hard on you, my dear. But that being her last wish almost, we can be married this side of Christmas or just after and plenty of time left us to be——' He hesitated.

'Comfortable,' suggested Jane. 'You was going to say "happy." 'Tisn't quite the same thing, eh, is it?'

They walked on a short way, John pondering this nice distinction. Jane turned round on him.

'If you think I'll marry now, to go and housekeep in that tall barrack as *she* did . . .'

'No need.' Whether by luck or good management John had brought her to the very spot for his answer. 'I shall sell up the business and retire—I've had offers—good ones. And you can keep on the "Norseman" or not, as you choose. But see there.'

He pointed up to a thatched building, something larger than a cottage, set in a clear glade of the woods, untenanted, with boarded windows. It had served in its time as office and miners' pay-house.

'Eh, Jane?'

'Sure I remember. But why? Mouldering, it must have been, inside, for years and years.'

'Fifteen,' said John triumphantly. 'Seventeen years back

I bought it, on the very next day after winding up father's affairs. And the rest has been my secret, to surprise you when the time came. Windows all blocked up, as you see: but plate glass behind 'em; and all indoors clean as a pin, walls scraped and two dozen rolls o' flock paper and my own make, and to last for ever—cupboarded up for your choosin'—but some other day, o' course.'

On their way back Jane asked: 'But parting from your business will be a wrench, John?'

'Not a bit'—success of his surprise still buoyant in him. 'Year by year I've been drawing in and selling out all father's investments—at a tidy profit, too, being able to bide my time. None so easy, though; for whatever the old man got he'd search about to use, to add more.'

'Ay,' Jane agreed, 'and you, John, was always content to possess.'

VII

Three Sundays later their banns were called.

The news thrilled Reselda parish, but agitated no breast so violently as Emma Peascod's, whom Jane had been careful not to warn.

'And next thing,' she broke out, 'you'll be shuttin' up the place, and me turned out like a—like a——'

'Before you find the image to fit,' said Jane, 'perhaps you might stop sobbing: sit down, and try not to behave like a fool.'

On the Saturday before the third calling of the banns John arrived, his right pocket bulging.

'It's my will,' he announced, extricating a long envelope. 'You may read it, or else—and I'd rather—put it aside—until afterwards.'

'I'll put it aside in my desk,' said Jane.

'And now,' said he, pulling out a wad from an inner pocket, 'I reckon 'tis usual for the man to make a wedding present.

I've thought it out, and here are two hundred in notes, to fare and buy whatever suits you for the cottage—furniture, fittings, and kitchen gear, and such-like odds and ends.'

Jane's eyes brimmed of a sudden. 'Thank you, John. But I was minded to do a bit on my own money.'

'Then you mustn't,' said John firmly.

Next morning: 'You and me are going to Exeter, Tuesday morning early,' Jane announced to Emma Peascod.

Emma's eyes widened. 'Good sakes! but what for?'

'To buy furniture and things. We can catch the first train and put up for the night at some hotel, if pressed for time.'

'But—but there's Truro handy—and there's Plymouth, full of shops. What's put Exeter in your head? And if it's an hotel, I was at Plymouth once—mother took me to meet father. That was coming home on the *Formidable*—and we waited in a bow-window of the "Globe." I can see it now with the military passin' up and down Bedford Street, and each with a little cane twiddling in his hand, and his girl tucked under t' other arm.'

'The farther from here,' said Jane, 'the nearer to find something new.'

VIII

They drove off by spring-cart at six o'clock next morning and caught an early train, which landed them at St. David's, Exeter, within half an hour of noon. Having deposited Jane's antiquated valise and Emma's carpet bag in the cloak-room, they walked up to view the city and the shops; these all gay with Christmas shows and decorations. Emma Peascod would have hung at heel for minutes before every one of them, babbling her wonder as she had been babbling it since—entering the train, this being her second journey by rail and her first beyond Plymouth. Indeed she had only stopped exclaiming at the size of the world to scream and clutch at Jane's arm in the tunnels.

It was now Jane's turn to clutch Emma's, which she did a dozen times, pulling her forward.

'But you're not taking in the half of it,' Emma protested. 'All these beautiful things and you scarce even looking!'

'Time enough, later on,' she was told. 'We must walk around first.'

Jane, indeed, had been curiously silent all day and on the journey, gazing down at her lap, rousing herself now and then, as out of a brown study, to answer one of Emma's excited questions—for the most part curtly with a 'yes' or 'no.'

From the display of a jeweller's, with the electric lights at full play on its diamonds, Emma required a deal of budging.

'It makes me feel all over like a Queen of Sheba! . . . But I don't see no wedding rings. . . . I wonder now, if Mr. John will remember about the ring?'

'Come along, foolish woman!'

They reached the Close in time, and Jane had a fancy to enter the Cathedral. Great sounds met them within, rolling, reverberating along naves and aisles, evoked by unseen hands at practice upon the grand organ above the screen. She seated herself to listen, and sat while the music lasted and for many minutes after, motionless, while Emma wandered about, vaguely awed, but with growing impatience.

At length Jane rose and announced that it was time they picked up lunch somewhere.

At the Royal Clarence, close by, they found a good meal; of which Emma ate ravenously, Jane little; and again, after it, she dallied, playing absently with her spoon while her coffee went cold.

'It turns dark towards four,' Emma suggested.

Jane paid the bill, and they fared forth anew down High Street and then into Queen Street. But not even in the furniture shops, though Emma called her attention to each in turn, could she awake Jane to any lively interest.

By the Market House steps, however, on which stood a

shapely little Christmas-tree about five feet in height, set in a tub, Jane halted. 'How much,' she asked the salesman, 'without the tub?'

'Four and sixpence, madam.'

'I'll take it at five shillings if you'll have it wrapped up in hessian within twenty minutes. Plenty of earth round the roots, please, and damped, but not too much. It has to travel.'

She turned on Emma. 'Wasn't that a toy-shop we passed, not twenty yards back?'

To this they retraced their steps and at once Jane started to buy. Emma thought her demented as she plunged about from counter to counter in a riot of spending—dolls, drums, trumpets, hobby-horses, golliwogs, toy guns; boxes of bricks, of wooden farmyards, a Noah's Ark, a miniature railway engine; boxes also of crackers, Christmas candles, glass danglers, tinsel. When all this had been assembled in a pile, she demanded a large crate, two crates. These packed, and the bill (some eighty-five shillings) discharged, a four-wheeler was ordered and the load hoisted on its roof by two obsequious attendants, who received largess. A halt was made at the market, the Christmas-tree also hoisted aboard, and the cabman told to drive to St. David's.

'And there, I reckon,' Emma guessed hopefully, 'we pick up our traps, and go back to the Clarence. Where we'll hope the beds are aired . . .'

'We're going home by next train.'

'What! . . . and not a stick nor stitch——'

Without answer Jane led the way into the station; handed their cloak-room tickets to Emma, and exchanged for two first classes for Truro. They found an empty compartment, twenty minutes later, in a westward-bound relief express.

All the journey homeward Emma Peascod had to solace herself with the plumpness of the cushions. For the night had fallen pitch dark by now, and Jane sat obstinately taciturn, with eyes turned to her corner window, fixed out upon the rushing blackness as though probing it.

At Truro they loaded up the back of the spring-cart and jogged in a drizzle for home. Jane—who observed her own interpretation of all victualling laws—had put up a window notice early to announce that 'The Norseman's Arms' would be closed for two days. But nearing the foot of Reselda Hill the travellers were surprised by a light ahead faintly crossing the road. The 'Norseman' was lit within, and a group of dark figures stood clustered by its porch. Another vehicle stood drawn up a few yards below.

'I knew it,' said Jane. She handed the reins to Emma, clambered down, and passed with set face through the hush of the little crowd into the house.

In her parlour by the lamp-light stood a short white-haired gentleman, kindly faced, grave; behind him the yet shorter figure of the postmistress, who ran forward, twittering.

'I couldn't help it, Miss Jane!—and all so concerned—so sorry!'

'Be quiet, woman,' commanded the short gentleman, and held out an open telegram. 'I sent this early, Miss Trewman: being anxious, I followed it up. Be very sure you have my sympathy.'

Jane took the missive and read:

'*Deeply regret John Berrycombe passed away early hours this morning suddenly and to all appearance peacefully.*—ATTLEY & SON, SOLICITORS.'

While Jane perused this, brows bent and face inscrutable, Emma—having given over mare and trap to be stabled by willing hands—came bursting in and would have clung to her, but was thrust back firmly into an arm-chair, where she curled over, burying her face.

'And his own ch-chair, too, the poor dear!' she sobbed: then, turning about fiercely on the postmistress: 'Which I said it from the first, when I see'd that venom pole going up. Naught ever but ill news from they tellygraphs.'

'Emma, get up at once!' Jane commanded, steady as a statue.

* o

'Fit and fetch the kettle, quick, Mr. Attley must have a glass
before he goes.'

'Which I made free to light the fire in the bar parlour, too,'
put in the postmistress, 'and the kettle near on the boil.'

While Mr. Attley sipped his grog in the bar-parlour Jane
slipped upstairs to her desk. She reappeared with a long
envelope in her hand and motioned him to bring his drink and
follow her back to the sitting-room.

'It's John's will.' She handed him the envelope. 'He
gave it to me on Saturday to keep.'

'I know its contents, of course. Indeed I done it myself,
almost on his dictation.'

'I doubt if you know it quite all. There's a note at the end
in his own handwriting. It only says that 'twas his wish, when
his time came, to be buried at Reselda.'

'Will it relieve you, Miss Trewman, if I make all the
arrangements?'

'It will indeed. Thank you, Mr. Attley.' He bowed.

'But there's one thing—if I can explain. I read it all through
last night: but not, Mr. Attley, because I was impatient, or
curious. Maybe 'twas the beginning of what's been sitting at
my ear all day.' She passed a hand over her forehead. 'You
see, I've been so used to thinking a bit ahead of John—catching
up aforehand—as one might say. . . .'

IX

A post-mortem revealed that John Berrycombe had died of
fatty degeneration of the heart.

He was buried as he had wished, in Reselda churchyard.
Custom in Reselda parish forbade women, if related or nearly
concerned, to attend funerals. So Jane and Emma, having
pulled down the house blinds, sought the parlour at first note
from the tolling-bell, and sat the time out in silence.

Towards next afternoon (Christmas Eve) a hired vehicle

descended the steep hill to 'The Norseman's Arms.' At a bend
of the road below Reselda church it had passed the village
schoolhouse ablaze with lights and ringing with the indoor
noise and merriment of children.

At the 'Norseman's' porch it disgorged three passengers,
whom Emma Peascod ushered into the parlour, where Mr.
Attley sat with John's will open before him under the lamp.
He rose and, bowing, indicated chairs. Mrs. Burslade (*née*
Matilda Berrycombe), a stoutish matron in flounces of black
crêpe, sank upon the small sofa and lifted her veil upon a face in
which the very sharp eyes pierced a plaster of enamel. Miles
Berrycombe seated himself, with back stiff as a ramrod, on
Mr. Attley's right. The Reverend Coningsby Berrycombe,
after a glance around, settled himself beside his sister.

'I should apologize for Miss Trewman,' said the solicitor.
'She has just returned from a children's Christmas-tree, and
will be here in a minute or two. Here is a copy, Mr. Miles, of
the will, as promised when you called on me this morning.'

Miles Berrycombe took the copy, spread it, and adjusted his
glasses.

'A Christmas-tree, did you say?' shrilled Mrs. Burslade
from the sofa. 'And dear John scarcely cold in his grave!
Well, of all——'

But at that moment Jane entered, dressed quietly in grey.
With an inclination of the head she comprehended the visitors,
and, moving to the fire-place, stood facing them.

'These gentlemen, Miss Trewman, and their sister desire a
talk with you respecting their brother's will. The relevant
sentence, Mr. Miles, is plain enough and concise?'

'Quite!'

'After a few legacies the testator leaves—here are the words—
"the residue of my worldly estate to my dear wife, Jane Berrycombe, absolutely and at her sole use and disposition." Those
were his own words: he insisted on them.'

'Yes, of course, of course—no reflection at all upon you,

Mr. Attley. Every man his own lawyer, eh? But'—pricking
the paper with his pencil—'here is the point, Miss Trewman.
Were you my brother's wife at the date of his signing?'

'Of course not.'

Mr. Attley interposed. 'The Court, sir—if that be your
ground, and I have suspected it since this morning—would
almost certainly take account of plainly declared intentions.
And seeing that the parties' banns were out as recently as last
Sunday, I shall positively advise my client——'

Jane broke in. 'Your pardon, dear Mr. Attley; but I shan't
take any one's advice in this. I knew John's intentions well
enough, though in these years never told. These people want
to dispute the will: but they have something at back of their
minds, and 'twill save time if they speak it out.'

'To come to the point, then,' said Miles Berrycombe after a
pause, choosing his words, 'we are certainly inclined to question
the validity——'

'Tut!' interposed Mr. Attley.

'—but we have consulted. The estate will probably realize
seventy thousand pounds (I put this not too optimistically,
Mr. Attley). And if, in consideration of your natural disappointment, one thousand down or perhaps an annuity——'

Jane had turned to a small mirror above the chimneypiece,
and seemed to be studying the lines of her face in it while she
spoke to it, slowly:

'Mr. Attley, you are a gentleman, and would work for my
rights on your honour's sake. But there's two sorts of pride
—one that has ruined the best of John's life and mine, and another that stamps on it and all such: and that sort happens to
be mine. The best service in life you can ever do me is here
and now; to show these people to the door.' She put a hand
in her bodice and pulled out a wad of notes. 'Tell them I'll
never touch a penny of Berrycombe money and let them take
this.' She put out her hand behind her. 'John gave it to me
to spend in setting up house. I haven't spent a penny of it.'

'Well, and that's over!' said Jane to Emma half an hour later. 'Let's sit and have a cup of tea.'

'Highly satisfactory I call it, and a credit in a way to all concerned,' said the Reverend Coningsby Berrycombe after dinner that evening, as he held up a glass of John's forty-five port against the candlelight.

'Though,' said his sister, 'I can never forget the impudent way that woman carried it off. . . . Hark!'

Outside the lit windows, in the drive, a chorus of childish voices had started to trill:

> 'Good Christian friends rejoice,
> With heart and soul and voice. . . .'

SURSUM CORDA
1940

SULLEN against the east a cloud
   Darkened the church from choir to nave,
O'er heads in supplication bowed,
   O'er hearts that whispered, 'Heart, be brave.'

Then . . . framed amid Crusader shields,
   Held in the space of one clear pane,
Acre on acre shone the fields
   Our fathers ploughed and sowed again.

And lo! the altar caught their shine:
   The cross was hilt upon a sword—
'Lift up your hearts!   Accept the sign.'
   —We lifted them unto the Lord.

BYRON

A S generations are counted, more than a generation has passed since Matthew Arnold made bold to prophesy, of Wordsworth and Byron, that 'when the year 1900 is turned, and our nation comes to recount her poetic glories in the century which has then just ended, the first names with her will be these.'

Even when we have consented with George Eliot that of all forms of human error prophecy is the most gratuitous, and have asked ourselves in vain what profit can come of constructing a hierarchy among the poets of any given century (which, after all, is no more than a conventional division of arithmetic), there remains the question why Arnold should have chosen to hit on two men rather than on one, or on three, or more. He had no need to consider Westminster Abbey, where the space for interment is limited, and where in fact neither Wordsworth nor Byron reposes; no need to practise any such frugal anxiety as William Basse's for Shakespeare:

> Renowned Spenser, lye a thought more nye
> To learned Chaucer, and, rare Beaumont, lye
> A little neerer Spenser, to make roome
> For Shakespeare in your threefold, fowerfold Tombe.

Poets live in memory, which neither calculates room nor assigns marks for competition. For their corporal dust—Wordsworth rests now in Grasmere churchyard, Byron at Missolonghi, and Arnold himself by the Thames at Laleham—ἀνδρῶν ἐπιφανῶν πᾶσα γῆ τάφος.

For the prophecy, it came true—or, rather, remained true— of Wordsworth: but the year 1900 has long since been turned, and yet where on the sea is the returning sail of Byron?

He died in exile: and those of us who would bring Byron's fame back among his countrymen must, first of all, recognize their neglect of it for an obstinate neglect, a positive reluctance to readmit him. For this we must give most honourable acquittal to his English publishers. No publishers have ever done more for an author than John Murray, his sons, and his grandsons have done for Byron: and, as though to be punctual at the advent foretold by Arnold, they began to issue in 1898, and completed in 1904, a magnificent edition of the Letters and Journals as well as of the Poems. Moore's 'Life,' whatever else may be said of it, was an ample monument: the literature of personal curiosity has been copious, and from time to time provokingly scandalous. Yet every attempt hitherto made to bring Byron back from exile has been met, in his own country, with no Prodigal Son's welcome.

This reluctance begins and ends at home. On the continent of Europe, through which his poetry first ran as a flame, the admiration it kindled has never died out. In the estimation of all but his countrymen he ranks to-day as a greater poet than Shelley. Execrated at home, he died at Missolonghi on the 19th of April 1824, and the Greek Provisional Government closed all shops and proclaimed with salute of guns a public mourning for twenty-one days. Over a hundred years later, after British denunciation had long given place to neglect, one opens a volume by an eminent foreign critic surveying the field of nineteenth-century literature and finds him assigning 33 of his pages to Wordsworth, no fewer than 119 to Byron. What, then, is the matter with Byron, or with the faithful foreigner, or with *us*? Easy talk about 'reaction' will not carry us far; or will carry us in a direction clean contrary to the truth: for any one who seeks to re-establish Byron's fame will find himself not only forced to rely for his brief—and to rely almost exclusively—on the later poems, but forced also to recognize that Byron's true work took its start from the social disaster of 1815–16; that he fell then, in some ways like Lucifer, but, as a poet, most certainly not like Lucifer, 'never to hope again.' Indeed I believe it to be substantially true that if we take 25 April 1816—the day on which he sailed from England for ever —and set it in our 'Byron' for a book-marker, by that simple expedient we can divide his false from his true contributions

to literature. Technically he never, to the end, took the
trouble to equip himself. He had abundance of wit, and
with the aid of it developed (as *Don Juan* throughout bears
witness) an amazing command over mere rhyme. But wit will
never teach rhythm to a naturally defective ear; and, set beside
Shelley's, for instance, Byron's rhythms are performances on
the banjo. Also he lacked sense of the poise and pause of
blank decasyllabic verse: while, strange to say, this revolutionary, with his own amateurishness of scansion, chose to
parade himself as a true-blue disciple of Pope. At all these
joints Byron's poetical armour gaped to receive the barbed
arrows of Swinburne's later criticism, which have possibly
killed his claim to be an artist in song. Nor are these arrows
of Swinburne's criticism any the less deadly because foreigners
are congenitally doomed to miss the nuances of form in English
rhythm and diction, as we no doubt are as heavily handicapped
as critics of *their* native strains. I can only make what I believe
to be a fair statement—that our national neglect of Byron to-day
has next to nothing to do with his life and opinions, everything
to do with his carelessness as an artist. It weighs not, at this
distance of time, that for three heady years Byron poured out
such tales as *The Giaour, The Bride of Abydos, The Corsair,
Lara*—written 'while undressing after coming home from balls
and masquerades in the year of revelry 1814,' written and
admired for being written 'with the careless and negligent ease
of a man of quality.' Snobbery in criticism prevails in its day,
but nothing in criticism suffers more cruelly from exposure
to time and weather. As Crabbe gave warning—Crabbe,
Byron's favourite—in his preface to *Tales of the Hall*:

Our estimation of title also in a writer has materially varied from
that of our predecessors; *Poems by a Nobleman* would create a very
different sensation in our minds from that which was formerly excited
when they were so announced.

For three years Byron enjoyed a wild popularity, and played
up to it with an insolence apparently negligent, actually self-

conscious, and in its carefulness of affectation artistically ignoble. But when disaster fell, Byron found his soul. Abandoned by the world on whose adulation he had floated, he caught at the real thing valuable in his ancestry, its tradition of indomitable courage, and, with that courage, the gift of sincerity, without which no poetry can be better than flashy.[1] Genuine anguish in the winter and spring of 1815–16 probed Byron and found the man. The first two cantos of *Childe Harold*, on which society had heaped applause, simply fade from our minds as we open Canto III (read the exordium composed in the first hours of disillusion with its anguish), pass the stirring account of Brussels before Waterloo, and turn, with hearts swelled as by a trumpet, back upon such a recessional as the stanza which commemorates young Howard, killed and carried from the field:

> There have been tears and breaking hearts for thee,
> And mine were nothing, had I such to give;
> But when I stood beneath the fresh green tree,
> Which living waves where thou didst cease to live
> And saw around me the wide field revive
> With fruits and fertile promise, and the spring
> Come forth her work of gladness to contrive,
> With all her reckless birds upon the wing,
> I turn'd from all she brought to those she could not bring.

If that stanza be not poetry, I say, with all submission to his critics, that neither they nor I know yet what poetry is. One has but to turn back to Canto I and read

> For who would trust the seeming sighs
> Of wife or paramour?
> Fresh feeres will dry the bright blue eyes
> We late saw streaming o'er. (etc.)

to feel that the Rubicon of poetry has been crossed. Macaulay's

[1] Compare the insincerity, e.g. of the poem to *Thyrsa* (1811) with the real poignancy of 'So we'll go no more a roving'; in which, moreover, his heart dictates a true rhythm.—Q.

famous passage appraises at their true worth the impulses on which his countrymen denounced Byron and drove him into exile. Yet the late M. Scherer was utterly mistaken in his dictum that 'this beautiful and blighted being is at the bottom a coxcomb. He posed all his life long.' It is, at any rate, far nearer the truth to say that in its surgery the knife cut down through a fop and found a man. He screamed under the operation—as how should he not, being Byron? It converted him into the fiercest of egoists, but a sincerer egoist can hardly be found in our literature. He was utterly, recklessly unrepentant—as *Manfred* testifies, if we recall the circumstances under which it was thrown at the public. Tribulation and evil fame had not power to convert the spoilt child, the ingrained self-worshipper and idolater of his own rank and title; no power to abase his disproportionate sense of his own importance. Outcast from England, he 'trailed' through Europe 'the pageant of a bleeding heart.' But he had the ferocious power to make a real pageant of it; and posterity cannot deny that the heart bled proudly, or that it was quenched at last in a noble cause.

With his doom upon him he wrote, but did not live to finish, *Don Juan.* Critics who frame their definition of an epic upon a few specimens acknowledged as best, and demand conformity to rules constructed upon these, may easily deny the title of epic to this poem. Certainly it is extremely unlike *Paradise Lost* or even the *Odyssey.* But it has the great undulating flow which some of us recognize as *the* quality above qualities in Homer and Milton; it flows because all things within his ken are seized upon, liquefied, and made malleable by the combined heat of indignation, wit, genius; it belongs, heart and soul, to its period in human history; and it paints that age with such lively intensity, with such a sweep of power, that no generation to come will ever be able to dispute the picture. As the late Professor Nichol puts it, 'in writing *Don Juan* Byron attempted something that had never been done before, and his genius so chimed with his enterprise that it need never be done again.'

In face of their achievements in poetry—huge in the mass,

frequent in eminence, with peaks super-eminent over all literature of the modern world—the inhabitants of this small island
are often charged with a general indifference to verse, and in
particular with indifference to poetic artistry, concerning which
(I have heard it argued) our carelessness amounts almost to
proof of a congenitally defective ear. The charge is baseless
in fact: but it has a root—in the very anxiety which accuses
us of lacking anxiety. Poetry in England, as in every other
nation, has always been the treasure of a few amid the populace.
These few do well to be anxious for it; but it might easily be
maintained, rather, that the countrymen of Shakespeare have
too often, in despite of his example, surrendered themselves to
the slavery of 'form,' of poetic 'laws' and 'rules.' We admit
this of the eighteenth century, and blame that century for its
formalism. Yet nine-tenths of Swinburne's depreciation of
Byron will be found, when examined, to resolve itself into cavil
against his technical faults, against his defect of ear. We allow
ourselves to be irritated by hasty workmanship which the
foreigner has no skill to detect. That is an error on the right
side; and yet it turns into a serious error when it blinds our
vision to the fine power in the man, or deadens our sense of the
daemonic brain out of which verses teemed like armed men and
stanzas in troops, a revolutionary host. Be it granted that to
the end he could never surely separate poetry from rhetoric.
Yet who can recite the roll—*Childe Harold, Chillon, The Dream,
Prometheus, Manfred, The Lament of Tasso, The Prophecy of
Dante, Cain, The Vision of Judgment, Heaven and Earth,
Beppo,* and (feat above all) *Don Juan*—and deny Byron the
title of 'maker,' a strong 'man of his hands'?

He himself, during those years, dreamed of action, of em-
battled war against the enemies of freedom:

> And I will war, at least in words (and—should
> My chance so happen—deeds), with all who war
> With Thought: and of Thought's foes by far most rude
> Tyrants and sycophants have been and are.

That chance came with the revolutionary uprising of Greece, and he took it. For a brief while he shone as the bright particular star of that dawn, until death quenched the light with a miasma from the marshes by Missolonghi. His last utterance was Δεῖ με νῦν καθεύδειν—'It is time for me to sleep.' As Swinburne has written—and no recantation can cover the words—'With all things unfinished before him and behind, he fell asleep after many troubles and triumphs. Few can ever have gone wearier to the grave; none with less fear. . . . He had seen and borne and achieved more than most men on record. He was a great man, good at many things, and now he had attained his rest.'

A LIMERICK

THERE was an old man of St. Omer
  Who objected, 'This town's a misnomer;
    You've no right to translate
    And beatificate
A simple digamma in Homer.'

A CLERIHEW

1942

THE remarks of Alexander of Macedon
Would have been somewhat more than sub-acid on
    An enemy that used wings
    To drop things.

TO AN OLD LEADER

WHEN to the breach, across thy body spent
    The rearward rush assured now to attain,
Leap over thee, to close on the event,
    And tread thee unregarded 'mid the slain,
    Neither accuse them nor the gods arraign.

Rise to thy knees; grope for the bugle bent,
    Set it to lip, and sound the Charge amain!

So back. . . . Lace up the curtain of thy tent,
And lay thee down, too manly to lament,
      Too careless to complain.

BASIC ENGLISH

A CHALLENGE TO INNOVATORS

I

A LIFE-LONG lover of English may be pardoned that his suspicion awakes and takes alarm at any suggestion to twist it to some new purpose. The purpose may be plausible enough; but he will ask, as his first question: 'How is the innovation likely to affect the future of this particular glory of our blood and State?' I have written elsewhere:

Our fathers have, in the process of centuries, provided this realm, its colonies, and wide dependencies, with a speech malleable and pliant as Attic, dignified as Latin, masculine, yet free of Teutonic guttural, capable of being precise as French, dulcet as Italian, sonorous as Spanish, and of captaining all these excellences to its service.

and (I might have added) of adapting itself to include with ease the names for the new discoveries, inventions, processes, as they occur, of modern science. I have quoted this simply to follow it up with the assertion that precisely because we have so wonderful a heritage, it behoves us to be jealous for it. We may find it heavy, be restive under it, but the past has laid upon us a burden of greatness obligatory almost as that of our freedom: and as great nations must deserve a language to fit high deeds, high thoughts, high policies, or wither; as the fate of a city may hinge on the watch at its postern gate; I hold that under whatever new guise of English alternative or substitute seek admittance, and whether on plea of expediency, convenience, barter, labour-saving, or religious propaganda, or even all these together, it should be held up to give strict account of itself.

The want of some common 'world language' is, I assume,

pretty generally admitted : certainly it has been felt by educated
Europeans ever since Latin faded out as the common language
of churchmen, scholars, and diplomatists.   But these men, being
educated, could to some extent fill up the void by learning other
tongues than their own; not without compensation and even
great profit to their own languages and literatures.   But the
men who opened the waterways all over the world and the
venturers who followed these trade routes to plant factories in
Muscovy, China, the Indies, and Americas were not scholars
but travellers and merchants and so the demand for a world
language starts naturally upon the needs of travel and commerce, its urgency increasing as travel quickens its pace and
commerce multiplies.   It has been primarily to meet this demand
that ingenious people at home have invented Esperanto, Ido,
Novial, and other vocabularies on which nothing need be said
here save they are all admittedly artificial, composed of various
'root-woods' in various foreign tongues.

II

Now, as I remember, Basic English also first came to us with
this as its primary and modest claim, the convenience of the
trader and traveller, but offering, as English, the great (and
flattering) advantage of being a form of our native speech.
Dr. I. A. Richards—'whom I name,' as Cicero might say, 'for
the sake of honour'—in his *Basic English and Its Uses*, devotes
some pages to claiming (*a*) that for this reason it excels Esperanto
and other artificial experiments; and (*b*) that it holds the victory
on many grounds over any other native language.   Well, let
both these claims be granted, and, for the second, let the French
or Chinese protest as they will!

My own first objection to Basic English lies against its calling
itself 'Basic' while in its working it cuts out all but eighteen
verbs.   Indeed, it amazes me that so capable a writer as Mr.

Ogden and so philosophical a critic as Dr. Richards—joint authors, too, of *The Meaning of Meaning*—should ignore the plain fact that in all civilized speech the verb is the very nerve of a sentence; and for preference the active verb. Nouns and adjectives are but dead haulage, prepositions and conjunctions inert couplings, until the verb (*verbum*, the 'Word') comes along, supplies the motive power, starts and keeps the whole train going. Dr. Richards prefers to call his small handful of verbs 'operatives,' and that is just what they are. He informs us that 'the reduction of the verbs to eighteen was the key to the discovery of Basic.' Very likely! Indeed, most probable, had Basic confined itself to the purposes it first professed and under which it first appealed to public suffrage; a few mere nouns may serve for taking a railway ticket, or shortening an advertisement, or clinching a bargain. But in matters of intellectual or emotional persuasion the verb takes charge, insomuch that, as a rough general rule for judging of a writer's style whether it be forcible or feeble, one may usefully note if by instinct or habit he uses active transitive verbs in preference to laying them on their passive backs and tying his nouns and particles together with little auxiliary 'is's' and 'was's.' By this kind of operation upon his 'operatives,' Dr. Richards tells us, they can be made to 'translate adequately more than 4,000 verbs of full English.' I take his word for their number. I deny their adequacy.

Adequacy for what?

On page 20 of his book Dr. Richards admits: 'It is true that if we go outside the field of general interests and into special branches of the sciences, the arts, or the trades, we shall have to use other words not listed among the 850. But the senses of these other words may be made clear in footnotes, or by teaching given through Basic English. Or they may be seen in the General Basic English Dictionary, which, using only the Basic words, gives the senses of twenty thousand other English words.' Again I accept his figures, remarking on them only that a system designed for the help of mankind yet demanding footnotes or specially trained teachers or a dictionary of its own (or possibly all together) to clarify the meaning of some 20,000 extra words is on its way to be a trifle cumbrous in itself. Further, be it noted, this new language has to be learnt not only by the supposedly receptive foreigner but by the English speaker on top of his own; so that the relief to him threatens to approach vanishing point. While I stare at the assertion that Basic's eighteen verbs 'in combination with other Basic words translate adequately more than 4,000 verbs of full English,' and am asking myself how this can be, if 'adequately' means the same to Dr. Richards and to me, he backs it up with:

And they do it sometimes with gain in force and clarity. . . . Students of the history of English knew, of course, that words like make, take, put, get, and give had been extending their spheres of influence in the language, but no one before Ogden's demonstrations realized how vast a domain these unobtrusive little words had won.

Willing, serviceable little workers, they were less impressive than the more literary verbs, but handier and safer. . . . A public unblessed by and unprotected by a sound training in philology escaped multiple dangers. So did the language itself. Every language is under constant attack by the tongues of its less expert users. One has only to watch—in a Chinese university, for example—the degradation of such learned words, when used without awareness of their implications, to see that they need protection. Basic English, by providing invulnerable but adequate substitutes for these more delicate instruments, can serve our language as a fender.

So the best protection for a nation's taste in music would be to limit the number of violins and substitute saxophones! Staggered for a while by Dr. Richards's argument I was closing the book on the comforting reflection, 'Well, at any rate these "willing, serviceable little workers" must leave our poetry unprotected,' when an advertisement at the end caught my eye: *Julius Caesar* (B.E.P.C.) *Shakespeare's tragedy with parallel Basic Version and Notes.* I have not yet been able to acquire a copy of this venture; but hope, as soon as the paper shortage permits, to discover what the editor has made (for example) of:

> Between the acting of a dreadful thing
> And the first motion, all the interim is
> Like a phantasma, or a hideous dream:
> The genius and the mortal instruments
> Are then in council . . .

III

But just here lies the trap for innovators, however well intentioned. Flushed with first and speedy success they let the pace get into their heads: they rush on, trusting in the same missionary fervour, to involve themselves in new and other enterprises, thereby, in Bacon's phrase, 'mixing up things that differ.' I remember passing a church in the East End on which some enthusiast had chalked up in large capitals, 'I do not care where I go so long as I go forward. (Signed) David Livingstone,' and a cynical companion suggesting that we might add, 'Agreed, on behalf of the Gadarene Swine.'

The mischief of it is that the general public catches the infection and with it the notion, quickly rooted, of Basic as a substitute for true English. Mr. Churchill (himself having as fine a command of our language as any man alive; in writing and speaking, if we take the two into account together, perhaps the finest), having incautiously praised Basic for its right purpose, and appointed a committee to consider and report on its applicability for that, has now to protest vehemently: 'I have tried to explain that people are quite purblind who discuss the matter as if Basic English were a substitute for the English language.' But while paying lip-service to his protest, the promoters of Basic go far to nullify it in practice, and occasionally in their theorizing. As for practice, Mr. Ogden soon pushed on to produce a Basic version of a German novel (*Carl and Emma*), Dr. Richards to abridge Plato's *Republic*; and, as we have seen, the B.E.P.C. to offer an alternative to Shake-speare's *Julius Caesar,* presumably for the use of schools. Finally, or finally so far, a new version of the New Testament is perpetrated, advertised with loud trumpetings, and one of the Old Testament promised for 1944. All this looks strange beside a modest disclaimer of any intention to substitute, etc.

IV

But why attempt this Bible? If its purpose be merely to facilitate commerce, travel, the pedestrian business of life, where was the need of all this machinery? 'Working with the Orthographical Institute, a committee under the direction of Dr. S. H. Hooke, Professor of Old Testament Studies in the University of London, has been responsible for a new form of the Bible based on the Hebrew and the Greek . . . and when the Basic form was complete it was gone over in detail by a committee formed by the Syndics of the Cambridge University Press.' Or is the design a missionary effort to ease the con-version of the savage? Does it help any one's intelligence to be taught 'I have knowledge' as a step towards saying 'I know' or any one's grasp of a doctrine hallowed by centuries of faith to alter the Virgin into 'unmarried woman' ('See, an unmarried woman will be with child'), the two terms meaning quite different things, as any heathen can tell his teacher?

Ask, and it shall be given you; seek and ye shall receive; knock, and it shall be opened unto you: for every one that asketh receiveth; and he that seeketh findeth; and to him that knocketh it shall be opened.

Compare the Basic rendering:

Make a request and it will be answered; what you are searching for you will get: give the sign and the door will be open to you because to every one who makes a request it will be given, and he who is searching will get his desire: and to him who gives the sign the door will be open.

'Ask,' 'seek,' 'knock'—how the imperative sinks, the authority loses accent, the assurance fades out, in the Basic version!—with the whole further debilitated by the substitution of 'will' for 'shall': 'shall' being superior or master wherever authority speaks or a promise is affirmed.

Compare again the famous passage in Romans viii, A.V.:

> For I reckon that the sufferings of this present time are not worthy to be compared with the glory which shall be revealed to us. . . . Who shall separate us from the love of Christ? For I am persuaded that neither death nor life, nor angels, nor principalities, nor powers, nor things present, nor things to come, nor height, nor depth, nor any other creature shall be able to separate us from the love of God . . .

with the Basic:

> I am of opinion that there is no comparison between the pain of this present time and the glory which we will see in the future. . . . Who will come between us and the love of Christ? . . . For I am certain that not death, or life, or angels, or rulers, or things present, or things to come, or powers, or things on high, or things under the earth, or anything that is made, will be able to come between us and the love of God . . .

and observe how the virtue has trickled out of it all; out of the strong 'shalls,' and out of the 'nots,' which, with their 'ns' as hammers, nail the assurance.

I turn with relief to Basic's proper function, and will end with a note or two on its practicability for that.

(1) To begin with, in my observation the foreigner's chief trouble in learning English lies in its chaotic spelling and his consequent puzzles with pronunciation. If English be chosen for our international language I should put spelling reform well ahead of any shortening of the dictionary. It would be a mighty task and, unless entrusted to scholars, very dangerous: but how well for us all if well done!

(2) If Basic English become the international language, the Englishman and the foreigner will each have to learn a new

language: for it is just as 'artificial' as Esperanto actually, being an invention, not a growth, using English words for material but lacking native idiom, lacking also the life-giving virtue of the verb.

(3) Whatever the plea, Basic should not be imposed on the already overcrowded curriculum of our junior schools. This would not only weigh intolerably on children and teachers, it would directly menace the English of our tradition and pride. For two languages would never keep their motion in so narrow a sphere.

NOTES

Page 8. Old Aeson. This story was evidently inspired by the birth of Q's first child (a son) in October 1890.

Page 18. The White Moth. The first stanza is supposed to be the beginning of a poem that Annie's bereaved lover is writing about her. Her return in the form of a moth is reminiscent of *Psyche*.

Page 31. 'Maarten Maartens' was the pseudonym adopted by the Dutch novelist, Joost Marius Willem van der Poorten Schwartz (1858–1915), in his English writings.

Page 33. The Looe Die-hards. This short story was first published in *The Illustrated London News*, where it was entitled *The Power o' Music*. The Die-hards provide the theme of another of Q's stories (*Hi-spy-hi!*) in his *Merry Garden and Other Stories* (1907).

Page 54. Alma Mater. In later versions Q changed *flits* (line 4) to *haunts*, *stonier faces* (line 7) to *other faces*, and *short laugh* (line 17) to *poor laugh*.

Page 56. Eckington Bridge. Eckington is a village on the Warwickshire Avon, down which Q made a journey in 1887 in the company of Alfred Parsons, the artist. Their experiences were afterwards recorded in Q's book, *The Warwickshire Avon*, published in 1892 with illustrations by Parsons. In this we find the prose original of Q's *Ode*: 'A small discovery awoke us. As we rested our elbows on the parapet, we noticed that many deep grooves or notches ran across it. They were marks worn in the stone by the tow-ropes of departed barges.

'These notches spoke to us, as nothing had spoken yet, of the true secret of Avon. Kings and their armies have trampled its banks from Naseby to Tewkesbury, performing great feats of war; castles and monasteries have risen over its waters; yet none of them has left a record so durable as are these grooves where the bargemen shifted their ropes in passing the bridge. The fighting reddened the river for a day; the building was reflected there for a century or two; but the slow toil of man has outlasted them both. And, looking westward over the homely landscape, we realized the truth that Nature, too, is most in earnest when least dramatic; that her most terrible power is seen neither in the whirlwind, nor in the earthquake, nor in the fire, but in the catkins budding on the hazel—the still, small voice that proves she is not dead, but sleeping lightly, and already dreaming of the spring.'

Page 58. Dolor Oogo (or Dollar Hugo) is a big cave in the serpentine rock on the south coast of Cornwall near Ruan, a couple of miles from Lizard Point.

Page 60. The Planted Heel. Polperro, where the Quillers and the Couches lived for centuries, is a hamlet in the parish of Talland, and a number of Q's ancestors consequently lie buried in Talland churchyard.

Page 64. The Famous Ballad of the Jubilee Cup was afterwards reprinted in *From a Cornish Window,* in which Q wrote: 'The following verses made their appearance some years ago in the pages of *The Pall Mall Magazine.* Since then (I am assured) they have put a girdle round the world, and threaten, if not to keep pace with the banjo hymned by Mr. Kipling, at least to become the most widely diffused of their author's works. I take it to be of a piece with his usual perversity that until now they have never been republished except for private amusement.

'They belong to a mood, a moment, and I cannot be at pains to rewrite a single stanza, even though an allusion to "Oom Paul" cries out to be altered or suppressed. But, after all, the allusion is not likely to trouble President Kruger's massive shade as it slouches across the Elysian fields; and after all, though he became an enemy, he remained a sportsman. So I hope we may glance at his name in jest without a suspicion of mocking at the tragedy of his fate.'

Page 71. Chant Royal. Becrowns is Q's emendation of his original *beseems.*

Page 73. Sir Patrick Spens. Isaac Todhunter (1820–84) and Robert Potts (1805–85) were Cambridge mathematicians whose textbooks were in great demand during Q's undergraduate days.

Tod-hunting, fox-hunting.

Page 92. The Room of Mirrors tells the same story, in miniature, as Q's last completed novel, *Foe-Farrell*, published in 1918.

Page 178. The Mental Deficiency Bill attacked by Q in these three open letters was withdrawn before it reached its third reading in Parliament. It was reintroduced in the following year, but in a different form.

Page 207. A. W. Verrall was the first King Edward VII Professor of English Literature at Cambridge. He died in June 1912, after only sixteen months in office.

Page 261. L.M.B.C. Lady Margaret (St. John's College) Boat Club.
Caius. The name of this college is always pronounced 'keys' at Cambridge.

Rupert Brooke, whose poem, *The Old Vicarage, Grantchester*, is parodied on pages 264 and 266, had been approached by Q to give a course of lectures on English literature, but the proposal fell through owing to Brooke's foreign travels in 1913–14.

Page 279.   *Thither where her secret prelude,*
        Darkling in the grove of Jesus,
        Throats the nightingale.

This was written in 1914. In 1928 Q wrote: 'The nightingale no longer sings in our grove; it has been driven out (one is told) by the brown owl.'

Page 282. Archdeacon C——. William Cunningham, Fellow of Trinity College, Archdeacon of Ely, and 'a pioneer in the teaching and writing of economic history in Great Britain.'

Page 285. The Tempest. This is Q's condensed version of his three lectures on *The Tempest* included in his *Shakespeare's Workmanship*.

Page 311. A Sexagenarian's Apology. The title is mine.

Page 368. Q has here fallen a victim to the modern amateur yachtsman's stunt of omitting the definite article before the names of ships.   He knew better, but he was guilty on occasion of bowing the knee to Baal.

Page 399. Byron. This essay is Q's much shortened version of a lecture that he delivered at Nottingham University College on 31st January 1919 (printed in 1922 in *Studies in Literature*, 2nd Series).   I have deleted from the sentence beginning at the bottom of page 402 a reference to the volume for which Q wrote this essay as an introduction.

INDEX

INDEX

Titles are in italics

Opening words of poems are in quotation marks